Drama Workshop Plays
for
Young People

*A collection of modern one-act
royalty-free plays*

by

PAUL T. NOLAN

Publishers   PLAYS, INC.   *Boston*

Copyright © 1969
by
PAUL T. NOLAN

All Rights Reserved

Library of Congress Catalog Card Number: 75–79110

MANUFACTURED IN THE UNITED STATES OF AMERICA

CONTENTS

For Peggy and John,
Peter and Anne

Introduction

American drama, in its main twentieth-century tradition, has been generally *realistic*. That is, most successful American plays are written for a stage that has a setting that looks like some place offstage. Furthermore, the characters in realistic drama look, act, and talk like people we know, and the events dramatized are like those we see about us in offstage life. The principle of *realistic* drama is based on the theory that if the playwright selects his materials from "real" life, his plays will be closer to the truth.

In truth, any theatre-goer knows that the stage setting, no matter how realistic it may appear, is, in reality, artificial. The "real" bricks we see onstage are painted canvas. This obvious contradiction has led some critics to conclude that the more a play tries to appear realistic, the more untrue it becomes. Whether or not such criticism is valid is not of any concern here, but at least there is an argument for other kinds of drama than that which we call realistic, especially when they are being used not merely for entertainment but also as an introduction for young people discovering what theatre has to offer them.

Non-realistic theatre is older than realistic theatre, and it is also younger. Before the success of realism as a theatre form at the end of the nineteenth century, all drama was essentially non-realistic in its representation of persons, places, and events. The Greeks, for example, found it advisable to represent people with masks rather than with bare faces; the Elizabethans represented places with signs rather than with painted sets. In twentieth-century experimental theatre, which has been characterized by such terms as *expressionism, impressionism, absurdism,* the playwright has created settings, characters, and language that intentionally avoid showing places, people, and events as they seem to look offstage, in order that he may show his audience how things seem or feel to him.

The plays in this collection deal with a variety of subjects of general concern to young people—dating, organizations, marriage, going steady, job training, and the pursuit of happiness. That these are subjects also of interest to people of all ages should indicate that it is not, primarily, the subject matter of these plays that has given rise to this grouping of "workshop plays." At the same time, however, it should be noted that these plays are not theatrical experiments of interest only because the form is unusual. The content is important, and the forms were selected as the best forms for the material.

None of these plays is narrowly realistic; each uses whatever dramatic style seems best to fit the material. In each, the stage setting has been designed to indicate the nature of the play and to give scenic pleasure, without regard to whether it is a photographic representation of such a scene as it would appear offstage. The setting of *An Anton Chekhov Sort of Evening* is, to be sure, generally realistic, for the intent of this play is to show that even in the midst of the familiar, the unexpected can happen. Even in this play, however, the job of the set designer should be less to imitate a normal living room one would see offstage than to give the sense of normalcy. In such plays as *The Moon's Up There, A View of the Sea,* and *Tree to the Sky,* the settings—except for a central property (a bench, a set of stairs, a mound of dirt)—have to be created by the convictions of the actors and the imagination of the audience.

It is not only in the matter of the stage setting that the workshop nature of these plays must be realized in productions. Most of the actions in these plays are not imitations of actions we see in life. Rich men, like the father in *A Young Man of Considerable Value,* do not stay in their treasure rooms counting their assets. Young girls, like the heroine of *Going Steady,* do not change their opinions in a minute because of a dream. People like the characters in *The In-Group* do not sit around in narrow little circles complimenting themselves—at least not literally. In the worlds of these plays themselves, these actions are just as serious to their citizens, the actors, as the actions of the people in the world offstage. Anyone who has observed people behaving absurdly—threatening to murder umpires because they have made "bad calls"—will realize that the more absurd the action, the more seriously the characters involved seem to behave. I believe that these actions, artificial and unrealistic as they be, are as much representative of the real world as are the actions—such as ball games, popularity contests, and some elections—that one may see offstage. While the audience knows the stage actions are artificial and unrealistic, the actors, the characters of these worlds, must believe as much that finding the "happiest hat" will bring bliss as characters in the offstage world believe that finding such things as money, popularity, and sports competence will make them better.

These plays are an attempt to shift the emphasis in the school theatre from the carpenters to the actors. The physical building of a realistic set, most school directors complain, often takes more time, effort, and money than the building of the play that is going to be performed before that set. Such plays as *The In-Group, The Moon's Up There,* and *This Younger Generation* were first conceived in terms of what actors could do on a bare stage, what they could do with the craft of acting, with voice, expression, gesture. At the same time, most of these plays have attempted to create vehicles for acting groups, rather than for stars. In many of these plays, *The Happiest Hat, This Younger Generation,* and *The In-Group,* for examples, there are no "leads" and no "minor roles." An attempt has been made to limit the performance of each actor to that which a young performer can *master,* not merely memorize. Nor can actors in most of these plays be content merely to give an imitation of people they have seen off-stage. They must conceive of the characters in terms of the world of the play itself.

Finally, although each of the plays has a theme and does suggest some sort of statement that can be made about life, they are not intended to be moral preachments. The plays cannot justify themselves *after the curtain has gone down* on the basis that they "taught a worthwhile lesson." Rather, these plays must justify themselves minute by minute. Moreover, they will not be exciting in terms of satisfying the audience's desire to "know what is going to happen." If they are to please at all, the pleasure must come from the entertainment they offer in how things are happening. In realistic drama, it is often enough if the actor gives the sense of his lines. In most of these plays, each speech fits part of a pattern of "instant entertainment." The dialogue moves not by the narrative method of realistic drama, but rather by the method of the joke. With all of these plays, even including the sentimental *The Whole City's Down Below,* the success of the play can be tested by a single piece of action. If it is not interesting in itself—if it does not amuse, provoke, arouse—the play as a whole will not succeed.

In producing these plays, the group should think in terms of such entertainment as the circus, the vaudeville show, TV comedy sketches and quick blackouts rather than the realistic theatre, for their models. This is the theatre of fun-and-games and intentional pretense. It is a theatre for the performers who wish to entertain, rather than a drama for the mechanics who wish to give a sense that the world onstage is as physically real as the world offstage.

Paul T. Nolan

A View of the Sea

Characters

ANNE KELSON
AMOS KELSON, *her brother*
OLD CAP
SUSAN BIDDLE   ⎱ *classmates of*
GEORGE ADAMS III ⎰   *the Kelsons*
MRS. VAN CLEVE
MRS. CONTONIO
OFFICER SMATHERS
MISS PRINGLE, *a private secretary*

SETTING: *The stage is empty except for a doorstep, at center, and a trash can, labeled* THE KELSONS, *which stands up left.*

AT RISE: ANNE *is standing on the top step of the doorstep, sweeping. Her brother,* AMOS, *sitting with a book in his hand, is half reading and half looking out toward the audience.*

ANNE: Go on, Amos, go on reading. If I am to do all the physical work, you must do the brain work.

AMOS (*Reading from book*):
"The sea is calm tonight.
The tide is full, the moon lies fair

1

Upon the straits;—on the French coast the light
Gleams and is gone; the cliffs of England stand,
Glimmering and vast, out in the tranquil bay."
(*Looks out at audience*) You know, Anne, Matthew
Arnold must have been looking at a scene like this when
he wrote this poem. Of course, there's no moon yet, but
there will be one.

ANNE: There's no French coast, either.

AMOS: No cliffs of England, either.

ANNE: But there is a sea. And it is calm.

AMOS: Yes.

ANNE: I wish I were calm.

AMOS: Now, Anne, don't start that again.

ANNE (*Coming down steps*): But I'm worried, Amos. We're
going to get caught.

AMOS: We're not doing anything wrong. Are we?

ANNE: I suppose not. But . . . well, I just wouldn't want
the kids at school to know.

AMOS: I don't care if they do know. . . . That George
Adams the Third. He thinks he's the King of England.

ANNE: Oh, George is all right.

AMOS: Yeah? Well, then why does he call himself George
Adams the Third?

ANNE: Because that's his name. That's why.

AMOS: Nobody's name is the Third, unless it's Louis
or Henry or something like that. And he asks questions
all the time.

ANNE: It's not his fault. It's that Susan. She puts him up
to it.

AMOS: They can both go jump in the ocean as far as I'm
concerned. But not in our ocean, not in front of our
steps.

ANNE: Amos, I'd just die if they found out we were lying.

AMOS: We're not lying.

ANNE: You don't think so?

AMOS: I just told them that our front steps face the ocean, and they do.

ANNE: But they think you meant our house.

AMOS: That's their fault. I didn't mention a house. Just front steps. (*Getting up and going over to steps*) And these are our steps. (*Pauses*) Do you think they need painting, Anne?

ANNE: You just painted them last week.

AMOS: I know, but I wouldn't want them to look shabby. A man ought to have pride in what he owns.

ANNE: They don't need painting, Amos.

AMOS: Maybe I ought to put a railing along the steps. I saw a good iron one at the junk yard.

ANNE: I like them just as they are.

AMOS: I do, too. (*Sits on steps*) You know, Anne, I guess I feel a little guilty, too. But I don't know why. These *are* our steps. I made them.

ANNE: But it's not our lot.

AMOS: No, but we keep it all neat and clean. It had a lot of weeds in it when we first came here.

ANNE: It does look nice.

AMOS: We're not doing anyone any harm. We just come here at noon and eat our lunch. And then we come after school and read and watch the sea. There's no harm in it.

ANNE: There's not a bit. (*Pauses*) Then why do we feel guilty?

AMOS: I don't know.

ANNE: I just wish that we hadn't told the kids at school that our steps face the sea.

AMOS: I'm not sorry. All those kids talk about is what kind of houses they live in. What was I going to say when George the Third asked me what our house faced? Was I going to say it faces a gasoline station?

ANNE: I'm not ashamed of our house.

AMOS: I'm not either. . . . I don't think I am.

ANNE: Then why did we lie about it?

AMOS: I didn't lie. I just said our steps face the sea. And they do. And I don't care if they do find out.

ANNE: I'd hate for Mother and Dad to find out.

AMOS: Well, I wouldn't. Dad has a gold watch chain, and he doesn't have a watch.

ANNE: That's different.

AMOS: He said it was good for a man to have a fine watch chain. It gave him a reason to work for a watch. We have a fine view from our doorstep, even if we don't have the house that goes with it.

ANNE: I wouldn't really want to live here.

AMOS: Dad doesn't really want a watch either. He likes his watch chain for the same reason that we like our steps. He said it gives him a better view toward life.

ANNE: Mother would think we were ashamed of our house if she knew about all this.

AMOS: No, she wouldn't.

ANNE: She asked me why none of the girls from school ever come to see me at home.

AMOS: Sometimes I wish that we didn't go to Fair Park High School.

ANNE: All the kids there are rich.

AMOS: We ought to go to Central.

ANNE: Fair Park is closer. We'd have to ride the bus if we went to Central. Besides, Dad bought the house just so we could go to Fair Park.

AMOS: Let's not talk about it anymore. Let's just watch the sea. Maybe, if we just sit and watch and don't say anything, we'll be able to see the gleaming lights on the French coast.

ANNE (*Joining him on the steps*): And the cliffs of England, "glimmering and vast."

AMOS: I think we're looking the wrong way. Europe is east, and we're looking west. (OLD CAP *enters down left, goes to trash can, looks in, and takes out a book and an apple.*)

CAP: This book is full of lies.

AMOS: I thought you liked *Moby Dick.*

ANNE: You said you liked it. That's why I brought it for you.

CAP (*Sitting down and opening book*): I do like it. It's a good book, full of lies. (*Takes bite of apple*) Don't you want an apple?

ANNE: No, thank you.

AMOS: We're not hungry.

CAP: Now, that's a lie. Young people are always hungry. If you don't like apples, I could bring walnuts.

AMOS: No, we like apples.

CAP: That's good. If you ate walnuts, there would be shells all over. Wouldn't look nice. Wouldn't look nice at all.

ANNE: It does look nice here, doesn't it, Cap?

CAP: I said it did, didn't I? Do I have to tell you every day?

ANNE: And we're not doing anything wrong by being here, are we, Cap?

CAP: I said you weren't, didn't I?

AMOS: I wonder what the owner of this lot would say if he knew what we were doing here on his property. I don't even know who he is.

CAP: Old Man Lewis owns this lot. (*Points offstage*) Lives in that big house up there on the hill.

AMOS (*Whistles*): He must be the richest man in the world.

CAP: He's the richest man around here, anyway. But don't worry about him. He's not very bright.

ANNE: He must be smart, or how did he ever get all the money to build a house like that?

CAP: If he were smart, why would he build a house there when he had a view of the sea here?

AMOS: He must have a view there, too.

CAP: Nope, he has a house there. You can't have a view and a house, too. The doors get in the way. The curtains get in the way. The servants get in the way. If a man's really going to have a view, all he needs is a good doorstep and a good solid trash can to keep his valuables in. (*Goes to trash can, puts book back in, and takes out a telescope.*) But don't worry about Old Man Lewis. You've been here three months now, and if he were going to bother you, he'd have done it by this time. (*Sits down and looks through telescope*)

ANNE: Can you see the French coast, Cap?

CAP (*Swinging the telescope around so that he is looking offstage left*): No, but I see a couple of foreign ships approaching. They look like enemy submarines.

AMOS (*Jumping up and looking off left*): It's George the Third.

ANNE (*Looking off left*): And Susan Biddle. I can't face them. I'm going to hide. (*Runs behind steps and hides under them*)

CAP (*To AMOS*): If you're going to hide in the trash can, be careful of my sandwiches. They're peanut butter, and if you sit on them, they won't be fit to eat.

AMOS: I'm not going to hide.

CAP: Good. I never could stand peanut butter sandwiches after someone had been sitting on them. (*Goes to trash can, puts telescope back, and rummages around with his head in the can. GEORGE ADAMS and SUSAN BIDDLE enter left, panting as though they have just climbed up a hill. They look at AMOS and the steps and then walk downstage and look out at the sea.*)

SUSAN: It *is* a pretty view.

GEORGE: If you like the sea.

SUSAN: It's probably better than the railroad tracks.

GEORGE (*Turning upstage*): And what a lovely house. Who lives in it, the invisible man?

SUSAN: It has a nice color.

GEORGE: And it suits its owner.

SUSAN: Yes, you can see right through it. (*To* AMOS) Where's your sister, Amos?

GEORGE (*Defensively*): Anne doesn't have anything to do with it. She probably doesn't even know about this.

SUSAN: Ha. I'll bet.

ANNE (*Rising behind the steps*): I do, too. It was all my idea.

SUSAN: I thought as much.

AMOS: No, it was my idea.

ANNE: It was *our* idea—if it's any of your business.

GEORGE (*To* ANNE): It really isn't any of our business, I guess. But he (*Points at* AMOS) is always bragging about his house, and I just wanted to see it.

SUSAN: Yes, we just wanted to see what you two had to be so stuck-up about.

AMOS: Us stuck-up?

SUSAN: You never come to any of the school dances or anything.

CAP (*Taking his head out of the barrel*): How did you know that, young lady?

SUSAN (*Embarrassed*): I never see him there.

CAP: Oh? Do you look for him?

SUSAN: No. Well, I . . . well, I've just never seen him, that's all.

CAP (*Lifting up a bag of apples he has taken out of can*): Have an apple, Eve?

SUSAN (*Taking apple from bag*): Thanks. (*Pauses, puzzled*) My name's not Eve. It's Susan. Susan Biddle.

CAP: I must have been thinking of another young lady who likes apples.

SUSAN (*Biting apple and walking downstage*): It is a beautiful view. I like the sea.

AMOS (*Walking down to her*): I didn't know you thought I was stuck-up. I thought *you* were.

SUSAN: I am. This is a good apple. (*Takes bite, and then turns upstage to* CAP) And if I'm Eve because I took the apple, you know what that makes you.

CAP (*Sighing*): Paradise lost again. (*He puts his head back in barrel.* AMOS *and* SUSAN *walk down left.* GEORGE *goes over toward* ANNE.)

GEORGE: I don't know why we followed you.

ANNE: Why are you George Adams the Third?

GEORGE: Gee, I don't know. Why are you Anne Kelson? You sure are a funny girl.

ANNE: I mean why do you call yourself "the Third"? It sounds as though you're trying to be a king or something.

GEORGE: Oh, that. Yeah. That's what my father says.

ANNE: Oh?

GEORGE: He wanted to name me Gus, after his brother. But my mother wanted to name me George, after my father. But my grandfather lives with us, too; and his name is George. If I didn't do something, everybody would be reading my mail.

ANNE: Do you get lots of mail?

GEORGE: No, but I might some time. I wish I were named Gus.

ANNE: Yes, it would be easier.

GEORGE: Of course, if I were, my Uncle Gus—he's my father's partner, too—would probably get my mail. Boy, it sure isn't easy being born after all the names are gone.

ANNE: I guess not. I never thought of that before.

GEORGE (*Looking around*): There wasn't a house here, was there? I mean it didn't burn down or anything?

ANNE: We never said we had a house here. We just said our doorstep faces the sea. And it does. This is our doorstep. Amos made it.

GEORGE: If you like it here, why doesn't he build a whole house?

ANNE: Maybe he will. Maybe he'll just do that. . . . (*Suddenly*) Why did you follow us?

GEORGE: I didn't want to. Susan suggested it. I think she likes Amos. At every dance, she always looks around for him, and she never talks about anyone else.

ANNE: Well, she doesn't like me.

GEORGE: She thinks you don't like her. She'd like you if she knew you.

ANNE: How do you know?

GEORGE: Because you're likable, that's why. Very likable. (*A long pause*) Do you live in a house? I mean a house you can see.

ANNE: Of course, I do.

GEORGE: Oh. (*Looks back of steps*) Down there?

ANNE: No, not down there. (*Takes a deep breath*) We live on the corner of Walnut and Green. I'll bet you don't even know where that is.

GEORGE: Walnut and Green? Oh, the white house across from the gasoline station.

ANNE: Yes. Right across from a gasoline station.

GEORGE: George and Gus's Station. That's my dad's station. We live on the street back of it, two doors from the Biddles' house. So you and I are practically next-door neighbors.

ANNE: Oh. I thought . . . I mean . . . that is a coincidence.

GEORGE: Yes, it certainly is. (ANNE *looks off right, and* GEORGE *sits down on the bottom step and looks downstage toward the sea.*) Anne?

ANNE: Yes?

GEORGE: Why did Amos build these steps here?

ANNE: The view. Because of the view.

GEORGE: But why steps?

ANNE: We like to sit on the steps and watch the view. It makes us feel . . . well, it makes us feel as though the sea really belongs to us. (*Quickly*) It doesn't, of course.

GEORGE: You don't intend to build a house here and move here, do you?

ANNE: Oh, no.

GEORGE: That's good. I mean I was thinking . . . we're neighbors and all. And if you moved here, we wouldn't be neighbors anymore. Might not even be going to the same school.

ANNE: We wouldn't want a house here. We just want the view.

GEORGE: It is a nice view.

ANNE: Yes.

GEORGE: Do you think it would be all right if I came here sometime and sat on your steps and watched the view, too?

ANNE: I'm sure that would be all right. Just anytime you want.

GEORGE: When are *you* here? (CAP *finally pulls his head out of the barrel. He has a croquet mallet and a cotton ball.*)

CAP (*To no one in particular*): Well, it's about time. If I had had to keep my head in that can for one more minute, I'd have died of suffocation. I guess Amos is going to have to put a porch on those steps so old folks will have a place to sit when young folks are courting. (*Puts cotton ball down and hits it lightly with the mallet.*) So much for physical exercise. (*Picks up the ball, puts it and the mallet back in the can, takes out a book, and sits down, crosslegged, to read.* AMOS *and* SUSAN *go upstage toward steps.*)

AMOS: Anne, guess what?

SUSAN: George, guess what?

AMOS *and* SUSAN: We're neighbors.

GEORGE: I know.

GEORGE: I know.

ANNE: He just told me.

GEORGE (*At the same time*): She just told me.

AMOS: You know, Anne, I think we ought to start going to the dances at school. Susan says they have a lot of fun.

ANNE: Do you think so?

GEORGE: We could all go together. Being neighbors and all.

SUSAN: If you want to.

CAP: Now, that's the way all problems should be solved. (*Looks off right*) Uh-oh. Another invasion. And this time it looks like destroyers. (MRS. VAN CLEVE, MRS. CONTONIO, *and* OFFICER SMATHERS *march onstage, one after the other.*)

MRS. VAN CLEVE (*Pointing at doorstep*): There it is, Officer.

MRS. CONTONIO (*Pointing at young people*): And there they are.

MRS. VAN CLEVE: Do your duty, Officer Smathers.

AMOS: What's the matter? We haven't done anything.

SMATHERS: Young fellow, is that your doorstep?

AMOS: Yes, sir. The can's mine, too.

MRS. VAN CLEVE: I told you. See, I told you.

ANNE: Excuse me, Mrs. Lewis. We didn't mean any harm.

MRS. VAN CLEVE: What did you call me, young lady?

ANNE: Mrs. Lewis. Aren't you the lady who lives up there on the hill in that big house?

MRS. VAN CLEVE: Well, no. I'm not really related to the Lewises. But we are very good friends—neighbors. And

I want to know what you all mean by turning our neighborhood into a public park.

MRS. CONTONIO: A junk yard is more like it.

ANNE: We keep it neat and clean.

MRS. VAN CLEVE: Not by the standards of *this* neighborhood.

SMATHERS: Now, now, let's get this settled peacefully. You young folks brought this doorstep and this can here, right?

AMOS: Yes, sir, I did.

GEORGE: I helped him. So if there's any blame. . . .

SMATHERS: Now, we don't know if there's any blame or not.

MRS. VAN CLEVE: Don't know? You see what they have done, don't you? If this is any example of police efficiency, I shall call Mayor Wilkins today. His wife and I are very good friends.

CAP (*Rising*): Close neighbors, I assume.

MRS. VAN CLEVE: Who are you?

CAP: Better still, who are you?

MRS. VAN CLEVE: *I* am Mrs. Van Cleve.

MRS. CONTONIO: And *I* am Mrs. Contonio.

SMATHERS: They live in the neighborhood, and they've complained about the activities going on here.

CAP: I'm here all the time.

MRS. VAN CLEVE (*To* SMATHERS): Probably a vagrant. He doesn't look either clean or honest to me.

CAP: I may not be honest, madam, but I am a nice clean old man.

MRS. CONTONIO: Then what are you doing on other people's property?

CAP: I don't see what being on other people's property has to do with being clean. You're clean, aren't you, madam?

MRS. CONTONIO: Humph! What a question to ask! Officer, are you going to do your duty or aren't you?

SMATHERS: Now, now, let's not rush into anything. What *exactly* is it that you want me to do?

MRS. VAN CLEVE: Want you to do?

MRS. CONTONIO: We want you to remove this . . . this garbage and arrest these people.

SMATHERS: Arrest them? What for?

MRS. VAN CLEVE: For trespassing. For invasion of privacy. For damage of property. How do I know what for? You're the policeman. That's your business.

CAP: Do you think people should be arrested for trespassing, Mrs. Van Cleve?

MRS. VAN CLEVE: I certainly do. I insist upon it.

CAP: Well, maybe you're right.

AMOS: Cap, you're turning against us.

GEORGE: Boy, if I'm arrested, I'll bet Gus will be glad my mother named me after my father.

ANNE: Cap, aren't you going to help us?

CAP: If you've broken the law, there's nothing I can do. Criminals must be punished. Don't you agree, Mrs. Van Cleve?

MRS. VAN CLEVE: Don't you try to get around me, you old man. You are trespassing, too. Officer, I want the lot of them arrested.

CAP: For trespassing?

MRS. VAN CLEVE: Yes, for trespassing.

CAP: I guess we might as well go quietly. (*Starts to put his hands out as though he is to be handcuffed.*) By the way, what is trespassing?

MRS. VAN CLEVE: It's being on somebody else's property without permission.

CAP: Oh, that's what I thought, but I wasn't sure. I've got no mind for the law.

SMATHERS: Now, wait a minute. I don't think there's any
need for any arresting. If you kids will just move your
things and promise not to come back, I'm sure these two
fine ladies here will be willing to forget all about it.

MRS. CONTONIO: Indeed we will not.

MRS. VAN CLEVE: You must make examples of them.

AMOS: This gets worse and worse. I'll never look at the
sea again.

SUSAN: I may not even be able to look at a glass of water.

CAP: There's just one point. (*To* MRS. VAN CLEVE) This
is your property, isn't it?

MRS. VAN CLEVE: That's none of your business.

CAP: Oh? Now, I would think it should be. I guess it might
be your property, Mrs. Contonio?

MRS. CONTONIO: No, not exactly. It's Mr. Lewis's property.

CAP: Oh, Old Man Lewis's property.

MRS. VAN CLEVE: But we are very good friends.

CAP: And he, of course, gave you power of attorney over
this property?

MRS. VAN CLEVE: Not in so many words—(*To* SMATHERS)
Officer, they have already admitted they are guilty, so
why don't you just take them off to jail?

CAP: Now, just a minute. Mr. Lewis gave you permission
to be on his property?

MRS. VAN CLEVE: I don't intend to answer any of your
questions. I'm not on trial here.

CAP: I think you are. If you are on this property without
the permission of the owner, you're trespassing.

MRS. CONTONIO: I've never heard of such a thing!

MRS. VAN CLEVE: Officer Smathers, are you or are you not
going to do your duty? Mr. Lewis is going to be very
annoyed when he hears of this.

CAP: I'll bet he will be. He's a mean, crotchety old man;
and if anyone's on his property that he doesn't want
there, he's going to be meaner than he's ever been.

ANNE: I wonder if they have dances in jail.

AMOS (*A little uneasily*): You're just making this up, Cap. He can't be as mean as all that.

CAP: He's a mean old man. You'll see.

MRS. VAN CLEVE: And in addition to seeing that Mr. Lewis is informed about the damage done to his property, I will also see that he is informed of the slander against his good name.

CAP: Old Man Lewis with a good name? Ha!

MRS. VAN CLEVE: Officer Smathers, I don't intend to continue this nonsense a moment longer. Are you going to arrest these people, or do I call Mr. Lewis?

CAP: Yes, that might be a good idea. We ought to get Old Man Lewis here and find out just how many of us are trespassers.

MRS. VAN CLEVE: Well . . . I certainly don't intend to bother such a busy and important man as Mr. Lewis just to satisfy an old coot.

CAP: I'm not an old coot, Mrs. Van Cleve. I'm just as good a man as Old Man Lewis. In fact, better.

MRS. VAN CLEVE: I'm not going to call Mr. Lewis. That's the end of it.

CAP: Then let Officer Smathers call him.

MRS. VAN CLEVE: If Officer Smathers wants to chance making Mr. Lewis angry, it can be on his head. (*To* SMATHERS) I don't need to tell you that he is a very important man.

MRS. CONTONIO: Yes, I wouldn't want to be in your shoes.

CAP: Officer Smathers, it's your duty. Instead of finding that you have five dangerous trespassing criminals, you may find you have seven. (*Stares at the two ladies*)

SMATHERS: I guess maybe I'd better call him. You all stay here. I'll just go to the car.

MRS. VAN CLEVE: Now, just one minute, Officer Smathers. I don't want dear Mr. Lewis bothered. It's against my principles, but let's just forget the whole affair. These people can leave here—and promise never to return—and we'll forget it.

ANNE: Oh, we will.

SUSAN: We'll leave right now.

GEORGE (*Going to one side of the steps and lifting them*): Come on, Amos, I'll help you carry the steps.

CAP: No. I think he ought to call Old Man Lewis.

MRS. CONTONIO: Now, see here, whoever you are. . . .

CAP: Cap, ma'am, honest old Cap, the Terror of the Trespassers.

MRS. VAN CLEVE: Why don't you just stay out of this?

CAP: I tried to, but now I think he ought to call Old Man Lewis.

AMOS: Aw, Cap, why can't you just let us leave?

CAP (*Sitting down on the steps as he knocks them loose from* GEORGE's *hands*): Nope. I'll just wait for Old Man Lewis. I like this view, and I like these steps; and I'm not going to leave here until he orders me to do so.

SMATHERS (*To* MRS. VAN CLEVE): What do you want me to do?

MRS. VAN CLEVE: This is insulting. When Mr. Lewis hears. . . .

SMATHERS: Shall I call him, Mrs. Van Cleve?

MRS. VAN CLEVE: I don't care what you do. I'm leaving. I've tried to perform my civic duty and this is the thanks I get. Come, Althea.

MRS. CONTONIO: Coming, Constantina. (*They start off right, and* MRS. VAN CLEVE *turns around.*)

MRS. VAN CLEVE: But don't think that Mr. Lewis won't hear about this. (*They exit.*)

SMATHERS: I hope you all understand that I didn't want to cause you any trouble.

AMOS: Gee, Cap, they were just bluffing, and you out-bluffed them.

GEORGE: You sure did.

SUSAN: I'll bet they don't even know Mr. Lewis.

CAP: Nobody knows Old Man Lewis. He's a mean old man. Now that the storm has blown over, let's watch the sea again.

GEORGE (*Sitting on steps*): It certainly is a nice view, isn't it, Anne?

ANNE (*Sitting*): Especially at this time of the afternoon.

SUSAN: Let's go up there, on that little hill. (*Pointing up-stage right*)

AMOS: Yes, that is a good view. (SUSAN *and* AMOS *start up right.*)

SMATHERS: No, wait a minute.

CAP (*Leading him down left*): Now Officer, you said you didn't want to cause any trouble.

SMATHERS: I don't, but I don't want them to cause any trouble either. These kids have to get these things out of here, and they have to stay off this property.

CAP: Now, who says so? Those women won't be back.

SMATHERS: Maybe not. But if Old Man Lewis hears about this—and he will—there's going to be trouble.

CAP: Oh, he won't hear about it. He's a little deaf.

SMATHERS: Nope. They have to go.

CAP: Suppose I get Old Man Lewis to deed the property to these kids. . . .

SMATHERS: Now, look, old-timer, you may be able to bluff those women, but you're not going to fool me. I want you all to get out of here, and I don't want to hear any more arguments.

CAP: They're nice kids, and this is a nice place for them. I'd sure hate to see them lose this place.

SMATHERS: They don't look as though they're in need of a place to live.

CAP: A person needs more than a place to live. He needs a place to dream, too.

SMATHERS: Let them dream on their own property.

CAP: I didn't want to do it, but you've forced me to. Officer, I own this property.

SMATHERS: It's not going to work, old-timer. I've seen you bluff once, and you're not going to bluff me.

CAP: I really do.

SMATHERS: Now, don't you go too far. If you owned this property, you'd be Old Man Lewis himself.

CAP: That's who I am.

SMATHERS: Old-timer, you're making me angry.

CAP: I told you Old Man Lewis was a mean old man. He makes everybody angry.

SMATHERS: All right, I'll just ask these kids.

CAP: Now, wait a minute. They don't know.

SMATHERS: No, nobody knows, except you and me. And I'll tell you what I'm going to do, old-timer, if you don't tell anybody, I won't tell anybody. Now, for the last time, are you going to move along peacefully or . . . (MISS PRINGLE *runs in from right.*)

MISS PRINGLE: Mr. Lewis . . . Mr. Lewis. (*To* CAP) Mr. Lewis, I know that you told me never to bother you here. . . . And you can fire me if you want to. . . .

CAP: Now, calm down, Miss Pringle. It's all right.

SMATHERS (*Gasps*): You really are Old Man . . . I mean, Mr. Lewis.

MISS PRINGLE: The Governor is at the house. He said he's your house guest.

CAP: The Governor? I completely forgot that I asked old Bob to come by this week.

MISS PRINGLE: What'll I do? What'll I do?

CAP: Give him something to eat and listen to him talk, and tell him I'll be there shortly—just as soon as I complete a major business transaction.

MISS PRINGLE: All right, Mr. Lewis. But the Governor! (*Starts off right*)

CAP: And, Miss Pringle, make out a deed to this lot, transferring it to Mr. Amos and Miss Anne Kelson.

MISS PRINGLE: Yes, sir, Mr. Lewis. Right away. The Governor, in our house! He looks just like Richard Burton. (MISS PRINGLE *exits right.*)

CAP: He looks more like a sixty-year-old Elizabeth Taylor, but he can certainly draw the women voters.

SMATHERS (*Stunned*): You really are Mr. Lewis.

CAP: Cap's the name. (*Calls to* AMOS *and* ANNE) Hey, you two, do you know what just happened? (*They move toward him as he walks up center.*)

GEORGE: Old Man Lewis found out, and we're all going to jail.

CAP: Nope. He did hear about it, but he's deeded the property to you two, Amos and Anne.

AMOS: What?

ANNE: Why would he do that?

CAP: With the understanding that you use it only as you have in the past. No house, you understand.

AMOS: I don't understand anything.

CAP: Maybe, he would let you put a porch up. But no house. He doesn't want you to ruin the view.

ANNE: He's just giving us the lot?

CAP: Yep, the old coot's losing his mind, I guess.

AMOS: But you said he was a mean old man.

CAP: He is, so look around. The place is probably covered with poison ivy. (*Stage lights dim*)

SUSAN: Look, the first star is up. (*Points up over audience*)

GEORGE: Make a wish, Anne.

ANNE: I wish that I never wake up and this dream goes on forever.

CAP: But look out for the poison ivy. (*Curtain falls as he exits.*)

THE END

Going Steady

Characters

SHARON JENNINGS
KAY, *her friend*
MRS. JENNINGS
WOODY PATE
PRITCHARD MERTON, *a movie actor*
AGNES BROTH, *Dean of Women*
MR. JACKMAN, *a representative of the Peace Corps*
MR. FLYBOY, *a representative of the Space Agency*

SETTING: *The Jennings living room.*
AT RISE: SHARON JENNINGS, *a high school girl, and her friend,* KAY, *are sitting on the sofa and talking.*

KAY: But the dance is just two weeks from this Saturday, and you don't even know if you're going to be invited yet.
SHARON: I think Woody is going to ask me.
KAY: But you don't *know*.
SHARON: No, I don't know. But I think he is.
KAY: Think, think, think! Girls aren't supposed to think. Now, if you were going steady . . .
SHARON: If I were going steady, I would know that I had

a date. I know, Kay. You've told me that often enough.

KAY: Then why don't you do something about it? Honestly, Sharon, why don't you go steady?

SHARON: I don't want to. And Woody hasn't asked me.

KAY: Why don't you ask him?

SHARON: Oh, I couldn't. Woody is a funny kind of boy.

KAY: I know.

SHARON: I don't mean funny that way. I mean . . . well, he thinks things ought to make sense.

KAY: Make sense? I've never heard of such a thing. What is he, some kind of nut?

SHARON: He says people do a lot of things that don't make sense just because other people do them.

KAY: Why, that's silly. If other people do them, they must make sense. Well, I have to go. Johnny is through with practice now.

SHARON: Oh, stay a while, Kay. I want to talk to you.

KAY: I can't. Johnny is waiting for me. It's my turn this week to carry his books.

SHARON: Why are you carrying Johnny's books?

KAY: Because we're going steady.

SHARON: But that's silly.

KAY: Now you're talking like that Woody. And I have to go. Johnny's waiting, and Johnny doesn't like to wait.

SHARON: Oh, I don't care what Johnny likes.

KAY: Well! That's what comes of not going steady. It makes people disagreeable. Goodbye. (*Exits*)

SHARON: That's what Johnny says. The big ape. (SHARON *walks about the room, thinking, and kicking the furniture.* MRS. JENNINGS *enters.*)

MRS. JENNINGS (*After observing* SHARON *for a moment*): Now, what's the matter?

SHARON: Nothing's the matter. What makes you think something's the matter?

MRS. JENNINGS: Oh, I don't know. When people walk around kicking furniture, I just think something is the matter. Excuse me. (*Starts out*)

SHARON: Mother?

MRS. JENNINGS: Yes, dear?

SHARON: Mother, is it all right with you if I . . . if I go steady?

MRS. JENNINGS: Where is that, dear?

SHARON: Oh, you know what I mean. You're just like Woody Pate. When a boy and a girl go out together, and he gives her his pin or a letter or something, that's called *going steady*.

MRS. JENNINGS: Oh, that sounds all right to me. But where are you going? You can't go out on school nights, you know. Not unless you are going to a lecture or something. Where are you going?

SHARON: I don't know where we're going.

MRS. JENNINGS: I don't think that's very steady. I would think that a steady person would be dependable, know where he was going. Has Woody asked you to "go steady," dear?

SHARON: No, he hasn't, Nobody has asked me.

MRS. JENNINGS: Doesn't it take two to go steady?

SHARON: Yes, it sure does.

MRS. JENNINGS: *Surely,* dear.

SHARON (*Without much enthusiasm*): Does that mean it's all right with you, Mother?

MRS. JENNINGS: I mean, dear, that you say, "it *surely* does," not "it *sure* does." Adverbs modify verbs, not adjectives.

SHARON: Oh, Mother, you talk just like Woody.

MRS. JENNINGS: Well, I'm sure that all of this makes a great deal of sense, dear, but I have to get dinner on the table. (*Starts out, then turns back*) Oh, Sharon. I forgot.

Woody is on his way over to see you. He called a few
moments ago.

SHARON: Oh?

MRS. JENNINGS: Shall I tell him you don't wish to see him?

SHARON: Now, Mother, why should you do that? I'm not
mad at Woody or anything.

MRS. JENNINGS: Well, I didn't know. You sound as though
you're angry. (*Bell rings.*) That's probably Woody now.
(*Starts off*) And if Woody wants you to go steady with
him, it's all right with me. Just as long as it's not on
school nights. (MRS. JENNINGS *exits.* SHARON *dashes to
wall mirror and quickly fluffs her hair.* WOODY *enters.*)

SHARON (*Formally*): Well, this is a pleasant surprise. Hello,
Woodrow.

WOODY: Surprise? Didn't your mother tell you I just
called?

SHARON: Ah . . . oh, yes. She did say a young man called.

WOODY: Were you expecting somebody else?

SHARON: Well, I . . . I don't know. When a girl isn't
going steady or anything, all sorts of people might drop
by. That's the way life is.

WOODY: That's true. Life is a lot more adventuresome that
way.

SHARON: Yes, it is. Of course, something can be said for
going steady.

WOODY: Some people like it. (*Pauses.* SHARON *smiles.*) And
then, again, some don't.

SHARON (*Frowning*): Some people are sure dumb.

WOODY: That should be *surely,* shouldn't it? *Surely* dumb.

SHARON: Oh, grammar. Is that all you can think about?
Grammar?

WOODY: That's what I came by to tell you. Miss Finley
posted the grades in English. You got a ninety-nine.

SHARON: Ninety-nine? I wonder what I missed. (*Quickly*

changes back to her new pose) Well, I mean I don't care. Grades aren't everything.

WOODY: They are a great deal if you expect to go to college.

SHARON: I don't know if I want to go to college.

WOODY: You do, too. And you're going to win a scholarship.

SHARON: Maybe I'm not.

WOODY: Grades are important if you expect to get any kind of interesting job.

SHARON: Maybe I don't want an interesting job.

WOODY: You don't want to go to college and you don't want a job? Sharon, what do you want?

SHARON (*Desperately*): Woody, do you want to go steady?

WOODY: *Steady?* But why, Sharon?

SHARON: Well, you wouldn't have to worry about my dating somebody else.

WOODY: I don't mind if you have other friends.

SHARON: And we'd always be sure that we had a date.

WOODY: Any time you want to go any place, I'm glad to take you. Do you want to go to the dance two weeks from Saturday? I really came over to ask you about that.

SHARON: Now I might see somebody I like better, but if we were going steady, I'd have to go with you.

WOODY: But if you wanted to go with someone else, I'd want you to go with him.

SHARON: Why? Do you have another girl, Woody? Woodrow, tell me the truth. Don't you like me any more?

WOODY: No, I don't have another girl, and of course I like you. I walked all the way over here just to tell you that you got a ninety-nine in English.

SHARON: Then why don't you want to go steady? All the kids go steady.

WOODY: Maybe I am some kind of nut, and a lot of the

kids do say they are going steady. But I still don't know what it means.

SHARON: It means that if we were going steady, I wouldn't date anyone else.

WOODY: If you don't want to date anyone else, you don't have to.

SHARON: And it means you wouldn't take any other girls out.

WOODY: I don't.

SHARON (*Desperately*): You wouldn't even want to.

WOODY: Well, I don't want to. But I didn't know that going steady meant that. Bill Slattery is going steady, and every time he sees a girl, he says, "Boy, if I weren't going steady!" Does that sound as if he doesn't want to date anyone else?

SHARON (*Trying to ignore his arguments*): And when people go steady, they like each other better.

WOODY: I never would have guessed that. All the kids I know who go steady fight all the time.

SHARON: Oh, you're just hopeless. Well, I don't care. And I don't want to talk to you any more, so you can just go home.

WOODY: All right. (*Starts off*) Look, Sharon, if it really means something to you, I don't care one way or the other. I just say I don't know what it means. Do you want to go to that dance with me?

SHARON: Maybe I do and maybe I don't. You can call me tomorrow, like any other casual acquaintance, and I'll give you an answer.

WOODY: Why should I call you? I just live next door.

SHARON: *Call* tomorrow, *Mr.* Pate.

WOODY: All right, I'll call you. (*Starts out and then turns back with mock seriousness*) Shall I ask for Sharon or Miss Jennings?

SHARON: You get out of here, or I'm going to throw something at you. (WOODY *flees, and* SHARON *slumps in a chair, her face in her hands.*) A lot I care whether he goes steady with me or not. He'll beg me now before I'll even speak to him. (*While she is muttering, the stage lights dim.*) You'd think he was doing me a favor or something. (*Yawns*) Everybody picks on me. It just makes me tired. (*The stage is in darkness; then the lights come on again, and* SHARON *is asleep.* WOODY *bounds into the room, wearing a knight's helmet and carrying a bunch of artificial roses, as though it were a sword. He drops to one knee in the style of King Arthur's knights.*)

WOODY (*To* SHARON, *who has just awakened*): Fair lady, I have returned.

SHARON: Woody, what are you doing with that silly hat on?

WOODY: I am a knight, sweet lady, your knight.

SHARON: Woody, what's wrong with you?

WOODY: Nothing is wrong with me. I am as you have dreamed me.

SHARON: Oh, then I'm dreaming. I'm still asleep.

WOODY: Thou speakest true, fair lady.

SHARON: If I pinched myself, I'd wake up, wouldn't I?

WOODY: Indeed you would.

SHARON: I'm not going to do it. I like this dream.

WOODY: Good. Then I shall go on. Sweet lady, on bended knee I come to you.

SHARON: Yes?

WOODY: I request, I implore, I urge that you go steady with me.

SHARON: You didn't say *beg.*

WOODY: I implore you, I urge you, I *beg* you to go steady with me.

SHARON: All right, you silly man. I consent.

WOODY: This means my ways shall be your ways.

SHARON: And my ways shall be your ways.

WOODY: You will never look at another boy.

SHARON: And you will never look at another girl.

WOODY: You shall have no plans but *our* plans.

SHARON: And *you* shall have no plans but our plans.

WOODY: Then it is agreed. We are going to go steady.

SHARON: We are going steady. Now, leave, brave knight. For I would get on to the good parts of the dream. I have found that when awake, people who go steady are happier apart, so it should be the same in a dream.

WOODY (*Rising and backing out, as before royalty*): Farewell, lovely Lady Steady.

SHARON: Farewell, Sir Knight Steady.

WOODY: (*Out of knight's character for a moment*): I shall think of you each moment we are apart.

SHARON: Now, you get out of here before I wake up, Woody, or I really will be angry. Going steady gives me the right to be angry at you any time I want.

WOODY (*Back in character*): Farewell, sweet lady. "Sleep dwell upon thine eyes, peace in thy breast!— Would I were sleep and peace, so sweet to rest!" (*Exits*)

SHARON: That went very well. Woody came crawling to me, as I knew he would. And now I am going steady. Let Kay carry books for Johnny—Woody is carrying a torch for me. (**PRITCHARD MERTON**, *the movie actor, enters, dressed in sport coat with white muffler at the throat, beret, and dark glasses.*)

MERTON: I've found you! At last!

SHARON: Pritchard Merton, the movie actor!

MERTON: At last I've found you.

SHARON: Have you been looking for me?

MERTON: I saw you but once a few years ago.

SHARON: Oh?

MERTON: It was in a production at elementary school number seven.

SHARON: Oh, yes. I remember the role well. I was a buttercup.

MERTON: A wonderful, beautiful buttercup. You were most believable in the role.

SHARON (*Modestly*): Thank you.

MERTON: I knew then that I must have you for my leading lady.

SHARON: Of course, dear boy.

MERTON: But when I searched for you, your mother came between us. She told me you were taking your nap.

SHARON: She's jealous of me.

MERTON: But now, it is all right. My producer wants me to do *Romeo and Juliet*. And you are my Juliet.

SHARON: I know the part well. (*Quoting*) "Sleep dwell upon thine eyes . . ."

MERTON: That's Romeo's part. My part. But no matter. I've found you, and if you want to play Romeo, I shall be Juliet.

SHARON: We shall be wonderful together.

MERTON: Then you'll accept?

SHARON: Of course, dear boy.

MERTON: You have no ties? No family to object?

SHARON (*Slowly*): Well, as a matter of fact . . . there's Woody. We're going steady.

MERTON: Egad, that it should come to this! To have found you at last, but too late. Too, too late. Then I must go. I'll join the French Foreign Legion. Goodbye, Bright Star.

SHARON: Goodbye, Pritchard—co-star who might have been. (MERTON *exits*.) Oh, what a price we pay when we give our vow to go steady. And I would have made such a wonderful Juliet. (AGNES BROTH, *Dean of Women, enters, dressed in academic robes.*)

DEAN BROTH: I am Dean Agnes Broth of the International Universal Global College.

SHARON: I've heard of you, Dean Broth.

DEAN BROTH: And you, I hope, are Miss Sharon Jennings?

SHARON: Yes.

DEAN BROTH: *The* Miss Sharon Jennings?

SHARON: I believe so.

DEAN BROTH: *The* Sharon Jennings who made a ninety-nine on Miss Finley's English test?

SHARON (*Modestly*): Oh, it was nothing. I don't know why I missed the one point.

DEAN BROTH: Miss Jennings, I have been given authority by the president of International Universal Global College to offer you a four-year scholarship.

SHARON: Really? What are the terms?

DEAN BROTH: First, all your fees and tuition are paid.

SHARON: Of course.

DEAN BROTH: Then, you get ten thousand a year for housing, books, and so forth.

SHARON: Of course.

DEAN BROTH: And then you get twenty-five thousand a year for incidentals—soap and things like that.

SHARON: A very generous offer.

DEAN BROTH: Then you'll take it? Frankly, Miss Jennings, our president is insistent that you join our student body. And if I fail, I'm in the soup.

SHARON: A Broth in the soup. How odd. But, have no fears, I'll accept.

DEAN BROTH: Thank you, Miss Jennings. You have saved my academic career.

SHARON: There is just one thing. You'll have to allow a certain Mr. Woodrow Pate to attend as a student, too.

DEAN BROTH: That will be quite out of the question. International Universal Global College is a women's college. But don't worry. It is surrounded by eight men's colleges; and as soon as all the students at those colleges heard you might join us, they immediately requested permission to take you to all their dances. Your program is filled for the next four hundred dances.

SHARON: But . . . but it just won't do, Dean Broth. Woody and I are going steady.

DEAN BROTH: Oh, I didn't know. Well, then, I'm sorry. We don't give scholarships to girls who go steady. They are so . . . so unsteady, you know.

SHARON: Of course.

DEAN BROTH: Goodbye, my dear. (*Pauses*) And you are young to have your life behind you. (DEAN BROTH *exits.*)

SHARON: Woody was right. Going steady certainly closes the door of opportunity. At least, in this dream it does. Well, I'm not going to have any more of it. I'm going steady and that's the end of it. I don't care who comes next. I'm not going to listen to him. I'm simply going to tell him that I'm going steady. That I like going steady. And I'm not interested in fame and fortune and scholarships. (*Pitifully*) I do, too, like going steady. I do, too. It's lots of fun. (MR. JACKMAN, *a representative of the Peace Corps, wearing a pith helmet, and* MR. FLYBOY, *carrying a space helmet, enter.*)

JACKMAN: After you, Mr. Flyboy.

FLYBOY: No, after you, Mr. Jackman.

JACKMAN: But you were first.

FLYBOY: No, you were first.

JACKMAN: But I insist.

FLYBOY: And I insist.

SHARON: For heaven's sake. One of you go first. And it doesn't really make any difference. I'm not interested.

JACKMAN: But you will be interested when you hear. I am a representative of the Peace Corps.

FLYBOY: I am a representative of the Space Agency.

JACKMAN: I am going to make you the most exciting offer of your life.

FLYBOY: Mine is even more exciting.

JACKMAN: Please, Mr. Flyboy. I was here first.

FLYBOY: No, you weren't. I was here first.

JACKMAN: I insist.

FLYBOY: I insist.

SHARON: Stop it, both of you. I told you I'm not interested.

JACKMAN: But I'm offering you an opportunity to be one of the leading women of the world—the first teenage head of the United Nations Peace Corps.

FLYBOY: Listen to me, and you will be *the* leading woman of the universe. The first woman to explore outer space.

SHARON (*Weakly*): I'm . . . I'm not interested.

JACKMAN: If it's money, we have millions . . .

FLYBOY: We have billions.

SHARON: Oh, it's not money.

JACKMAN: There's no danger.

FLYBOY: Lots of adventure, but no danger.

SHARON: I'm not afraid. It's not that.

JACKMAN: It's not that you're . . . you're . . . Oh, I can't say that word.

FLYBOY: No, it can't be. Not Sharon Jennings, who was a buttercup at P.S. No. 7 and now makes ninety-nine in English with Miss Finley. It couldn't be.

SHARON: It is. It's true.

JACKMAN: You're . . . you're . . . ?

FLYBOY: You're . . . you're . . . ?

SHARON: I'm not afraid to say it. I'm *going steady*. (JACK-MAN *and* FLYBOY *shrink back.*)

JACKMAN: Let me out of here. (*Starts out*)

FLYBOY: No, me first. (*He pulls* JACKMAN *back and dashes out.* JACKMAN *exits after him.*)

SHARON (*Sinking into chair*): Now I've lost my chance to

go to India . . . to go to Africa . . . to go to the moon. And all because that Woody Pate insisted that I go steady with him. Oh, I hate him. (*The lights dim, go out, and as they come back on again,* MRS. JENNINGS *enters.*)

MRS. JENNINGS: Sharon, don't you think . . . (*She stops.*) Why, Sharon, what's the matter?

SHARON: I fell asleep. At least, I think I fell asleep.

MRS. JENNINGS: I want to know what's going on.

SHARON: I had the most horrible dream.

MRS. JENNINGS: I don't mean in your sleep. I mean while you're awake. Woody is in the kitchen, and he asked me to ask you if you're still angry at him. Are you?

SHARON (*Standing up*): That Woody! You bet I'm still mad at him. I could have been a movie star, a scholarship student, a space pilot . . .

MRS. JENNINGS: Sharon! What in heaven's name are you talking about?

SHARON: I . . . I guess I'm not really awake yet. No, Mother, I'm not mad at Woody. I was just being silly. Boy, was I being silly.

MRS. JENNINGS: Good, then I'll send him in. He's eating me out of house and home out there. (*Starts out, but turns back*) What was that about a horrible dream?

SHARON: Nothing. I just wasn't awake. (MRS. JENNINGS *exits.*) But I'm awake now. Boy, that was a horrible dream. (WOODY *enters.*)

WOODY: Sharon? Your mother says you're not mad at me any more.

SHARON: No, I'm not, Woody. Come on in.

WOODY: And about that going steady. If you really want to . . .

SHARON: I don't.

WOODY: Well, if you do, it's all right with me.

SHARON: I don't, Woody.

WOODY: I mean—maybe it's a good idea.

SHARON: It's a terrible idea. I'm sorry I even thought of it.

WOODY: I mean, if you want me to beg you, that's all right, too. I'll even wear a knight's suit and bring flowers.

SHARON: You do, Woody Pate, and I'll really be angry.

WOODY: But if you want to go steady—

SHARON: Steady is one place I don't want to go. I mean it, really. The moon maybe, steady no.

WOODY: All right. I was just thinking about it.

SHARON: Don't. Don't ever think about it again.

WOODY: I won't. Well, what shall we talk about?

SHARON: Sit down, Woody. (*Dreamily*) Sit down, Woody, and tell me about space travel.

WOODY: Space travel? You told me you weren't interested in things like that.

SHARON: Yes, but I've been thinking—a girl never knows what she'll be called upon to do. I might be a woman astronaut. Who knows?

WOODY: Yes, who knows? (*Puzzled*) You orbit faster than any girl I've ever met. (*Curtain*)

THE END

The In-Group

Characters

ONE
TWO } *dressed in white*
THREE

FOUR
FIVE } *dressed in blue*
SIX

SEVEN
EIGHT } *dressed in white and black*
NINE

TEN
ELEVEN } *dressed in green*
TWELVE

SETTING: *An elevated platform, on which are three kitchen stools, is at center, slightly upstage. Several mats and pillows are downstage from platform. Five chairs and an easel are down left, and down right are five more chairs and a typewriter on a table.*

AT RISE: ONE, TWO, *and* THREE *are sitting on the stools.* FOUR, FIVE *and* SIX *are sitting on the mats.* SEVEN *and* EIGHT *are sitting in chairs left, reading, and* NINE *stands in front of the easel, painting.* TEN *and* ELEVEN *are sitting in chairs right, and* TWELVE *sits at typewriter, ready to type.* (NOTE: *The action of the actors in the areas around the platform is done in exaggerated pantomime, as quietly as possible.*)

ONE: I don't think anyone could honestly say we are snobbish.

TWO: But let's face it, One. We are the in-group.

THREE: It may not be fair, but . . .

ONE: We are better than other people.

TWO: We are all dressed in white.

THREE: And sit on fine stools.

ONE: On a fine platform.

TWO: Which naturally makes us better than other people.

ONE: I am very grateful.

TWO: I am, too.

ONE: *That* proves we're not snobbish.

TWO: Snobs *think* they are better than other people.

ONE: But we really are.

TWO: Everyone would like to be in our group.

ONE: Naturally, Two.

THREE: But we have no room for anyone else.

ONE: We have only three stools, and there are three of us.

Author's Notes on THE IN-GROUP

The In-Group is a play about two groups of people: one, people who are satisfied with themselves, and two, people who want to do things. The first group, the in-group, sets its standards in terms of what it has. Its dress is proper; its speech is correct; its position is the best. The rest of the world is unaware it exists, except when someone wants to leave the activity of the world. Anyone may join the in-group whenever he sees there is an empty place from which to watch the world, and anyone may join the others in the world whenever there is something he wants to do. Belonging to the in-group gives one protection from hurt, but it also removes one from the joy of being alive. All the original members of the in-group desert it to join life, but some of their places are taken by others who want to escape the hurt of being human, of being involved, and of failing. The play *suggests* that being involved, despite the failures, is more honest and exciting than being removed.

THREE: Of course, we could make some more stools.

ONE: Then we would be crowded, Three.

TWO: Besides, there are plenty of seats for everyone—over there. (*Points to area left*)

THREE: And over there. (*Points to area right*)

ONE (*Snickering*): And down there. (*Points to area down center*)

TWO: But up here, there are just enough stools for the members of the in-group.

ONE: That's the way it should be, because we were born to sit on stools and look down on the out-groups around us.

TWO: I am very grateful that I am a member of the in-group.

THREE: I am, too.

ONE: Everyone would like to change places with us and sit on a fine stool on this fine platform and have such a fine view of the world below.

TWO: They certainly would.

THREE: But . . .

ONE: But what?

TWO (*To* ONE; *indicating* THREE): Are you sure Three belongs to our group? He sounds like a dangerous radical.

ONE: Or a reactionary, which is just as bad.

TWO: Or a conservative.

ONE: Or a liberal.

TWO: Or a moderate.

ONE: Or even a middle-of-the-roader.

TWO: Whatever that is.

THREE: I just said *but*.

ONE: I wish we had soap. I'd wash his mouth out.

TWO: I've always been suspicious of him.

ONE: Now he'll be accusing us of exploiting the lower classes.

Two: Or revolting against the upper classes.

One: Or selling out to the middle classes.

Two: Or of advocating a classless society.

One: Or of joining . . . of joining . . .

Two: We've run out of classes.

One: It's Three's fault. He's the one who brought up this whole class business.

Two: I agree. I think there's entirely too much talk about class. (*Pointing to other groups*) They talk about class, but *we* don't.

Three: I didn't say anything about class.

One: You did, you did. (*To* Two) Didn't he, Two?

Two: I don't think so. He said *but*.

One: That's the same thing.

Three: I wasn't even thinking of class. I was just thinking. (Nine, *the painter, throws his hands in the air in glee, steps back and looks at easel. All, except those on the platform, rush over and look at the picture. They clap* Nine *on the back, shake his hand, admire picture.* One, Two, *and* Three *walk to edge of platform nearest easel and look.*)

One: What are they doing now?

Two: They are looking at a picture he painted.

Three: Is it any good?

One: I don't know whether it's any good or not. I can't even see it.

Two: I can see it.

Three: Is it any good?

Two: I don't know anything about art. I know what I like, but that's as far as I go.

Three: Do you like it?

Two: I'd rather not say. I might be wrong. (One, Two *and* Three *return to stools. Others return to original positions.* One *and* Two *sit, but* Three *remains standing.*)

ONE (*To* THREE): Well.

THREE: Well, what?

ONE: Sit down.

THREE: I don't want to sit down.

ONE: You don't want to sit down?

TWO: On a stool?

THREE: No.

ONE: You just want to stand there?

TWO: Forever?

THREE: I want to sit down. There! (*Points to left area*)

ONE: Traitor!

TWO: Quisling!

ONE: Benedict Arnold!

TWO: George Washington!

ONE (*Turning to* TWO, *somewhat aghast*): George Washington? What does George Washington have to do with this? He was no traitor.

TWO: I was thinking of the matter from the British point of view.

ONE: You *do* have a point, but I wish you hadn't made it. (*To* THREE) I suppose you feel sorry for them.

THREE: Why should I feel sorry for them? They look happy.

TWO: Don't listen to him, One. It's just that business with the painting. He thinks they have a group.

THREE: I do not. My back is tired, and I want to sit down. That's all.

ONE: Are you saying that their chairs are more comfortable than our stools?

THREE: Yes, I am.

TWO: That's a crime. Every day in every way we are better than anyone else. Even if we are too polite to say so.

ONE: Look, Three, I've always liked you. Perhaps those chairs do *look* more comfortable than our stools.

Two: The grass always looks greener in the other fellow's pasture.

One: *Perhaps*—and mind you, I say *perhaps*—their chairs might be a little more comfortable. Are you going to sacrifice your position in our group for that?

Three: What's so great about our group?

Two: Oh, I do wish we had soap to wash out his mouth.

One: Patience, Two, patience. After all, he is a member of our group.

Two: I know. And that means he is worth saving. At least in theory.

One: At least, he deserves a chance. (*To* Three) What was that question again?

Three: What's so great about our group?

One: What's so great about our group?

Three: There must be an echo in here. That's exactly what I asked.

One: Don't be fresh.

Two: Or insolent.

One: Or outlandish.

Two: Or freakish.

One: I'll tell you what's so great about our group. We're the in-group.

Three: So's the group at the State Penitentiary.

One: But they don't dress in white.

Two: Or sit on fine stools.

One: And they weren't born into their group.

Three: I wish I hadn't been.

One: You may leave, you know.

Three: May I really?

Two: Right now, if you wish. (Three *walks to edge of platform and puts one foot over edge as though testing the water. He wiggles his foot.*)

Three: It seems pleasant enough out here.

ONE: Of course, once you leave, you can't come back.

TWO: Never.

ONE: That's a rule.

TWO: Of long standing.

THREE: I wonder if they'll have me.

ONE: Of course.

TWO: Why not?

ONE: There's always room at the bottom.

TWO: So stop being silly. Come back and sit down.

THREE: No, I'm going to do it. (*Starts to step forward*)

ONE: Well, go ahead.

TWO: But you'll be sorry.

ONE: Forever.

THREE (*Stepping back*): I suppose I will. (TWELVE *gets up from typewriter, waves sheet of paper in air. All except* ONE, TWO, *and* THREE *rush around him. He pantomimes reading from paper. Others take out large handkerchiefs and pantomime crying.*) What are they doing now?

ONE: Twelve has written a poem.

THREE: Twelve?

ONE: That's his name. People out there have very funny names. Like Four, Five, Six, Seven, Eight, Nine, Ten, Eleven, Twelve.

TWO: Some you can't even pronounce.

ONE: If they belonged to the in-group, they would have nice names.

TWO: Like Two.

ONE: And One.

THREE: And Three?

ONE: I suppose.

THREE (*Looking at them carefully*): Why are they crying?

ONE: The poem.

TWO: It's very sad.

ONE: They cry a great deal in the out-group.

Two: They are sad.

One: It's their own fault. If they want to listen to poetry, they must expect to be sad. (*Others pantomime laughter, clap* Twelve *on back, and shake his hand.*)

Three: Now they're happy.

One: Of course. They are not very dependable.

Three: I think I'll join them.

Two: You'll be sorry.

Three: I *am* going to join them. (*He steps off platform carefully, looks about, smiles, flexes his muscles, runs over to a chair in left group, and sits.*)

Two (*Staring after* Three): He did it.

One: He did what?

Two: He left us. He deserted our group. (*Gets up*)

One: Who deserted our group?

Two: Three did. See him sitting there? (*Others return to their original positions.* Eight *gives* Three *a book, and* Three *starts to read.*) See, he's reading.

One: Who's reading?

Two: Three is.

One: I never heard of him.

Two: Oh. Oh, of course not. (*Still staring at* Three) But he does look like someone I used to know.

One: Stop that, Two. Come back and sit down. (Two *returns, but can't decide which of the two empty stools to take.*)

Two: Where shall I sit?

One: On the stool, of course.

Two: But there are two stools.

One (*Looking at* Two, *puzzled*): Is there only one of you?

Two: Why, yes, I think so.

One: Are you sure?

Two (*Pointing to himself*): One. (*Seems about to point to a second*) Yes, I'm sure. There is only one of me.

ONE (*Rising and looking concerned*): This does present a problem.

TWO: Maybe I could sit on two stools.

ONE: Not if there's only one of you.

TWO: Maybe we could just leave one stool empty.

ONE: That would utterly ruin property values.

TWO: What are we going to do?

ONE: It's all your fault. You drove what's-his-name off.

TWO: I did not. He left of his own free will.

ONE: I don't like that expression—*free will*. It sounds . . . well . . . unruly.

TWO: Unruly?

ONE: Yes, undisciplined. If people just go around doing things from free will, what happens to law and order?

TWO: And what happens to the extra stool?

ONE: Exactly. (SEVEN *walks up to platform.*)

SEVEN: Psst!

ONE: Two, did you hear something?

TWO: No.

ONE: I didn't either.

SEVEN: Psst. Hey, I mean you.

TWO: Are you sure you didn't hear anything, One?

ONE: Not unless you did.

TWO: I heard . . . well—(*Points at* SEVEN)

ONE: Do you want to speak to him?

TWO: Do you?

ONE: Not unless you do.

TWO: You speak first. You're One.

ONE: All right. (*Goes over near* SEVEN *and bends over as though speaking down from a great distance*) Did you call us?

SEVEN: I sure did. Is that stool empty?

ONE: Why do you want to know?

SEVEN: I'd like to sit on it.

Two: It's not as easy as that. These stools are for members of the in-group only.

Seven: I know; I want to join your in-group.

One: You can't just *join* our group. You have to be born into it.

Seven: I know. I want to be born into it.

One: Oh. (*Turning to* Two) What do you think?

Two: What do *you* think?

One: Do you want me to speak for the group?

Two: Yes, of course.

One: Will you give me authority to speak with one voice for the whole group?

Two: Yes, of course.

One: And you won't complain later?

Two: I probably will.

One: If that's understood, I'll speak to him. (*Returns to* Seven) In our group, we all sit on stools.

Seven: I like stools.

One: We all wear white.

Seven: I am wearing black and white. (One *reaches out, takes* Seven's *hand, and helps him onto platform.*)

One: Welcome aboard, then.

Seven: Shouldn't we all sit down?

One: Of course. (*Goes to stool and sits*)

Two: To be sure. (*Sits on stool*)

Seven: It's perfectly natural. (*Sits on stool*)

One: Everyone would like to be in our group.

Two: Naturally.

Seven: But we have no room for anyone else.

One: We have only three stools, and there are three of us.

Two: Of course, we could make some more stools.

Seven: But then we would be crowded. Besides, there are plenty of seats for everyone.

One (*Pointing left*): Over there.

Two (*Pointing right*): And over there.

SEVEN (*Snickering*): And down there. (*Points to area down center*) But up here, there are just enough stools for the members of the in-group.

ONE: And that's the way it should be.

SEVEN: Because we were born to sit on stools and look down on the out-groups around us.

ONE: I'm grateful.

Two: Me, too.

SEVEN: Everyone would like to change places with us and sit on a fine stool on this fine platform and have such a fine view of the world below.

ONE: I guess they would.

Two: But . . .

SEVEN (*Rising and pointing at* Two): He said *but*. Two said *but*. Did you hear him, One?

ONE: I heard him.

SEVEN: Are you sure he belongs to our group? He sounds like a dangerous non-conformist. (ONE *shrugs*.) A radical. A conservative. A liberal. A moderate. A middle-of-the-roader.

ONE: Whatever that is.

Two: I did say *but,* and that's what I meant.

SEVEN: I wish I had soap. I'd wash out his mouth.

Two (*Standing and walking to edge of platform right*): I'm going to write a poem, too.

SEVEN: You'll never do it. It's easy enough to talk. But you'll never leave. You'll never do it. You know which side your bread's buttered on. You'll never go. (Two *steps off platform and goes to typewriter. He taps* TWELVE *on shoulder.* TWELVE *looks around, sees* Two, *gets up and goes to another chair.* Two *sits down at typewriter.*) He did it.

ONE: I hope he writes a short poem. I hate long poems.

SEVEN: It's all your fault. You've become soft in your position, One. You've been up on top too long.

ONE (*Getting off stool and rubbing his hip*): I think I have been.

SEVEN: I think there should be an election for a new leader.

ONE: All right.

SEVEN: Isn't it the tradition of our in-group that people don't vote for themselves?

ONE: Of course. We are ladies and gentlemen. We serve only when we are forced to do so.

SEVEN: All right then, how many votes for One? (*Looks about to count*) No votes. Now then, how many votes for Seven? (*Looks at* ONE) Aren't you going to vote for me?

ONE: I don't think so.

SEVEN: Why not?

ONE: I don't like you. You're too traditional.

SEVEN: Oh. (*Raises hand*) And how many votes for Seven? (*Looks up at own hand*) One. Gentlemen, I accept this high office that has been forced upon me. Although I would prefer to lead a private life, tending my sheep, collecting stamps, whistling Brahms, I know my duty. Since you, my fellow citizens, have insisted that I take the helm of state, I can do no less than accept. (*Bows*)

ONE: You broke the tradition of our in-group when you voted for yourself.

SEVEN: I have just started a new tradition.

ONE: Very well. I submit.

SEVEN: Well, then, let's all sit down. (*Sits on stool*)

ONE: Which stool shall I sit on?

SEVEN: Is that my job to decide?

ONE: Of course, you're the leader.

SEVEN: It's not easy to lead, is it?

ONE: I wouldn't know.

SEVEN: True. Only we who have accepted the burden of command know its weight.

ONE: What stool shall I sit on?

SEVEN (*Pointing to one stool*): How about that one?

ONE: (*Pointing to other*): That one will be empty then.

SEVEN: Then why not sit on that one?

ONE: Then that one (*Points to other stool*) will be empty.

SEVEN: There does seem to be a problem. Why can't a stool be empty?

ONE: Ruins property values.

SEVEN: Couldn't you sit on both stools?

ONE: That would be pushy.

SEVEN: Couldn't we burn the stool?

ONE: That would be wasteful.

SEVEN: Oh, the burden of command. (NINE *moves away from easel, stretches, and walks up to platform.* SEVEN *looks down at* NINE) Hello there, Nine.

NINE: Hi, Seven, what's new?

ONE: You are not supposed to speak to those out there.

SEVEN: I used to know him.

ONE: We never used to know anyone out there.

SEVEN: I didn't know him very well.

ONE: You're not supposed to know him at all.

NINE: Hey, Seven, is it all right if I take that stool up there?

SEVEN (*To* ONE): Is it?

ONE: It's up to you.

SEVEN: It would solve our problem.

ONE: Of course, he'd have to be a member.

SEVEN: Nine, do you want to be a member of the in-group?

NINE: Will I be able to sit on the stool if I do?

SEVEN: Of course.

NINE: And look down on the rest of the world?

SEVEN: Of course.

NINE: All right, I'll join.

SEVEN (*Giving him a hand to help him onto the platform*): You're very lucky, you know. Everyone wants to be a member of our group.

NINE: I know.

SEVEN: Let's all sit down. Everything is solved now. (*NINE and SEVEN sit on stools. FOUR rises from his mat and stands on his head. Others rush over and applaud. After he rights himself, they shake his hand and clap him on the back. Then they return to their original positions.*)

ONE: I could do that, too.

SEVEN: Do what?

ONE: Do what Four down there just did. Stand on my head.

NINE: That's an odd ambition. In all my years as a member of the in-group, I never heard any of our members express a desire to stand on his head.

SEVEN: One hasn't been feeling well, I'm afraid.

NINE: Are you sure he's a member of our group?

ONE: It shouldn't be too hard. (*Yells down to group down center*) Hey, Four, I can do that. Did you hear me?

NINE: Of course, he didn't hear you.

SEVEN: We have no communication with them, and they have no communication with us.

NINE: We don't speak the same language.

SEVEN: Or use the same accent.

NINE: I am grateful that I am a member of the in-group.

SEVEN: Everyone would like to change places with us and sit on a fine stool on this fine platform and have such a fine view of the world below.

ONE (*Yelling again*): Hey, Four. I can stand on my head, too.

SEVEN (*To NINE; indicating ONE*): Are you sure he belongs to our group?

NINE: He sounds like an outsider. Or an inside-outer. Or an upside-downer.

ONE (*Yelling again*): Hey, Four, I can do that.

SEVEN: You're just wasting your time, One. There is a wall between our world and theirs.

NINE: They can't hear us, and we can't hear them.

ONE: But I hear them.

SEVEN: Oh.

NINE: Well.

SEVEN: We hear them, but we can't understand them. Not really.

NINE: They are just different.

ONE: I understand them. I understand them all. (*Points to right area*) They are writers and orators, and they like to write poetry and cry and laugh. (*Points to left area*) And they are painters and builders and plumbers and artists like that. They like to paint things and build things and plumb things. (*Points to downstage area*) And they are athletes, and they like to do things. They are just like us.

SEVEN: They are not like me.

NINE: I don't like to do anything.

ONE: Some of them don't like to do things, either.

NINE: Those are just the bums.

ONE: You talk in circles.

SEVEN: Talking in circles is the proper way to talk.

NINE: If you really and truly belong to the in-group.

SEVEN: So stop that nonsense of trying to talk to the people out there and sit down. (FOUR *stands on his head again.*)

ONE: There, he did it again.

SEVEN: Really, One, you are being quite tiresome.

ONE (*Shouting to* FOUR): Hey, Four, I can do that.

NINE: He can't hear you.

ONE: How do you know he can't?

NINE: I shouldn't tell you, but I will. People out there— doing things, crying, laughing, and standing on their heads—they don't know what it is like just to *be* something. They are always proving things, doing things.

SEVEN: Helping people and hurting people and things like that.

NINE: Every day they want to do something new.

SEVEN: It's always just a lot of fuss and bother.

NINE: And they forget all about what group they are in.

SEVEN: And even how much more important the group is than anything else.

NINE: They write poems.

SEVEN: Poems that aren't even about their group.

NINE: They wander from group to group, just as if there were no walls separating people from each other.

SEVEN: I could forgive them if they would stay the same, even if they were always doing things.

NINE: But they don't. Look. (FOUR *goes over to* TWO *at typewriter, taps him on the shoulder,* TWO *gets up, and* FOUR *sits down.* TWO *goes to center and stands on his head.*)

SEVEN: You see. Everybody does everything out there.

ONE: Hey, Two, I can do that.

NINE: He can't hear you.

ONE: That's Two. I used to know him. He was a member of our in-group.

SEVEN: It doesn't make any difference. They can't hear us out there unless they come to us.

ONE: I'm going out there, too.

SEVEN: You won't like it.

NINE: You'll try to stand on your head and fall.

SEVEN: Then where will you be?

NINE: Do you want to be a failure?

ONE: I might not fail.

SEVEN: Stay here, One, and you know you can't fail.

ONE: I might succeed.

NINE: Stay here, One, and you know you can't succeed. We are safe here. We don't fail. We don't succeed. We just are.

ONE: We never laugh here.

SEVEN: We sneer a lot.

ONE: That's not the same. We don't laugh.

NINE: But we don't cry, either.

ONE: It doesn't matter if you don't cry as long as you don't laugh.

SEVEN: You may cry a lot out there.

ONE: It's better to cry than to do nothing. I'm going to go.

NINE: You'll be back.

SEVEN: We've been there. We know.

ONE: I *am* afraid to go. Hey, Two, help me to join you.

SEVEN: He won't help you.

ONE: You said that people out there help each other.

NINE: You're not out there.

SEVEN: They don't even know you exist.

ONE: I'm going out there.

SEVEN: You're afraid.

ONE: I know it. But I'm going to go anyway.

NINE: Suit yourself.

ONE: Goodbye, Nine. Think about me when I'm gone.

NINE: We never think about anyone here.

SEVEN: If we tried, it would ruin our in-group.

ONE: I'll think about you.

NINE: You won't have time.

SEVEN: Out there, you just do things. You'll forget all about us.

ONE (*Stepping off platform*): Goodbye. (*Looks about, then goes to* TWO) I can stand on my head, too.

TWO: That's nice. To whom were you speaking?

ONE: When?

TWO: Just then.

ONE (*Looking around without seeing* SEVEN *and* NINE): I must have been speaking to myself. There's no one else around.

TWO: I used to live over there. (*Points to typewriter*) I was a poet when I was young.

ONE: I am going to be a poet someday.

TWO: Next year, I am going to be a painter.

ONE: Say, that would be fun. I might try that, too. But now, I am going to stand on my head. I've always wanted to. (ONE *tries to stand on his head, falls, laughs, and* TWO *watches, smiling.* ONE *tries again and succeeds.* SEVEN *and* NINE *get up.*)

SEVEN: He has forgotten us.

NINE: You said he would.

SEVEN: We don't need him.

NINE: Or any of them.

SEVEN: We are the in-group.

NINE: We are better than other people.

SEVEN: We are all dressed in black and white.

NINE: And sit on fine stools.

SEVEN: On a fine platform.

NINE: While out there, they are alive.

SEVEN: And that means being unhappy and trying and failing.

NINE: And crying and writing poetry and fixing the plumbing.

SEVEN: Come on, Nine, let's sit down.

NINE: Where shall we sit? There are three stools, and there are only two of us.

SEVEN: Just sit on any one. Someone else will be along soon. (SEVEN *sits on a stool and looks glumly out.*)

NINE (*Hesitating a moment, then selecting a stool*): I am very grateful that I am a member of the in-group.

SEVEN: I am, too.

NINE (*Sighing*): Everyone would like to be in our group.

SEVEN (*Sadly*): Everyone envies us.

NINE: But we need a new member. Isn't someone somewhere tired of being alive? (SEVEN *and* NINE *sit, looking out, chins on hands.*)

ONE: Do you know what we ought to do? We ought to have a party.

TWO: And invite everyone?

ONE: Everyone who wants to come.

THREE (*Coming to center*): I want to come. (*Others join group at center.*)

FOUR: I'll bake a cake.

FIVE: I don't have a thing to wear, but I'll come anyway.

SIX: I'll have a friend I want to bring. I'm going out and make a friend right now. (*Runs off stage*)

EIGHT: I used to have some friends just like me. I wish they were here.

SEVEN: Eight is talking about us, Nine.

NINE: It will probably be a wonderful party.

SEVEN: I don't want to go, do you?

NINE: Not if everyone is invited.

SEVEN: Let's have a party of our own.

NINE: It wouldn't be the same.

SEVEN: Why not?

NINE: We don't have anyone to invite.

SEVEN: Then I'm going to One's party. Hey, wait for me. (SEVEN *leaps off platform and joins others, who form a line.*)

ALL (*Chanting*): We're having a party. (*They march off right, chanting.*)

NINE (*Sadly*): It's very nice being the only member of the in-group. That means I'm really exclusive. But it does get lonely. (*Pretending to phone*) Hello, Operator? Do you have a phone number for the Lonely Hearts

Club? . . . But that's my number. . . . No, thank you. Don't bother to ring. There will be no one there. Good-bye, Operator. (*Hangs up*) Hey, wait for me. I'm coming, too. (*Leaps off platform*) Wait for me. (*Runs off right, chanting*) I'm going to a party. I'm going to a party. (*Curtain*)

THE END

What's Zymurgy with You?

Characters

TIMOTHY, *a young man hoping to be noticed*
HIRAM, *a local hippy*
IRIS, *Hiram's girl*
JACK, *a young man with muscles*
MRS. POOLE, *a kindly woman*
MR. BONSIGNORE, *a barber*
MRS. NORTON, *a librarian*
JANIE, *a young lady*

SETTING: *A park in the small town of Centerville on a pleasant day in June. A bench is down center.*

AT RISE: *Two hometown hippies—HIRAM and IRIS—are onstage. HIRAM, seated on the bench, is a picture of studied indifference. IRIS is walking up and down in an equally unconvincing display of studied restlessness. They are imitation hippies in all respects—dress, language, gestures; and because they are imitations, there is a curious inconsistency to the roles they play. But they enjoy the roles and play them with the conviction that no one in their hometown can tell the genuine from the imitation.*

IRIS: Hiram, let's go. I mean, this place is a drag.

HIRAM: Cool it, Iris. Timothy will be here soon.

IRIS: So Timothy will be here soon. What should I do, send up red, white, and blue rockets?

HIRAM: Timothy's my friend, and he has troubles.

IRIS: Anybody who has Timothy for a friend has troubles, too.

HIRAM: It's a Romeo and Juliet hangup, Iris, right out of *Broadway Melody of 1936.* You'll hate yourself if you miss this.

IRIS: I don't care if it's right out of Nelson Eddy and Jeannette MacDonald in *Rosemarie.*

HIRAM: Aw, Iris, can't you wait five minutes?

IRIS: Come on, Hiram. We've been waiting ever since the big hand was on three and the little hand on four. Timothy's not going to come.

HIRAM: He'll be here.

IRIS: He'll be afraid to leave the house with that outfit you gave him. You can't make a hippy out of a hubcap just by polishing the chrome, Hiram.

HIRAM: Timothy's a good kid, Iris, and he needs help.

IRIS: He's not going to get a date with Janie no matter what we do.

HIRAM: Wait three minutes. You can wait three minutes more, can't you?

IRIS: Three minutes, three years, Timothy's not going to show up.

HIRAM: Two and a half minutes. Wait two and a half minutes.

IRIS: It won't do any good, Hiram.

HIRAM: One minute and thirty-five seconds?

IRIS: Hiram, come on, let's go.

HIRAM: One minute and eight seconds?

IRIS: Hiram, he's not coming, believe me.

HIRAM: Twenty-nine seconds? Just twenty-nine seconds? That's less than a half minute.

IRIS: All right. We'll wait five minutes more and then we go. (*She sits down on bench.*)

HIRAM (*Rising*): I'm not going to wait for that creep another minute.

IRIS: He's your friend. You can wait five minutes.

HIRAM: Five minutes for that square?

IRIS: Four minutes, then? Just four minutes.

HIRAM: Come on, Iris, this is a bad scene.

IRIS: One minute and four seconds? Just one minute and four seconds. No, make that one minute and three and a half seconds.

HIRAM: No. (TIMOTHY *enters in hippy outfit, obviously very self-conscious.*)

TIMOTHY (*Waving one hand tentatively*): Hi, Hiram. Hi, Iris.

IRIS: Hi, Timothy. You look groovy.

HIRAM: Hi, Tim. You look terrible.

TIMOTHY: It doesn't look very good, does it?

HIRAM: The outfit's great.

IRIS: It just looks rotten on you. You're not the hippy type, Timothy.

TIMOTHY: I know. My mother thinks I'm wearing these clothes as an initiation to get into a club. She said I looked very funny. She laughed a lot.

IRIS: Mothers are like that. She didn't mean to hurt your feelings.

TIMOTHY: I know. That's why it did hurt. Gee, if a man's own mother thinks he looks funny, what's a strange, lovely girl like Janie going to think?

IRIS: You always said that you wanted a girl just like your mother.

HIRAM: Not that much like her. (*Surveying* TIMOTHY) Yeah, Tim, boy, I'm afraid this isn't your bag.

TIMOTHY (*Sitting down*): That's great. That's just great. I go through all this, walk all the way through town dressed up like a kook, just because you two suggested it, and now it won't work either. (*Pauses*) I wonder if the Foreign Legion is still taking volunteers.

IRIS: (*Rising*): Not in that outfit, Tim. (*To* HIRAM) Well, we've done what we can for the overprivileged minorities today.

HIRAM: O.K., Iris. (*To* TIMOTHY) Sorry our plan didn't work out, Tim. I thought maybe if you had the right costume, you might pick up a little class. But I was wrong. (*Pauses*) You want to go with us, Tim? We thought we might go to the Center and bowl.

TIMOTHY: No, you two go ahead. Even I know that three's a crowd.

HIRAM: Oh, come with us, Tim. With you it's not like three's a crowd.

IRIS: No, it's more like two and a half.

TIMOTHY: No, thanks.

HIRAM: You sure, Tim?

TIMOTHY: I'm sure. I don't bowl very well, anyway. Besides, I have to think of some other way to get a date with Janie.

IRIS: We'll see you, Tim.

HIRAM: Yeah, Timmy, boy, take heart. The 7th Cavalry just left the fort. (HIRAM *and* IRIS *exit right.* JACK, *dressed in a sweatsuit and carrying a basketball, bounds in from left, as* TIMOTHY *takes off his hat.*)

JACK: What's that you have on, Tim?

TIMOTHY (*Sitting down wearily, trying to comb his hair with his fingers*): Don't pick on me, Jack. I'm an old man crushed by fate.

JACK: You're what?

TIMOTHY: I'm tired.

JACK: Oh. It doesn't surprise me. You don't take enough exercise. Look at you. You're all flab.

TIMOTHY: All flab and a broken heart, that's me.

JACK (*Looking him over carefully*): Your foundation is all right. You just need conditioning.

TIMOTHY: Conditioning to do what?

JACK: Why . . . to be in shape.

TIMOTHY: In shape to do what?

JACK: Look, Tim, I have this great set of weights I'll sell you. Cheap.

TIMOTHY: What do I want weights for?

JACK: So you can get in shape and look great, that's why.

TIMOTHY: I'm not the type, Jack.

JACK: Sure you are. You're a good swimmer.

TIMOTHY: I like to swim, that's all. I'm not interested in being a boxer or anything like that.

JACK: Oh, you're not, eh? Do you know how much a champion boxer gets for one fight?

TIMOTHY (*Interested*): Could I be a champion boxer?

JACK: As a matter of fact, you couldn't. (TIMOTHY *slumps down.*) I just gave that as an example. But you could be in a lot better shape.

TIMOTHY: I don't want to be in better shape, believe me, Jack.

JACK: All right, suit yourself. (*Starts off right.*) But girls like men with muscles, I can tell you that. (*Exits*)

TIMOTHY (*Sitting up straight*): They do? (*He thinks a moment, and then takes off his coat so that he is now dressed in jeans and T-shirt. He looks around carefully, and then tries to exercise. First he tries touching his toes, but doesn't quite make it. Then he starts doing push-ups. He does one, but can't quite get off the floor for the second.* MRS. POOLE *comes in left.*)

MRS. POOLE: Don't move, Tim. Stay still, and I'll call an ambulance.

TIMOTHY (*Rising to a sitting position*): Hi, Mrs. Poole.

MRS. POOLE: Is anything broken?

TIMOTHY: I beg your pardon?

MRS. POOLE: When you fell, did you break anything?

TIMOTHY (*Standing*): I didn't fall, Mrs. Poole. I was exercising.

MRS. POOLE: In heaven's name, what for?

TIMOTHY: I don't really know, to be perfectly honest. It seemed like a good idea at the moment.

MRS. POOLE: You're not thinking of becoming a prize fighter, are you? Don't do it, lad. My Uncle Louie went into the ring a handsome, young man and came out with a broken nose and two of the biggest ears this side of a lettuce patch.

TIMOTHY: I was just exercising, that's all. I told Jack that I'm not the type.

MRS. POOLE: You're right, Timothy. So right.

TIMOTHY: Mrs. Poole, Jack told me that girls like young men with muscles. Is that true?

MRS. POOLE: Not entirely. As a young thing, I liked a man with a bit of a muscle, to be sure. But there's some I know that aren't so choosy. My sister Belle, for example, married a little runt of a man just because he was a millionaire.

TIMOTHY: Oh. It's pretty important then? Having muscles?

MRS. POOLE: If you don't have millions, it's a reasonable substitute. Of course, that's just my opinion. Young Janie, now, she told me that she didn't care much for young men who spent all their time developing their muscles.

TIMOTHY (*Brightening up*): Oh? Janie said that?

MRS. POOLE: And if she's the young lady you had in mind, you might try developing your personality instead.

TIMOTHY: That's what Hiram and Iris told me.

MRS. POOLE: So that's the reason you were parading

through town in that outlandish garb. Don't be a hippy, Timothy. You're not the type.

TIMOTHY: I don't see why everyone keeps saying that. I'm as much the type as Hiram is.

MRS. POOLE: That's true, but your father's not a judge the way Hiram's dad is.

TIMOTHY: What does that have to do with it?

MRS. POOLE: When a young man sits across the breakfast table from a judge every morning, it's only natural that he must try to be different. It's the same thing with Iris. If her father weren't the Chief of Police here in Centerville, she'd probably want to be a librarian like Mrs. Norton. People know these things and are understanding. But you don't have to show that you're not the judge's son; everyone already knows it.

TIMOTHY: I guess what you're saying makes sense.

MRS. POOLE: Now what you need to do is develop your natural qualities. You were one of the best Cub Scouts Centerville has ever seen. Develop your Boy Scout qualities. Be helpful, courteous, kind, considerate, and then you'll be attractive to the opposite sex.

TIMOTHY (*Sarcastically*): Sure, I will. I tried that, Mrs. Poole, and it just didn't work. You remember the time I tried to do good deeds all the time and was trying to help Old Mrs. Gurney across the street. You know the trouble that caused.

MRS. POOLE: You shouldn't be helping old ladies across the street *unless they want to go.*

TIMOTHY: I thought she wanted to go. I asked her if I could help her.

MRS. POOLE: She's so deaf she didn't hear a word you said, and the first thing she knew, you were dragging her across the street—in exactly the opposite direction she wanted to go.

TIMOTHY: I'm not blaming her. I'm just not the type to go around doing good deeds. They always backfire. (MR. BONSIGNORE *enters right. He sees* MRS. POOLE *and sweeps his hat from his head and makes a great bow.*)

MR. BONSIGNORE: Ah, good afternoon, Mrs. Poole. You are looking charming today. But then, don't you always?

TIMOTHY: Hello, Mr. Bonsignore, how's the barber business?

MR. BONSIGNORE: Pretty good, Timothy, pretty good. Of course, it's not as good for me as it was for my German grandfather. Now there was a barber.

MRS. POOLE: I didn't know you were German, Mr. Bonsignore.

MR. BONSIGNORE: I'm not. My grandfather was—the one who was a great barber. He was such a great barber, he was known as Herr Cutter. (*Laughs at his own joke*)

MRS. POOLE: I don't think you should be laughing at your grandfather just because he was German, Mr. Bonsignore. We all can't be Italian, you know.

MR. BONSIGNORE: I wasn't laughing at my grandfather. I don't have a grandfather.

TIMOTHY: No grandfather? That's the strangest thing I ever heard. I thought everybody had a grandfather.

MR. BONSIGNORE: I mean, I had a grandfather, but his name wasn't Herr Cutter and he wasn't a barber. He wasn't even German. That's a joke, don't you get it? Herr Cutter? Herr. H-e-r-r. That's German for *mister*.

MRS. POOLE: I don't think people ought to joke about things like that.

MR. BONSIGNORE: I wasn't joking about anything. I was just joking . . . about nothing.

MRS. POOLE: I don't think people ought to joke about nothing. You spend too much time going to the movies. That's your problem.

MR. BONSIGNORE: Please, Mrs. Poole, I'll thank you not to criticize my wife.

MRS. POOLE: I never mentioned the poor thing.

MR. BONSIGNORE: You mentioned the movies. I met my wife at the movies. We didn't just meet there. We came to understand each other because of the movies. She saw the real me because of the movies. I learned everything I know in the movies. You noticed the way I tipped my hat to you?

MRS. POOLE: How could I help but notice? You almost knocked me down with your fine manner.

MR. BONSIGNORE: I learned that from John Barrymore. You notice the way I wear my clothes? Straight from Cary Grant. I comb my hair just like Frank Sinatra. I brush my teeth like Rock Hudson. As my wife said the night I proposed, how could any red-blooded American girl who goes to the movies six nights a week not love me? I'm all the movie heroes in America rolled into one. When we have corn-on-the-cob for supper, I even talk like John Wayne. (*To* TIMOTHY) Believe me, young man, if ever you want to have a young lady fall in love with you, go to the movies and learn how to walk and talk and smile and say clever things. Now, you see, Mrs. Poole, how you have insulted my wife? So I am going to walk away—just like Humphrey Bogart in the movies. (*He walks off down left.*)

MRS. POOLE (*Yelling after him*): And give my regards to Elizabeth Taylor when you get home, Mr. Burton.

TIMOTHY: Was he kidding?

MRS. POOLE: I'd like to believe so. But who knows with a man? Here you are trying to think of some way to catch a girl's attention, and how do you go about it? You wear funny clothes and start exercising in the park, when all the time, all you have to do is be helpful, cheerful, kind, willing, friendly, courteous, loyal . . . and the rest of it. Well, I've given you my advice and if you have any sense, you'll start following it.

TIMOTHY: Maybe what you say is true. Can I help *you* across the street, Mrs. Poole?

MRS. POOLE: Don't try any of that stuff on me, Timothy. I'm not poor Mrs. Gurney who can't defend herself. (*Stalks off down right.* TIMOTHY *stands dejected and then sits on the bench, arms folded, thinking.* MRS. NORTON, *the librarian, comes in up center, carrying a load of books that obstructs her vision. When she is almost to the bench,* TIMOTHY, *not seeing her, rises, mutters to himself, then turns up stage. They collide, sending the books flying.*)

TIMOTHY: Oh, my goodness, I'm sorry, Mrs. Norton.

MRS. NORTON: Timothy, where did you come from?

TIMOTHY: I was sitting on the bench.

MRS. NORTON: I didn't see you. I was carrying these books and thinking about something.

TIMOTHY: Oh, your books. (*He starts collecting books for her.*)

MRS. NORTON: It's really my fault.

TIMOTHY: No, it's mine. I was thinking about something.

MRS. NORTON: *You* were thinking, Timothy?

TIMOTHY: You don't have to sound so surprised, Mrs. Norton. I do think sometimes, you know.

MRS. NORTON: I'm sure you do, now that you mention it. But . . . well, I never see you in the library.

TIMOTHY: One can think without going to the library. I use the one at school.

MRS. NORTON: In the summertime?

TIMOTHY: Gee whiz, Mrs. Norton, in the summertime I think about things that aren't in books.

MRS. NORTON: In the summertime? I thought it was during

the spring that a young man's thoughts lightly turned
to love. I found *that* in a book.

TIMOTHY (*Who now has all the books picked up and is
stacking them on the bench*): Do you want me to help
you carry your books, Mrs. Norton?

MRS. NORTON: No, thank you, Timothy. I'm not going
far, and as a librarian, it's my job to help you with books
—not the other way around.

TIMOTHY: I've been thinking about reading a book this
summer. I'll be by the library one of these days.

MRS. NORTON: You may borrow one of these, if you like.

TIMOTHY: That would be very nice. But I wasn't thinking
about reading a book right now. I meant later in the
summer. I have this very important problem right now
and if I started to read a book, I might forget what I
was thinking about.

MRS. NORTON: That sometimes happens. But if the problem is important, you'll return to it—with a fresh mind.

TIMOTHY: There's a lot in what you say, I'm sure, Mrs.
Norton.

MRS. NORTON: Go ahead, Timothy. Take a book.

TIMOTHY: They all look so thick. I wouldn't know which
one to take.

MRS. NORTON: I could recommend one. Now, there's . . .

TIMOTHY: I'll just close my eyes and grab one. I used to
do that a lot in library period. It works about as well
as any system. Sometimes I got very interesting books
that way.

MRS. NORTON: I don't know what my old professor at
library science school would say about that, but go
ahead. Take a book.

TIMOTHY (*Closing his eyes and taking a book from top of
pile*): All right, I have a book. Thank you, Mrs. Norton.
I'll take good care of it and return it in a few days.

MRS. NORTON: Will you read it, Timothy?

TIMOTHY: Oh, yes, Mrs. Norton. I'll try.

MRS. NORTON: Aren't you even going to see what book you have before you promise to read it?

TIMOTHY: I'll *try* to read it no matter what book it is.

MRS. NORTON: I think you have taken my *Webster's New Collegiate Dictionary,* Timothy.

TIMOTHY (*Looking at book*): So I have. Now, that's interesting. I've never read this book. Of course, I've looked at it. To find out how to spell a word and things like that.

MRS. NORTON: The author has a wonderful vocabulary, but it doesn't have much of a plot.

TIMOTHY (*Thumbing through book*): I can see that it is going to be pretty slow reading.

MRS. NORTON (*Laughing*): Timothy, why don't you take another book? One that you will read.

TIMOTHY: No. No, I'll keep this one. And I'll read it— some of it, anyway. I said I would, and I'll do it.

MRS. NORTON: It really is a rather interesting book. Do you know that there're only two words starting with *Q* that aren't followed by *U?*

TIMOTHY: I didn't know that.

MRS. NORTON: It's so. *Qintar* and *Qoph.* (*Spelling words*) Of course *Qoph* isn't exactly a word; it is the spelling of the nineteenth letter of the Hebrew alphabet; so it's really a letter.

TIMOTHY: I never would have known that if you hadn't told me.

MRS. NORTON: Of course, I guess young men aren't interested in facts like that. But girls are. They are very much interested.

TIMOTHY: They are?

MRS. NORTON: Yes, indeed. Girls are always attracted by

young men who know things like that. It shows that the young man thinks.

TIMOTHY: It does?

MRS. NORTON: It certainly does. Let me ask you something, Timothy. What is the first word in that dictionary?

TIMOTHY: Well . . . er . . . well, *A*, I guess

MRS. NORTON: Right. *A*. That's good, Timothy. That shows you think. Now, what's the last word?

TIMOTHY: That's a little harder. I've never read the dictionary all the way through.

MRS. NORTON: Think about it.

TIMOTHY: I guess it begins with a . . . (*Silently runs through the last letters of the alphabet, forming "X," "Y," and "Z" on his lips.*) It begins with a *Z?*

MRS. NORTON: That's right. *Zymurgy.*

TIMOTHY: What do you know? *Zymurgy.* That's a very interesting word. But I never would have thought it was the last word in the dictionary.

MRS. NORTON: Oh, do you know the word?

TIMOTHY: Zymurgy?

MRS. NORTON: Yes, zymurgy.

TIMOTHY: Not exactly. But it has a most important sound. Zymurgy. It's rather catchy when you think about it.

MRS. NORTON: It's a scientific word.

TIMOTHY: I suspected that. It has that kind of ring to it.

MRS. NORTON: It's from the Greek.

TIMOTHY: Oh? Now I didn't know that.

MRS. NORTON: *Zymurgy* means the applied chemistry dealing with fermentation processes, as in brewing.

TIMOTHY: Now, that is something. Thank you, Mrs. Norton. This has certainly been a very interesting talk, and I'm sure I'll never forget good old zymurgy the rest of my life. Applied chemistry dealing with fermentation processes, as in brewing. That's most interesting.

MRS. NORTON: You should use the word every chance you

get. In that way, it will become a part of your working vocabulary.

TIMOTHY: I'll do that, Mrs. Norton. And I want to thank you for taking this interest in me.

MRS. NORTON: Not at all, Timothy.

TIMOTHY: It really makes a person feel good to know that people are trying to help him. And I'll keep practicing that word. *Zymurgy*. It's a mighty fine word. I'll use it all the time.

MRS. NORTON (*Laughing*): I wouldn't overdo it, Timothy. After all, except for chemists, I don't know many people who would have much use for the word.

TIMOTHY: Zymurgy's a fine word, and it's too bad that it's been neglected. Maybe if I started using it all the time, it would become really popular—like *hippy*.

MRS. NORTON: I wouldn't go that far.

TIMOTHY: And you're right, Mrs. Norton. Books are mighty fine. I just might come by the library this summer and check out one.

MRS. NORTON (*Gathering the books in her arms*): I wish you would, Timothy. I think you'll find that a man who reads knows how to solve lots of problems.

TIMOTHY: Are you sure I can't help you with these books?

MRS. NORTON: No. Just steer me toward the library and away I'll go.

TIMOTHY (*Taking her arm and gently directing her down left*): It's that way, Mrs. Norton.

MRS. NORTON: Thank you, Timothy. And keep reading.

TIMOTHY: Thank you, Mrs. Norton. I will. There's nothing that reading and a little zymurgy can't beat. (MRS. NORTON *exits down left.* TIMOTHY *stands watching her, as* HIRAM *and* IRIS *come in right.*)

IRIS: All right, Tim, come alive. Sweetness and light have returned.

HIRAM: I'm sweetness.

TIMOTHY: Hi, Iris; hi, Hiram. (*Sighs*) Mrs. Norton is really a very fine woman. We just had a very fine conversation. Very fine.

HIRAM: You and the lady with the books?

IRIS: The librarian?

TIMOTHY: Come on, you two know who Mrs. Norton is.

HIRAM: Not professionally, I don't.

IRIS: The only time we hippy types go to the library is to get out of the snow.

TIMOTHY: You read that in a book.

IRIS: I did not. It was a magazine—a way-out magazine with psychogenic punctuation, I might add.

TIMOTHY: With what?

IRIS: Psychogenic punctuation—that's like when you see the commas, but they're not there.

HIRAM: Only with Iris, it's question marks.

TIMOTHY: Psychogenic, eh? Just a minute. (*He walks to bench, opens book, and starts thumbing through it.*) How do you spell it?

IRIS: Like soul—p-s-y-c-h. . . .

TIMOTHY: That's what I thought. Ah-ha. I found it. (*Holds book up*) I found it—right in this book. I knew you were getting all this talk from a book.

HIRAM (*Looking at book*): Hey, Iris, this is wild. This is a dictionary—an honest-to-goodness dictionary.

TIMOTHY: That's right. And I've read it from *A* to *Zymurgy.*

HIRAM: To *what?*

TIMOTHY (*Sitting down on bench with air of victory*): Zymurgy. Z-y-m-u-r-g-y. You don't know what that means, do you?

HIRAM: Zymurgy? It's a dumb word.

TIMOTHY: It's a very fine word. And you don't even know what it means.

HIRAM: Sure I do. Tell him what it means, Iris.

IRIS: Why should I tell him? He asked you.

TIMOTHY: She doesn't know either. Mrs. Norton and I know.

HIRAM: Tell him what the word means, Iris. He says you don't know.

IRIS: What was that word again?

TIMOTHY: Zymurgy.

IRIS: You know something, Hiram, he's right. I don't know what zymurgy means. But I agree with you; it's a dumb word.

TIMOTHY: Oh, yeah? It just so happens that zymurgy is the last word in this dictionary, and it also happens to be my favorite word.

HIRAM: It's a dumb word, believe me, Timothy.

TIMOTHY: The Greeks were using zymurgy long before the word *hippy* was even thought of. And people will be using it a million years from now. Zymurgy is just that kind of word.

HIRAM: It's a dumb word. It was dumb when the Greeks used it, and it will be dumb a million years from now.

TIMOTHY: You're just saying that because you don't know what it means.

IRIS: All right, Timothy, what does zymurgy mean?

TIMOTHY: I'm not sure I should tell you. You said it was a dumb word.

HIRAM: You tell us what zymurgy means, Tim, or we'll never help you get a date with Janie.

IRIS: We didn't even go bowling, worrying about you. And now you won't tell us what a stupid word means.

HIRAM: I'll tell you one word you don't know the meaning of, Tim. Gratitude, that's what.

TIMOTHY: O.K. I'll tell you. But you shouldn't call it a dumb word.

HIRAM: It is a dumb word.

IRIS: Wait a minute, Hiram, let Timothy tell us what the word means before we make any judgment. (*To* TIMOTHY) What does zymurgy mean?

TIMOTHY: I know exactly. I just looked it up. (TIMOTHY *stands, lifts his eyes upward, and quotes from memory, with some strain.*) "Zymurgy. n. (That means noun.) Applied chemistry dealing with fermentation processes, as in brewing."

HIRAM (*Exploding*): I told you it was a dumb word!

TIMOTHY: It's my word, and I'm going to keep my faith in it. A person ought to be what he is, and zymurgy is my kind of word. If I had a son, I might even name him Zymurgy. How do you like that?

HIRAM: This is the dumbest thing I've ever heard. Look, Timothy, you're my friend, so let me tell you something. Forget that word. Don't ever use it again.

TIMOTHY: Oh, yeah. I'll never forget zymurgy. I'll use it all the time.

IRIS: If Janie ever heard you use a word like that, you'd never have a chance for a date with her.

TIMOTHY: Now let me tell you something. The next time I see Janie, zymurgy will be one of the first words I use.

HIRAM: If you do, it will be one of the last.

TIMOTHY: I'm going to do it anyhow. (JANIE *enters down left.*)

JANIE: Hi, Hiram. Hi, Iris. (*Slowly*) Hello, Timothy.

TIMOTHY: Janie!

HIRAM: O.K., Timothy, let's hear you say it. Here's Janie now.

JANIE: Were you waiting for me, Timothy?

TIMOTHY: I . . . I . . .

HIRAM: He certainly has been, Janie. He has this great word he wants you to hear.

JANIE: Is that right, Timothy?

HIRAM: It certainly is, unless he's turned chicken.

TIMOTHY: I do have a word, Janie. (*Gulps*) How's zymurgy with you?

JANIE (*Laughing*): That's precious. (*Then, very formally*) Well enough, Timothy, or at *yeast* I'm trying. (TIMOTHY *pauses a moment, then laughs.*)

TIMOTHY: That's very sharp, at *yeast* she's trying. (*To* HIRAM) Don't you get it? At *"yeast"* she's trying.

HIRAM (*To* IRIS): She's as dumb as he is.

TIMOTHY: You don't get it, Hiram. *Yeast* causes fermentation in bread, and zymurgy is the *fermentation* process. (*To* JANIE) Don't you think zymurgy is a mighty fine word?

JANIE: I never thought of it before—it was always just a scientific word we had in home economics chemistry class. (*Brightly*) But I do now. It's a very fine word.

HIRAM (*Almost to himself*): She knew what the stupid word meant. (*To* IRIS) How come you didn't know what zymurgy meant?

IRIS (*Raising her hands in protest*): Me? You said it was a dumb word.

TIMOTHY: Janie, would you be interested in having a Coke?

JANIE: I certainly would, Tim. It's very warm.

TIMOTHY: The Sugar Bowl all right?

JANIE: My favorite place. (*They start off down right together.*)

TIMOTHY: Do you think you might like to go to a show tonight, Janie?

JANIE: That's zymurgy with me, Tim. (*They exit laughing.* HIRAM *and* IRIS *stare after them.*)

IRIS: All he had to do all the time was just *ask* Janie.

HIRAM: It was that dumb word. Zymurgy.

IRIS: Oh, no, it was just . . .

HIRAM: It was that dumb word, I tell you. And you didn't even know what it meant. (*Pauses*) Do you know what, Iris? We should stop being hippies.

IRIS: That would make my father happy.

HIRAM: It's not that hippies don't have a lot of good ideas.

IRIS: It's just that Centerville isn't big enough. You know what I mean, Hiram?

HIRAM: Yeah, there's no sense in learning to boil if there isn't room for the steam.

IRIS: Centerville is more of a zymurgy town—with slow-rising dough.

HIRAM: That's still a dumb word, Iris. I haven't changed my mind about that.

IRIS: Well, it was at *yeast* worth trying once.

HIRAM (*Thinking deeply*): Maybe I'll be a hermit. (*Curtain*)

THE END

The Moon's Up There

SGT. AL KIMBALL, *an old soldier*
SGT. AL DIETLIN, *a young soldier*
GEORGE, *a small boy*
GRANDFATHER
ACTRESS
AGENT
MRS. HEFLEY ⎫ *cleaning women*
MRS. PATTON ⎭
JOHN
JOAN

TIME: *The present. Nighttime.*

SETTING: *The area in front of a rocket site. A low fence, about three feet high, runs for about six feet across the stage, down center. About five feet upstage from the fence are two benches. A large yellow paper moon hangs on back wall.*

AT RISE: SGT. KIMBALL, *a soldier in his late thirties, is marching in a leisurely fashion to center, with a rifle over his shoulder. Just before he reaches center, SGT. DIETLIN, a soldier in his early twenties, marches with a rifle over his shoulder from the other direction. Both soldiers bring their rifles to a diagonal position in front of them, the barrels at their left shoulders.*

KIMBALL: Al?

DIETLIN: Yes, Dietlin. Al?

KIMBALL: Yes, Kimball. (*They walk toward each other.*)

DIETLIN: It would be a lot easier changing guard every night if we both weren't named Al. It sounds kind of silly, you know.

KIMBALL: You could call me Albert. My mother calls me Albert.

DIETLIN: You have a mother, Al?

KIMBALL: Sure I have a mother. Best mother in Brooklyn. I should have listened to her. Twenty years ago when I signed up, she told me, "Albert, don't make yourself too important. They won't let you go."

DIETLIN: How come you stayed in twenty years, Al?

KIMBALL: I don't know. It's a kind of nice life. Back in Brooklyn now, there would be snow on the ground. I like it here.

DIETLIN: Not me. When my hitch is up, I'm getting out. Four years is enough.

KIMBALL: I don't know. Maybe I'll retire soon. Go back home and feed the birds in Prospect Park. On nights like this, I figure I've been in the service long enough.

DIETLIN: You'll never quit until they chase you out. It's just this crazy job. Here we are, sergeants. And what do we do? March up and down in front of that rocket out there. My father sent me to Kansas State College for four years just so I could march up and down in front of a rocket to the moon.

KIMBALL: I didn't know you went to college, Al.

DIETLIN: Studied psychology four years.

KIMBALL: Psychology? Oh, that's why you were given this assignment.

DIETLIN: Yes, they figured it would take somebody with some psychology to deal with the nuts we have around here.

KIMBALL: Ever since the government announced that rocket out there (*Waves in direction of audience*) is ready to go to the moon, every nut in the United States wants to be a stowaway on it.

DIETLIN: It's kind of hard to figure, isn't it? Why does anyone want to go to the moon?

KIMBALL: I don't know. Just because it's up there, I guess.

DIETLIN: You want to go to the moon, Al?

KIMBALL: No. No, I guess not. There's nothing up there.

DIETLIN: Maybe that's why everybody wants to go there.

KIMBALL: I guess so. Well, you'd better take off. You have to relieve me in four hours.

DIETLIN: O.K. (*Starts to exit*) See you, Al.

KIMBALL: See you, Al. (*He stands looking out, and then he looks up at the moon.*) Old moon up there, you stay up there and I'll stay down here. O.K.? (*He realizes that he is talking to himself, looks around quickly to be sure no one has heard him, and then marches off in a military manner.* GEORGE *and his* GRANDFATHER *enter.*)

GEORGE: It's still there, Grandpa. It hasn't gone yet.

GRANDFATHER: If your mother finds out I let you talk me into coming down here this time of night, we are going to wish we were on it.

GEORGE: I wish I were on it anyway. (GRANDFATHER *sits on the bench, and* GEORGE *stands at the rail.*)

GRANDFATHER: What would you do on the moon, George?

GEORGE: I could jump sixty feet up there, Grandpa.

GRANDFATHER: That's true. You could. Maybe I could jump fifty, or at least forty.

GEORGE: Sure you could, Grandpa. There's not much gravity there.

GRANDFATHER: There's where I'd like to be. Someplace

where there's not so much gravity. There's too much gravity here. Wars and stock markets and disease and crime and (*He sighs.*) . . . and growing old. Everything on earth is grave.

GEORGE: Oh, that's not what gravity means, Grandpa. It means—

GRANDFATHER: I know, George. It means we'd better get home and get you in bed before your mother gets back. (*He stands.*)

GEORGE: All right, Grandpa. (*They start off.*) Grandpa? Grandpa, are you afraid of Mama?

GRANDFATHER: It's not that, George. Your mama is still my little girl. But she's awfully grave. (*Quickly*) That's because she loves you. People on earth get awfully grave when they love someone or something.

GEORGE: I'll bet it's not like that on the moon. I'll bet on the moon that when people love, they are happy and they laugh.

GRANDFATHER: Maybe so, George. Maybe so. (*They exit. Actress, carrying a small suitcase, enters from the other side with her Agent, who is carrying a camera. They look around.*)

AGENT: It's all right. There's no one around.

ACTRESS: I don't know, Barney. I still think this is a kind of crazy idea. Why do I want to go to the moon?

AGENT: You want to be a star, don't you?

ACTRESS: Why, sure I do, Barney. But what's going to the moon have to do with it?

AGENT: Look up, baby.

ACTRESS (*Looking up*): Yes?

AGENT: What do you see?

ACTRESS: I see the moon.

AGENT: Sure, you see the moon. Don't you get it? Every night all over the world, people look up and see the moon. And after you get there, baby, every night when they look up and see the moon, they'll say, "There's that old moon, and Lola Luna is up there." That's what they'll say.

ACTRESS: Barney?

AGENT: Yes, baby?

ACTRESS: Why do I have to change my name to Lola Luna?

AGENT: *Luna* means *moon,* baby. Don't you get it? You'll be the moon actress.

ACTRESS: What's wrong with my own name? What's wrong with Greta? I think it's a pretty name.

AGENT: Greta! That's no name for an actress. It sounds like a Swiss cheese. Besides, baby, that wouldn't tell your public you've been to the moon.

ACTRESS: I don't know if I want to go to the moon. (*Points toward the audience*) I don't think that rocket looks very comfortable.

AGENT: The two astronauts are very handsome.

ACTRESS: Oh? Well, maybe . . .

AGENT (*Getting his camera ready to use*): Now, look, baby. Here's what you do. Climb over this railing and then run to that rocket. See that door?

ACTRESS: That little door way up there?

AGENT: That's the one. You climb up to that, pull it open . . .

ACTRESS: Aren't you going with me?

AGENT: Baby! If I went with you, who would stay here and take the pictures? Who would take care of all the offers you're going to have?

ACTRESS: Well, all right. (*She sets her suitcase over the rail and starts to climb over.*) I hope it's not cold there. I didn't even bring a sweater. (SGT. KIMBALL *enters.*)

KIMBALL: All right, hold it. Hold it, right there. (*He advances on them.*)

AGENT: It's the cops.

KIMBALL: All right, now, miss. What do you think you're doing?

ACTRESS: I'm going to the moon. In that rocket.

KIMBALL: Look, lady, where did you get an idea like that? Do you know the kind of preparation an astronaut needs? You wouldn't live through the blast-off.

ACTRESS (*Turning to* AGENT): You never said anything about a blast-off.

AGENT: Captain, believe me, I never saw this lady before in my life.

ACTRESS: Why, Barney Knowhart! You did, too. I'm going to take that camera . . . (*She starts toward him.*)

AGENT: General, you're not going to let this woman . . . (AGENT *turns and runs off, and* ACTRESS *chases him off-stage.* KIMBALL *looks after them and shakes his head. Then he notices the suitcase.*)

KIMBALL (*Shouting*): Hey! Wait a minute! Come back here! (*He picks up the suitcase and runs offstage, almost bumping into* MRS. HEFLEY *and* MRS. PATTON, *two cleaning women on their way home from work, who enter and stare back at* KIMBALL *offstage.*)

MRS. HEFLEY (*Gasping*): Did you ever, Mrs. Patton?

MRS. PATTON: Indeed I did, Mrs. Hefley. Many a time. It's the eternal triangle. They probably had some kind of lovers' quarrel. It happens all the time.

MRS. HEFLEY: They didn't look like lovers to me.

MRS. PATTON: Indeed, lovers never do. But you mark my word. We have just seen an elopement.

MRS. HEFLEY: An elopment? But what was that soldier doing with the suitcase?

MRS. PATTON: Probably the girl's father. Wanted to be sure she didn't forget it. You saw the gun he was carry-ing. He must be her father. I've been cleaning up for

forty years at the Shearer Building, Mrs. Hefley. And
there's little you don't learn about life, cleaning up after
those people. It's a sordid life people lead. Sordid. Sordid. Sordid.

MRS. HEFLEY: The rocket's still there.

MRS. PATTON: It's a pretty thing, isn't it? And on a night
like this, after my work is done, I could almost wish that
I were going to the moon on it.

MRS. HEFLEY: And what would you be doing on the moon?

MRS. PATTON: I'd be sitting on the edge, dangling my feet
over the earth, with never a thought about my bunions
and other people's dirt. That's what I'd be doing.

MRS. HEFLEY: If you go, save a place for me. It would be
nice to be up there looking down, with never a care for
what muddy boots are tracking over the floor you've
just cleaned. It would be nice to get away from the dirt
of the earth.

MRS. PATTON: Just for a vacation, mind you. I wouldn't
care to live there. (*They exit, passing* JOHN *who is just
entering. At the same time,* JOAN *enters from the other
side. Both* JOHN *and* JOAN *are looking back over their
shoulders as they move toward center, and they bump
into each other.*)

JOAN: Oh, my goodness.

JOHN: Oh, pardon me. I wasn't looking where I was going.

JOAN: I'm afraid I wasn't either.

JOHN: I'll stay out of your way so you can get by.

JOAN: I wasn't going by.

JOHN: Oh?

JOAN: But I'll stand out of your way so you can get by.

JOHN: But I wasn't going by.

JOAN: Oh? (*She turns downstage and looks toward audience.*) That's it, isn't it?

JOHN: Yes, that's the moon rocket.

JOAN: It looks very clean.

JOHN: Oh, yes. Yes, I'm sure it is.

JOAN: Is it going to the moon tomorrow?

JOHN: No one has said, but I think so.

JOAN: Well . . . well, I don't want to keep you.

JOHN: I wasn't going any place. But don't you stay on my account.

JOAN: You're just going to stay here?

JOHN: Why, yes. I'm just going to stay here.

JOAN: But why?

JOHN: I just want to, that's all.

JOAN: How long are you going to stay here?

JOHN: Oh, I don't know. Quite a while, I think. Does it bother you that I'm staying here?

JOAN: No. No, of course not. It's none of my business if you want to act like a fool and just stay here.

JOHN: I don't see why you have to insult me. If it's so foolish, what are you doing here?

JOAN: I—I just have something to do, that's all. (*She goes over and sits on the bench.*) I can stay here just as long as you can. But I don't see why you don't go home. Somebody is probably waiting for you.

JOHN: Waiting for me? That's a laugh.

JOAN: Oh?

JOHN: Nobody even knows I have a home. I work all day at the shoe store. Then I go to my room. Nobody's there. I just sit and write poetry.

JOAN: Oh, are you a poet?

JOHN: Yes. As a mater of fact, I am.

JOAN: Oh? I've never known a poet before. (*Pauses*) I read poetry.

JOHN: Longfellow, I guess.

JOAN: No. I like—well, somebody like Yeats.

JOHN: Oh?

JOAN: Yes, you know like—(*Quoting*)
"Suddenly I saw the cold and rook-delighting heaven"
JOHN (*Finishing it*):
"That seemed as though ice burned and was but the
more ice, . . ."
JOAN (*Very pleased*): Oh, you know it.
JOHN (*Very superior*): Everybody knows Yeats' "Cold
Heaven."
JOAN: Charlie doesn't know it.
JOHN: And who is Charlie?
JOAN: Charlie Milikin. He's—he's a young man who—who
comes to see me.
JOHN: Does he want to marry you?
JOAN: He thinks he does.
JOHN: Doesn't he know?
JOAN: It's really my mother. He likes my mother's cook-
ing, and my mother likes to cook. So he says he comes to
see me, but then he sits in the kitchen and watches my
mother cook.
JOHN: I wouldn't think he'd know anything about poetry.
JOAN: No, he doesn't. Jack doesn't either.
JOHN: And who is Jack?
JOAN: Well, his name's not really Jack. It's Joseph. But
he doesn't like to be called Joe, so he tells everybody
his name is Jack.
JOHN: Does he want to marry you, too?
JOAN: Well, he says he does. But it's really my sister Anne
that he talks to all the time.
JOHN: Oh? What do they talk about?
JOAN: Oh, things. Tennis and dancing and building a
house with a private swimming pool. They talk quite a
bit about building a house with a private swimming
pool.
JOHN: Oh? And what do you say?

JOAN: I don't say anything, except maybe "uh-huh" or "uh-uh." (*She shakes her head to indicate "yes" and "no."*)

JOHN:

Uh-huh and uh-uh lived on her lips,
Two dwarfish guards that kept
The castle of her mind safe
From the rampaging armies
Of small words, pontifically arrayed.

JOAN: Who wrote that?

JOHN: Nobody wrote it. I just said it.

JOAN: It's poetry, isn't it?

JOHN: It's a kind of poem, I guess.

JOAN: You just made it up because I said that?

JOHN: Yes, I just made it up.

JOAN: That's because you know how I feel.

JOHN: I guess so.

JOAN: There's Dick, too.

JOHN: Dick? He wants to marry you, too?

JOAN: He says so.

JOHN: But?

JOAN: It's really my father. He likes to come and talk to my father.

JOHN: Oh?

JOAN: They talk about baseball and fishing and television.

JOHN: What do they say about baseball?

JOAN: Mostly they just talk about the Yankees and the Dodgers.

JOHN: Oh.

JOAN. Sometimes they say, "Look out for Cincinnati," or "Look out for the Giants." But mostly they just talk about the Yankees and the Dodgers.

JOHN: And they all want to marry you? Charlie and Jack and Dick?

JOAN: They all say they do, but they don't. Mama tells me I should marry Charlie 'cause he has a good appetite, and a man with a good appetite makes a good husband.

JOHN: A pig has a good appetite.

JOAN: Anne says I should marry Jack 'cause he's a good dancer and smokes a pipe.

JOHN: A chimney smokes.

JOAN: And Daddy says I should marry Dick. (*She pauses.*) You don't want me to marry any of them, do you?

JOHN: It's none of my business. I wouldn't marry any of them if I were a girl.

JOAN: They're really very nice.

JOHN: If I were a girl, I wouldn't marry anyone who didn't talk to me.

JOAN: Do—do you have a girl?

JOHN: No.

JOAN: Don't you like girls?

JOHN: I like girls. There was a girl once. Her name was May, and she had hair the color of yours. But she said that poets never amount to anything.

JOAN: Oh?

JOHN: I didn't know her very well. She worked next door to the store, and I talked to her once and told her I was a poet. And then she said poets never amount to much. She had nice hair, just like yours.

JOAN: Do you like my hair?

JOHN: It's all right, I guess. There was another girl. Her name was Emily. She had eyes . . . sort of like yours.

JOAN: Didn't she like poets?

JOHN: I don't know. I didn't tell her. She liked men with big cars, she told me.

JOAN: Do you have a big car?

JOHN: I don't have any car. (*Sighs*) She had nice eyes . . . sort of like yours.

JOAN: Do you like my eyes?

JOHN: They're all right, I guess. There was another girl.

JOAN: Oh?

JOHN: She just came into the store one day. Took a size 5B shoe.

JOAN: I take a size 5B shoe.

JOHN: Oh? She had a nice mouth. It was—it was a little like yours. The same kind of lips and the same kind of mouth. And she smiled a little the way you do, too.

JOAN: Do you like my mouth?

JOHN: I guess so. It's all right.

JOAN: My name's Joan.

JOHN: Oh? How do you do? My name's John.

JOAN: I think that's a nice name.

JOHN: It's sort of like Joan, isn't it?

JOAN: Sort of, I guess. John, what are you doing here?

JOHN: I just came down to stow away. . . . (*Stops abruptly*) I don't know. I'm just here. What are you doing here?

JOAN: I'm here for the same reason you are. I want to go up there.

JOHN: Up there? To the—

JOAN: Yes, to the moon.

JOHN: Why, that's crazy.

JOAN: Then why do you want to go?

JOHN: Well, that's—I didn't say I did.

JOAN: Well, you do, don't you?

JOHN: Oh, I guess so. I just get so tired of never having anyone to talk to. If I'm going to be alone, I'd just as soon be alone on the moon. I'd be closer to the stars.

JOAN: I know.

JOHN: How can you know? You have all those fellows chasing you.

JOAN: They're not chasing me. They never even talk to me.

JOHN: Well, it's not the same.

JOAN: It is, too.

JOHN: What would you do on the moon?

JOAN: What would you do?

JOHN: I . . . I'd write poetry. There! What would you do?

JOAN: I . . . I'd read. I could read the poetry you write.

JOHN: You wouldn't even like it.

JOAN:

Uh-huh and uh-uh lived on her lips,
Two dwarfish guards that kept
The castle of her mind safe
From the rampaging armies
Of small words, pontifically arrayed.

JOHN (*Impressed that she remembered the poem*): Do you really think you'd like to read my poetry?

JOAN (*Nodding*): Uh-huh.

JOHN: Do you like baseball and private swimming pools?

JOAN (*Shaking her head*): Uh-uh.

JOHN: Do you like Robert Frost and T. S. Eliot and Auden?

JOAN (*Nodding*): Uh-huh.

JOHN: Do you like to walk?

JOAN (*Nodding*): Uh-huh.

JOHN: And concerts in the park, and museums on rainy afternoons, and old movies with Charlie Chaplin, and jazz records from old New Orleans?

JOAN (*Nodding*): Uh-huh, uh-huh, uh-huh, and uh-huh.

JOHN: Well, maybe . . .

JOAN: And I like you.

JOHN: Well, maybe we could . . .

JOAN: And I like peanut-butter sandwiches.

JOHN: I do, too. I guess it's all right then.

JOAN: Shall we go to the moon together?

JOHN: Together? (*They start over the rail, just as* KIMBALL *enters left.*)

KIMBALL: All right, all right, you two. Hold it right where

you are. (*He goes to them.*) Now, what do you two think you're doing?

JOAN (*Looking at* JOHN): I don't like to tell lies.

JOHN: I don't either. (*To* KIMBALL) We're going to the moon.

KIMBALL (*Impatiently*): On that rocket?

JOHN: Yes.

JOAN: It is a government rocket, isn't it?

JOHN: Paid for by the taxpayers.

JOAN: And we're taxpayers.

KIMBALL: All right. All right, so you're taxpayers. But you're not going to the moon on that rocket.

JOAN: Why not?

KIMBALL: Well, why would you? Why do you want to go to the moon?

JOHN: We—

JOAN: We just do, that's all.

KIMBALL: Look. The moon's up there. And you're down here.

JOHN: That's why we want to go.

KIMBALL: But if you go to the moon, it will be the same. You will be down there on the moon, and earth will be up here.

JOAN: That's true.

JOHN: I hadn't thought of that.

KIMBALL: I could run you in, you know. You're not supposed to be here. But I don't want to. You look like nice kids, so if you will just go home, I'll forget about it.

JOAN: Home. And Charlie and Jack and Dick.

JOHN: Home. And nobody there.

KIMBALL: Look, kids, you don't want to go to the moon. For thousands of years, young lovers have looked up there and figured the moon was the place to be. But now—now, it's just another bus stop. Now, why don't you go home?

JOAN: Well, I guess . . .

JOHN: I might as well.

JOAN: No. I'm not going to do it. I'm not going home and watch Charlie stuffing himself in the kitchen. I'm not just going to sit there while Jack talks to Anne, and Dick agrees with my father. I'm not going to do it.

JOHN: And I'm not going back to my room and write any more silly poetry.

JOAN: It's not silly poetry.

JOHN: It is, too.

JOAN: Well, it doesn't make any difference anyway. I'm not going home to Charlie and Jack and Dick.

JOHN: And I'm not going home to four walls and a rhyming dictionary.

KIMBALL (*To himself*): And I could be sitting in Prospect Park right this minute, feeding the birds. (*To them*) Look, I don't know what's wrong with you kids. Maybe you've had a quarrel. People always have quarrels. You'll make up. Go on home.

JOAN: You mean *together?*

KIMBALL: Sure, together. Look, what do you want? You're young, you're healthy, and the moon's up there. That's not going to last forever, you know.

JOAN (*To* JOHN): Would you . . . would you take me home?

JOHN: Me? What would your mother say?

JOAN: She'll ask you if you're hungry.

JOHN: Oh. If you think it would be all right with your folks . . .

JOAN: And when Mama asks you if you're hungry, you say no. And then if you are hungry, I'll fix you a peanut-butter sandwich.

JOHN: I'm not really hungry.

JOAN: And if my Dad asks you about baseball, tell him you never heard of the game. That will make him mad.

And if you really like baseball, I'll go to a game with you.

JOHN: That would be fine.

JOAN: And don't you even look at my sister Anne.

KIMBALL: All right, all right. Now that we have that all settled, are you going home?

JOHN: I think so.

JOAN: Yes, now we're going home. (*They start off left.*) What do you do when you're not working at the store and not writing poetry?

JOHN: Oh, not much. Two nights a week I go to night school.

JOAN: At the University?

JOHN: Yes. I'm studying architecture.

JOAN: What nights?

JOHN: Tuesdays and Thursdays.

JOAN (*Very excited*): I have a class on Mondays and Wednesdays in English literature.

JOHN: What do you know? Why don't we try to go the same nights?

JOAN: Yes, let's! Mama will be so pleased. She's always asking me why I don't bring home some of the people from school. But I never knew anyone before. (JOAN *and* JOHN *exit.*)

KIMBALL (*Watching them go, then looking toward the audience and whistling*): Whew. (DIETLIN *enters.*)

DIETLIN: Al?

KIMBALL: Yes, Kimball. Al?

DIETLIN: Yes, Dietlin. (*He goes over to* KIMBALL.) Quiet watch?

KIMBALL: Kind of. Some crazy actress wanted to stow away on the rocket.

DIETLIN: It takes all kinds.

KIMBALL: Then there was this young couple—

DIETLIN: Oh?

KIMBALL: You know, Al, what we really need is two moons —one that we can go to and another one that just stays up there, so we'll have something to dream about. (*Both look up at the moon.*)

DIETLIN (*Slowly*): Yes, Al, I know. (*Curtain*)

THE END

Happy Ending

Characters

FAUST
LUCIFER, *Prince of Darkness*
BALLIOL ⎫
BELCHER ⎬ *devils under Lucifer*
HELEN OF TROY
WILLIAM SHAKESPEARE
ROMEO
JULIET
ANTONY
CLEOPATRA
HAMLET, *a teen-age boy*

SETTING: *Faust's laboratory.*

AT RISE: *The stage is dimly lit with red lighting to suggest the Inferno. A high-backed chair up center on an elevated platform is in darkness.* LUCIFER, *wrapped in his cape, is sitting in chair.* FAUST *runs in, followed by* BALLIOL *and* BELCHER, *who are gleefully jabbing at him with small pitchforks.* FAUST *suddenly stops at center and faces them.*

FAUST: Stop jabbing me with those pitchforks. You have no control over me. I sold my soul to your master, Lucifer, not to you.

BALLIOL: You're a traitor, Faust. I charge you with disobedience to our sovereign lord, Lucifer.

BELCHER: If you don't stop trying to break your bargain with him, we'll jab more holes in you than a sieve.

FAUST: Sweet Belcher. Darling Balliol. You misunderstand. I am not trying to break my bargain with Lucifer.

BALLIOL: What were you doing, then, talking to that holy old man?

FAUST: I was trying to get him to join me, not offering to join him. Besides, my contract with Lucifer calls for him to grant all my requests, and if he once fails, the contract is broken and my soul is again my own.

BELCHER: Considering that it is the soul of a traitor, I don't see why Lucifer wants it.

FAUST: Nevertheless, if you jab me with a pitchfork again, I shall call on Lucifer to destroy you both.

BALLIOL: He wouldn't do that to *us!* We're his friends.

FAUST: If he refuses my request, our contract will be broken. (*A bright light comes on over chair up center.* LUCIFER *leaps to his feet and throws back his cape.*)

LUCIFER: Enough. (*Comes downstage*) You worthless devils. You have almost cost me my catch. Speak, Faust. If you give the command, I shall destroy them both.

FAUST: No, never mind, Lucifer. Let them go. They're good enough fellows—or girls—or whatever it is that little devils are made of. I wish them no harm.

BELCHER: Thanks, old Faust. And when you get to . . . well, to where you're going eventually, I'd like you to come over and have dinner with the family. My mother makes the best fried brimstone in all Hades.

FAUST: I can hardly wait.

BALLIOL: And I have a friend who can fix you up with an apartment that will just kill you. Southern exposure the year around.

LUCIFER: Begone, you two devils, or I'll destroy you for my own sake. (BELCHER *and* BALLIOL *run off right.*) I told Mephistopheles not to use women for this job. I believe in fair employment laws as much as the next fellow, but women are just plain silly as devils.

FAUST: Oh, they were women? I hope this doesn't hurt your feelings, Lucifer, but all you devils look alike to me.

LUCIFER: And all human beings look alike to me. So there.

FAUST: I didn't mean to hurt your feelings, Lucifer.

LUCIFER: *Mr.* Lucifer to you. Let's just keep this strictly business.

FAUST: You sound put out about something. What did I do?

LUCIFER: Don't pretend that you haven't been trying to break our contract. Century in and century out, that's all you've tried to do.

FAUST: To be perfectly honest with you. . . .

LUCIFER: Don't use that word *honest* in my presence.

FAUST: To be perfectly *frank,* then, I don't think I've had all the service I've paid for. After all, a soul is quite a bit to pay for the second-rate magic you've been performing.

LUCIFER: If I had known what a stingy little soul you have, I would never have made the contract with you.

FAUST (*Slyly*): I'm willing to let you out of the contract if you like. I don't want anyone to think I cheated *you.*

LUCIFER: You don't trick me like that. Whom do you think you're dealing with—some crummy third-rate devil still charred behind the ears? (*Drawing himself up proudly*) I am Lucifer, Prince of Darkness, and you'd better not forget it.

FAUST: I'm not trying to trick you. I just think that you haven't given me much excitement for my money.

LUCIFER: All right, what do you want?

FAUST: For one thing, let me ask this of you. I've always had a longing to see Helen of Troy. Maybe if I saw her, I wouldn't be so concerned with saving my soul.

LUCIFER: Faust, this or whatever else you shall desire shall be performed in the twinkling of an eye. (HELEN OF TROY—*best played by the heaviest tackle on the football team—comes tripping on stage from down left and takes a stance on low platform left.*)

FAUST (*Looking at* HELEN, *then at* LUCIFER, *aghast*): Was this the face that launched a thousand ships and burnt the topless towers of Illium?

HELEN: It is I, Helen of Troy, my very self, that is being described.

FAUST: Come, Lucifer, this is a trick. A cheap, shoddy trick.

LUCIFER: No, it isn't. That's Helen in all her glory. Styles change in different ages. Women haven't always been shaped like the twigs on trees.

FAUST: Better a twig than the trunk of an oak.

HELEN: Come, Faust, I'll make you immortal with a kiss.

FAUST: You'll just make me sick, that's what you'll do.

HELEN: Watch what you're saying, man. I'm heavenly.

LUCIFER: That, Helen, is a dirty word.

FAUST: Send her away, Lucifer.

LUCIFER: It's done. Begone, Helen.

HELEN (*Walking left, dejected*): If you change your mind, I'll be in the sulphur pit in North Hades. Pit number 3367.

LUCIFER: All right, Helen. But don't call us. We'll call you. (HELEN *exits.*)

FAUST: No wonder Troy fell.

LUCIFER: Helen has never been one of my favorites, but you asked for her.

FAUST: I'm beginning to think that black magic is not all it's cracked up to be.

LUCIFER: Digging up people from the past does have its problems. Styles change, you know. Some people around today even think you're a kind of joke, Faust.

FAUST: A lot you know. Some very famous people are still pretending to be me.

LUCIFER: To be *I*. If you are going to correct me, at least you might be grammatical.

FAUST: I don't want to be grammatical with people who say stupid things.

LUCIFER: If I were *people,* I would be offended.

FAUST: I read in *Variety*—just last week—that Marlowe's play about me went over very big in Boston.

LUCIFER: Big deal.

FAUST: And a scholar in Chicago is doing a new translation of Goethe's play about me.

LUCIFER: Scholars! I would think, Faust, that you above all men would know they don't mean anything. What kind of things did you do as scholar? Tried to turn brass into gold. And then everybody went off the gold standard.

FAUST: I also figured out how many angels can fit on the head of a pin.

LUCIFER: I'd like to fit some angels I know on a pin.

FAUST: You're letting your bias show, Lucifer. Angels have to live, too, you know.

LUCIFER: Not if I can help it. But enough of this shop talk. If you have another request, make it.

FAUST: Yes, I have a request. I want to talk to Shakespeare.

LUCIFER: Shakespeare? (*He hesitates.*) You mean William Shakespeare?

FAUST: Yes, William Shakespeare. You've heard of him, haven't you?

LUCIFER: Of course I've heard of Shakespeare. Do you think I'm ignorant or something? I know a lot about Shakespeare.

FAUST: Good. Conjure him. I want to talk to him about his plays. In my opinion, they leave a lot to be desired, and I want to talk some things over with him.

LUCIFER (*Almost pleading*): You wouldn't rather talk to John Milton?

FAUST: What's the matter, Lucifer? Don't you know how to conjure up Shakespeare?

LUCIFER: Sure, I know how. I'd just rather not, if you don't mind. Shakespeare is a very great man, and I hate to bother him.

FAUST: I didn't think you thought any man was great.

LUCIFER: He's the only exception. Besides, he left a curse on his tomb. And nobody but a stupid scholar would disturb him.

FAUST: Are you afraid of curses, Lucifer?

LUCIFER: Certainly not! I just don't see any sense in fooling around with things like that.

FAUST: You are scared.

LUCIFER: I am not. (*Limply*) I just don't want to.

FAUST: If you really don't want to. . . . I guess that ends our contract. (*Puts out his hand to shake* LUCIFER's) It's been nice doing business with you. If I ever think of selling my soul again, I'll look you up. But don't call me. I'll call you. (*Starts off right*)

LUCIFER (*Striking a pose of throwing a bolt of lightning*): Schzamm! (FAUST *freezes in place.*)

FAUST: But you refused my request. You have to let me go. It's in the contract.

LUCIFER: I did not refuse. I don't want to do it, but I will. Come back here.

FAUST (*Still frozen*): Unfreeze me then.

LUCIFER: All right. (*Lackadaisically*) Schzamm scram.

FAUST (*Returning to* LUCIFER): I'd think this over, if I were you, Lucifer. After all, getting my one soul is not worth the social embarrassment of disturbing the bones of William Shakespeare.

LUCIFER: Be quiet. (*Raises hands and speaks as to a spirit*)
Thrice to thine, and thrice to mine,
And thrice again, to make up nine.
Arise, Shakespeare, and appear before me.
(*Points to the platform*) Now! This very minute. (SHAKESPEARE *enters down left and stands on platform*.)

FAUST: He doesn't look like a great man.

SHAKESPEARE: I've been dead a long time, you know.

LUCIFER: Don't pay any attention to him, William. He has no taste. He has been criticizing your plays.

SHAKESPEARE: He jests at scars that never felt a wound.

FAUST: *Romeo and Juliet!* Right? You see, I've read all your plays. And I like them too, but. . . .

LUCIFER: But? What is there to *but* about in a play by William Shakespeare? I don't see how I'm going to get your soul. You don't have any. Don't listen to him, Willy.

SHAKESPEARE: Oh, it's all right, Lucy. I don't think some of my plays are so hot either.

FAUST: *Lucy!* Don't tell me that. . . .

LUCIFER: It's none of your business. But if you must know, I am a man. And I don't allow anyone in creation to call me *Lucy* except Willy; so don't *you* try it.

FAUST: I wouldn't even want to. I think it's a silly name.

LUCIFER: You're just trying to irritate me so that I'll break our contract, but it's not going to work. You asked me

to summon Shakespeare from the grave. Well, here he
is. I have kept our bargain.

FAUST: You're so suspicious, Lucifer.

LUCIFER: Never mind about me. Let's just stick to our
business. Are you through with Shakespeare?

FAUST: I haven't even started to talk with him yet. (*To*
SHAKESPEARE) I don't want you to misunderstand,
William, I think you're a great playwright.

SHAKESPEARE: It's a living. Well, it *was* a living.

FAUST: I think you have a great way with words.

SHAKESPEARE: I get by, I guess.

FAUST: Great insight into character.

SHAKESPEARE: I've been around.

FAUST: But. . . .

LUCIFER: There he goes with that *but* again. Sometimes
I think I must be out of my mind to bring someone like
you back home with me. (*Goes upstage and flops into
chair*) But I will. And don't think I'll forget all this,
either. You're making me very angry, Faust.

FAUST: You're too sensitive, especially for your job. Have
you ever thought of taking up some other line of work?

LUCIFER: As a matter of fact, when I was young I thought
about going on the stage. But I didn't want to disgrace
the family.

FAUST: It's still not too late. Actors are very respectable
now.

LUCIFER: No, you don't. You're not tricking me. I have a
contract with you, and when I have fulfilled all your
requests, off you will go—body, soul, and sneaky tongue.

FAUST (*To* SHAKESPEARE): As I was saying, Will . . . you
don't mind my calling you Will, do you?

SHAKESPEARE: Suit yourself. It's all the same to me.

FAUST: As I was saying, I like your plays fine—good stories,
fine characterization, first-rate dialogue; but your end-

ings—they're terrible. I'm talking about the tragedies now.

LUCIFER: The tragic endings are the best things in the plays. You don't know nothing about show biz, Faust. You're just ignorant, plain ignorant.

FAUST: I may be, but I don't use double negatives. "Don't know nothing!"

LUCIFER: That just shows how really ignorant you are. Shakespeare used double negatives lots of times.

SHAKESPEARE: Did I use double negatives? (*Half to himself*) Ben Jonson was right. I should have read those plays over.

FAUST: I don't really mind double negatives. I just don't like to be called ignorant, that's all. I think your double negatives are fine, Will.

SHAKESPEARE: I hope that my English teacher back in Stratford didn't see them.

FAUST: In fact, if it weren't for those tragic endings, you'd be the perfect playwright. Happy endings, that's what I like.

LUCIFER: Happy endings! Bah! Humbug!

SHAKESPEARE: It's too late now. The plays have been written, and I am in my grave.

FAUST: Black magic does have some advantages, you know. You can still change the endings.

SHAKESPEARE: I could? How?

FAUST: Lucifer here can summon up all the characters and you can just make the endings something else. I'll even help you. He has to fulfill all my requests. (*Turning to* LUCIFER) Don't you?

LUCIFER: I won't do it.

FAUST: Then our contract will be broken.

LUCIFER: I'll do it, but I won't like it.

SHAKESPEARE: All right, let's give it a whirl, then. Faust,

you tell me the changes you want; Lucy can bring my characters back, and we'll see what happens.

LUCIFER: I hate myself.

FAUST: Let's take Romeo and Juliet first. As *I* see them.

LUCIFER: And I'll hate myself tomorrow even more.

FAUST: Now, you had that nice couple dying pretty young, Will.

SHAKESPEARE: She was almost fourteen. That was no kid in my time.

FAUST: That's pretty young. I want a happy ending for them. Lucifer, bring back Romeo and Juliet twenty years later. They both survived, married, and have children. Now, call up the happy Romeo and Juliet.

LUCIFER: I'll hate myself a million years from now. All right, though. Romeo and Juliet, appear before me. Now! (ROMEO *and* JULIET *enter down right and cross to left as they speak. He is pushing a baby carriage and she is walking beside him complaining.*)

JULIET: You never do anything right, Romeo.

ROMEO: It's not my fault I couldn't find a baby-sitter, Juliet.

JULIET: From the day we married you've never done a single thing right. You almost botched up our elopement. I wish that I had listened to my mother and father and married the Count Paris. Now, *he* could find a baby-sitter. But, like a fool, I believed everything you told me.

ROMEO: Juliet, pet, I meant every word I said that night under your balcony.

JULIET: That's another thing. Before our daughter gets to marriageable age, I want that balcony torn down. If you had had to court me properly, without all the moonlight and poetry, we would have gotten a few things straight.

ROMEO: But, pet, I did try to get a baby-sitter.

JULIET: And one more thing. You didn't take the garbage out this morning. The whole kitchen is overflowing, but a lot you care.

ROMEO: But, pet, why can't Junior take the garbage out?

JULIET: Because he's no better than his father, that's why. Oh, if I had it to do over again, I'd have listened to my mother. She always said you were no good.

ROMEO: Yes, pet. (ROMEO *and* JULIET *exit left.*)

FAUST (*Rubbing his hands*): Now, wasn't that better than that dreary tomb scene? I do like happy endings.

LUCIFER (*Groaning*): I'll hate myself for a billion years.

SHAKESPEARE: Juliet's taken on a little weight, I think. She looks good, though. What's next, Faust?

FAUST: Ah, let me see. *Antony and Cleopatra.* Yes, that would be very nice.

LUCIFER (*Almost crying*): Not *Antony and Cleopatra.* That's one of my favorite plays. You're not going to have Antony pushing a baby carriage, and Cleopatra complaining about the garbage!

FAUST: Of course not. (*Sits on stool down right*) I see them somewhat differently, another sort of happy ending.

LUCIFER: I'm not going to like this. I just know I'm going to hate it.

FAUST: Do you want to break the contract?

LUCIFER: Not after I've gone this far. Antony and Cleopatra, appear before me. Now! (CLEOPATRA *enters down left. She is obviously a tourist, loaded down with cameras, etc., and wearing sunglasses and a funny hat. She stops and calls off left.*)

CLEOPATRA: Tony! Tony, get me one, too. (ANTONY *enters carrying two hot dogs.*) Did you put mustard on my hot dog?

ANTONY: Yes, Cleo dear. Lots of mustard.

CLEOPATRA: You're a sweet boy, Tony.

LUCIFER (*Leaping up and screaming*): Tony! Cleo! Antony and Cleopatra eating hot dogs! It's a travesty. A disgrace. (ANTONY *and* CLEOPATRA *freeze.* LUCIFER *comes down center and shakes his finger at* FAUST) You're a fiend, Faust. A devil.

FAUST: Why, thank you, Lucifer. I didn't know you cared.

LUCIFER: What am I saying? (*Walks back to his chair slowly*)

FAUST (*Yelling after him*): Do you want to break our contract, Lucifer?

LUCIFER (*Turning downstage*): Never. You'll not trick me out of your miserable soul. (*Dramatically*) O, what a rogue and peasant slave. . . .

FAUST (*To* SHAKESPEARE): *Hamlet,* Act II, Scene 2. Right?

SHAKESPEARE: I guess so. It sounds familiar. But I've always preferred the comedies to the tragedies myself.

FAUST (*To* LUCIFER): You want to keep the contract?

LUCIFER: Until my country freezes over. Go on with your travesty. (*He sits.* ANTONY *and* CLEOPATRA *go back into action.*)

CLEOPATRA: You know, Tony darling, I'm glad we had sense enough to quit the ruling business and retire while we're still young enough to enjoy it.

ANTONY: The smartest thing I ever did was to turn the business over to young Caesar. Not that he's doing much of a job.

CLEOPATRA: Now, Tony, don't start worrying about the business again.

ANTONY: I'm not worrying. I'm just voicing an opinion. Even an old retired man has a right to an opinion, hasn't he?

CLEOPATRA: Now, Tony, dear, don't get yourself upset.

ANTONY (*Shrilly*): Who's upset?

CLEOPATRA: That's right, dear. Remember what the doctor said about your nerves.

ANTONY: My nerves are fine, now that you've gotten rid of those snakes.

CLEOPATRA (*Sighing*): Yes, dear. I know that you are allergic to poisonous snakes. But I do miss the little darlings. Do you think maybe I could get just a little one— a little teeny asp?

ANTONY: No snakes. That's final.

CLEOPATRA: Yes, dear. If you say so.

ANTONY: Don't start that sniffling. Come on, I'll take you on a shopping tour of Cairo.

CLEOPATRA: Can I buy everything I want?

ANTONY: Everything, except snakes and pyramids. (*Looking off left.*) There's our bargeman. (*Raising his hand as though hailing a taxi*) Bargeman. Bargeman. (AN-TONY, *followed by* CLEOPATRA, *exits right.*)

LUCIFER (*Storming downstage and looking after them*): "Age cannot wither her, nor custom stale her infinite variety." That was the great woman Shakespeare created. (*Turning to* FAUST) Oh, how could you do such a thing? The finest tragic queen in all the world turned into a . . . a tourist! (*Turns to* SHAKESPEARE) And you, Will, how could you let him do it?

SHAKESPEARE (*Shrugging*): That's show biz, Lucy.

LUCIFER (*Throwing his hands in the air in defeat*): Oh, that it should come to this! (*To* FAUST) Now you're through. Right?

FAUST: Wrong. I want to change one more tragedy. I want one more happy ending.

LUCIFER (*Almost pleading*): Not *King Lear*?

FAUST: Certainly not.

LUCIFER: Not *Julius Caesar*?

FAUST (*As though considering it*): Well, no.

LUCIFER: Not . . . you wouldn't. . . .

FAUST (*Gleefully*): Yes, I would. *Hamlet*!

LUCIFER (*Dropping to his knees and pounding his fists on the floor*): No, no, no!

FAUST: You want to break the contract?

LUCIFER (*Rising and standing majestically*): You'll not win over me, Faust. Do your worst and then wait for the power of all Hades to rise against you.

FAUST (*Slowly*): Do you want to break the contract? (LU-CIFER, *hands in air, turns upstage, and walks to his chair, slumps in it, and glares at* FAUST.)

LUCIFER: Go ahead. Ruin *Hamlet* with your happy ending. Go ahead. I can take it.

FAUST: You'll like this, Lucifer. It will be a really wholesome, fun play now.

LUCIFER: Go on about your business. And don't talk to me.

FAUST: Call up Hamlet, then.

LUCIFER (*Pleading*): Do I have to?

FAUST: Unless you want to break the contract.

LUCIFER (*To* SHAKESPEARE): Will, aren't you going to do anything about this?

SHAKESPEARE: Who, me? What can I do? I'm only the playwright. The actors know it all. The director knows it all. The critics know it all. Even your Aunt Fanny from Scotland knows it all. But who ever asks a playwright what he thinks? (*Sits down on platform*) Besides, I like happy endings, too.

FAUST (*To* LUCIFER): Are you going to call Hamlet up or aren't you?

LUCIFER: All right. But when I am being blamed for all the evils of the world, I want one thing clearly understood. It was not the devil who made a travesty of *Hamlet*. (*Holds out his hand to raise the spirit*) Hamlet, appear before me. Now! Please? (HAMLET *enters down right. He is wearing short pants and carrying a picnic basket.*) Oh-h-h! What have you done to Hamlet?

FAUST: I just turned him into a clean-cut, decent boy, that's all. When a kid goes around with black clothes and a beard and long hair, he's just naturally going to get into trouble.

LUCIFER: Oh, I'll hate myself through three eternities.

FAUST (*To* HAMLET): Hi there, fellow.

HAMLET: Hi there, yourself. (*Points off left*) Is this the way to the picnic area?

FAUST: Why, yes, I think so. Are you going on a picnic, Hamlet?

HAMLET: Yes, it's a kind of father-son outing. My dad and I are going.

LUCIFER: Your dad! Hamlet, have you forgotten? Your noble father is dead, murdered by a villain, and heaven and hell both cry out for vengeance.

HAMLET: What? Oh, you're talking about Old King Hamlet. I mean Daddy Claudius.

LUCIFER: Claudius! That's the villain who killed your father, treacherously, while he was sleeping in the garden.

HAMLET: None of us is perfect.

LUCIFER: This has gone too far. Go back to wherever you've come from. Go! (HAMLET *runs off right, running backwards, like a movie film in reverse.*)

FAUST: You've broken the contract, Lucifer. I've won my soul back.

LUCIFER: Yes, I've broken the contract. I wouldn't have you in my kingdom—not even as a lump of coal. (*He storms off up center.*)

FAUST (*Jumping up and down in glee*): I won. I won. That's the happy ending I've been looking for.

SHAKESPEARE: I don't get it.

FAUST: I've beaten Lucifer and I have my soul back. I'm free of him forever. I didn't really want to change your plays, Will, but I figured there must be something that even the devil wouldn't do.

SHAKESPEARE: I don't know. I rather liked the Hamlet you dreamed up. (*Thinking*) Maybe he could have a twin brother, and then both brothers could have servants who were twins. Then . . .

FAUST: No, no, leave *Hamlet* the way it is. It's really a great play. I was just playing a trick.

SHAKESPEARE: All right, Faust, but what am I going to do now? Lucy seems to have left without getting me back to wherever it is I belong.

FAUST: Oh, don't worry. I've been thinking about it. I'd like you to stick around and write another play. A play about me!

SHAKESPEARE: I might as well. I'm not doing anything else. It might be kind of fun. (*Walks about thinking*) Now, as I see it, in this play, you are hiding in the Forest of Arden, and you meet a young boy. Well, you think it's a young boy, but it's really a young girl. Now there's this scene. . . .

FAUST: No, no, no. I don't want *As You Like It*. I want a serious play. A modern Tragedy of Faust, that's what I want. In this play, I'll trade my soul to the devil.

SHAKESPEARE (*Thinking*): It might have possibilities. How are you going to get out of this deal with the devil?

FAUST: I don't get out of it. That's just the point. It's a tragedy. I die at the end, and the devil drags me off. It could have all sorts of social overtones—about life and death and the fears of modern men.

SHAKESPEARE: It might have possibilities for some playwright, but not for me. I think I'll go back where I came from. So long, Faust. (*Starts up center, yelling*)

Lucy, Lucy. Lucifer, you forgot me. Lucy! Lucy! I'm ready to go home. (SHAKESPEARE *exits up center.*)

FAUST: Wait, Will. Wait. (*Turns to laboratory table down right*) I don't need him. I'll concoct a tragedy here in my laboratory. (*Holds a bottle up to the light*) I can do it. I can do it. I know I can. (*Stops*) No, I can't. I need Shakespeare. Oh, I'd give my soul to have him here. (*Puts his hands over his mouth and looks around in terror*) I wonder if Lucifer heard that.

LUCIFER (*Coming in up center*): I heard you. (*Lights gradually dim, and become red again.*)

FAUST: Then, I'm in your power again. But I'll do it. Our contract is on again, Lucifer. (*Puts out his hand to* LUCIFER)

LUCIFER (*Refusing to shake*): Not this time, Faust. I offered you a tragic ending, but you wouldn't have it. No, you liked happy endings. Well, from now on, I'll use my influence with playwrights so they'll make nothing but comedies about you.

FAUST: Oh, no. Not that. I'll give you anything you want.

LUCIFER: And that, Faust, is really a happy ending. For you, for me, and for anyone who ever had to sit through an evening of you as a tragic figure. Ha! (*Curtain*)

THE END

Trash and Treasure

Characters

MIDAS O'BRIEN, *the caretaker*
PAGE, *his friend*
PAULINE WARREN, *an actress*
MRS. LISTMAN, *a housewife*
HENRY LOFTIS, *a woodworker*
JUNE, *an unhappy young girl*
BOB, *her husband*
GEORGE, *a young boy*
PATTY MILLER, *a middle-aged woman*
ALVIN FOOTE, *a middle-aged man*

SETTING: *The basement of an apartment house, the room in which the trash cans are kept. Up center is a large trash can, in front of which is a bench. Six or seven medium-sized trash cans form an irregular border around stage.*

AT RISE: MIDAS O'BRIEN *and* PAGE *are sitting at a small table down right, playing checkers.*

PAGE: There, I have you this time.
MIDAS: You certainly have. (*Makes a move*) Here, take another of my poor pieces.

PAGE (*Laughing*): Ah, Midas, my friend. This does my heart good. You have no idea how long I've wanted to beat you at a game of checkers. (*Jumps a checker and takes it*)

MIDAS: That's your trouble, Page. You're greedy. You see? (*Makes a series of jumps and clears all of* PAGE'*s checkers from the board*) It's a rule of life, Page. Whenever you take something, leave something. Whenever you leave something, take something. Shall we set up for another game?

PAGE: I was so certain I had won this game.

MIDAS: Perhaps the next time. But watch carefully. Only the bud of a rose is without a thorn, the poets say, and we are faded roses now. To win at checkers, you must give freely and take cautiously. Do you want the reds or the blacks?

PAGE: The reds. This time I'll take the reds. They might be luckier.

MIDAS (*Setting up board*): Luck is a strange girl. She won't be flattered by charms, lied to by flatterers, or charmed by liars. Take me, for example. My good father, Daniel O'Brien, tried to flatter Miss Luck into treating me gently. He named me Midas—after the old fellow with the golden touch. "To let Lady Luck know the boy could do with a bit of money," he told my mother. And here I am—a half century and more later—tending to other people's trash, cleaning up·after the rich ones, none of whom is named Midas.

PAGE: But it's not a bad life, Midas. You have your health. It's warm here in the winter months, cool here in the summer. And you have a golden touch in checkers.

MIDAS: I'm not complaining—just explaining. You can't bribe little Miss Luck. My father would have done better if he had named me Job or Ishmael, or even

Jonah—one of those fellows that knew bad luck. Then I'd have been prepared for the worst. I'd have known as a boy that I needed to lose something to gain something.

PAGE: You've grown most philosophical here, Midas.

MIDAS: Taxi drivers, sailors, and janitors are always philosophers. Philosophy just naturally grows in places where people are going and coming, getting and spending, losing and finding. Well, we're ready to go. Shall I make the first move?

PAGE: Go ahead.

MIDAS (*Making move*): Here's an easy one for you.

PAGE: I'll think this time before I move.

MIDAS: You don't have to think yet.

PAGE: That's just what you said to me before you jumped my king in the last game. (*He stares at board.* PAULINE WARREN *enters with an armload of clothes.*)

PAULINE: Where shall I put this trash, Mr. O'Brien?

MIDAS (*Getting to his feet*): As I live and breathe, it's Juliet, and Rosalind, and Ophelia—all rolled into one.

PAULINE: Mr. O'Brien, would you call those roles one at a time? Every time my director sees me he tells me I have to lose weight.

MIDAS: The man's out of his mind. You're just perfect. I saw you last week as Lady Macbeth, and it was the best I've ever seen.

PAULINE: Why, thank you, Mr. O'Brien, but one of the reviewers said that I made Vincent Cassidy's Macbeth look like a henpecked husband.

MIDAS: What can they expect—if they cast you next to a little runt of a man like that? Sure, Mr. Cassidy is a fine actor, but he's a bit on the scrawny side for my money.

PAULINE: Well, *I'm* not scrawny. And these old costumes

tell me a sad story. I wore these twenty years ago when I did Juliet—and now. . . . Which trash can shall I throw my slim youth into?

MIDAS (*Going to can*): Here's an empty one, Miss Warren. But I hate to see you throwing those clothes away. They should be going to a museum of theatre arts.

PAULINE (*Throwing clothes into can*): No, no museum for me—not yet. (*Starts to exit, then turns back*) Good night.

MIDAS: Good night.

PAULINE: Parting is such sweet sorrow that I shall say good night till it be morrow.

MIDAS: Good night, Miss Warren, peace on thy brow.

PAULINE: Good night, Mr. O'Brien. (*Exits*)

MIDAS (*To* PAGE): She's a fine woman, that Pauline Warren—and she was almost a great actress once.

PAGE: Once? I thought you said she was playing Lady Macbeth the other night.

MIDAS: That was ten years ago I saw her opposite Vincent Cassidy. I lost a few years in talking to a great lady, and we both gained . . . a few dreams.

PAGE: It doesn't seem honest to me.

MIDAS: Have you made your move yet?

PAGE: I'm still thinking.

MIDAS: If you'd do your thinking about checkers and not mix in complex problems like time and ladies, you might be a better player, Page.

PAGE (*Moving checker*): All right. All right.

MIDAS (*Making a quick move*): It's your move again.

PAGE: You move too fast. I can't see what you're doing.

MIDAS (*Indicating*): I moved my checker there.

PAGE: Yes, yes, I see.

MIDAS: Now it's your move.

PAGE: I know it. Let a man think a minute, will you? You gave your Miss Warren ten years, can't you give me ten seconds? (*He goes into thinker's pose;* MIDAS *gets up and goes to trash can, pulls out a scarf and looks at it.* MRS. LISTMAN *enters with a small cardboard carton filled with blocks of wood.*)

MRS. LISTMAN: Good evening, Mr. O'Brien.

MIDAS: Good evening, Mrs. Listman.

MRS. LISTMAN: It's certainly comfortable down here.

MIDAS: It's a home. Of sorts.

MRS. LISTMAN: What shall I do with my trash? Mostly old blocks of wood, not good for anything.

MIDAS (*Looking in box*): It would have been good wood to start a furnace. But they're all oil now, oil and gas. (*Indicating another can*) Here, throw the junk in here.

MRS. LISTMAN (*Emptying wood into can*): That's a pretty scarf, Mr. O'Brien. A gift for a lady friend?

MIDAS: No, it's just something Miss Warren threw away. It is pretty, isn't it?

MRS. LISTMAN: It certainly is. And my favorite color, too.

MIDAS: Would you like it?

MRS. LISTMAN: I'd love it.

MIDAS: It's yours. (*Handing scarf to her*)

MRS. LISTMAN: Why, thank you, Mr. O'Brien.

MIDAS: Don't thank me. Thank Miss Warren—or the changing times and shapes. She threw away a whole arm-load of clothes.

MRS. LISTMAN: She did?

MIDAS: Right here. (*Reaches in and brings a few pieces of clothing to the top of can*) See?

MRS. LISTMAN: My goodness. They look so nice. Do you suppose . . . ?

MIDAS: If you want them, just help yourself. One person's trash is another's treasure. (*Walks back to table*) Well, Page, have you moved yet?

PAGE: Don't rush me. (*Moves a checker*) There. (MIDAS

sits down, looks at board a moment, then makes a move.)

MIDAS: There, I've given you a jump.

PAGE: Don't rush me.

MIDAS: If you have a jump, you have to take it.

MRS. LISTMAN (*Who has been filling up her box with clothes*): Do you think it's all right if I take *all* these things?

MIDAS: I'm sure it is. If you didn't, they would only go to the city dump.

MRS. LISTMAN: That would be a shame, you know. These are beautiful things. But I feel greedy. I'm taking everything, and that doesn't seem right.

MIDAS: You're not taking everything, Mrs. Listman. Just some old clothes—something someone else didn't want. You're leaving lots of things.

MRS. LISTMAN: You mean there's more? Where?

MIDAS: There's that can filled with wooden blocks.

MRS. LISTMAN: Oh, you mean the trash that I brought in. Who wants it?

MIDAS: You never can tell.

MRS. LISTMAN: Whoever wants that trash may have it and my blessings with it. (*Looking at clothes*) But these . . . these are real treasures. I'm going to make a costume out of one of these for my Mary. She's in the school play, you know .

MIDAS: Then be sure to tell her that a famous actress wore them, too. It will bring her luck on opening night.

MRS. LISTMAN: I will. (*Starts off left*) I can hardly wait to see her face when she sees them. Good night, Mr. O'Brien.

MIDAS: Good night, Mrs. Listman. (*She exits.*)

PAGE: Thought you said you couldn't bribe luck.

MIDAS: You ought to stop eavesdropping, Page. It's ruining your checker game.

PAGE: Eavesdropping! I like that. You said it right in front of me.

MIDAS: True, but I didn't say it *to* you. Go on, move. You have to jump.

PAGE: All right, but I think I'm being tricked. (*Jumps a checker and lifts one checker off table*)

MIDAS: It would please Miss Warren to know that her old costumes will be used for a young actress. She'd like that. (*Jumps two checkers, lifts them off board*) Your move.

PAGE: Hey! What are you doing with my checkers?

MIDAS: I just jumped them.

PAGE: I don't see how you did that.

MIDAS: Do you want me to make the move again?

PAGE: No, no, never mind. I just wish that you wouldn't move so fast.

MIDAS: And I wish that you wouldn't move so slowly. It's your move. (HENRY LOFTIS *enters, carrying bag of empty tin cans.*)

LOFTIS: Is Midas beating you, Page?

PAGE: He's ahead at the moment, Henry.

LOFTIS (*To* MIDAS): What can do you want me to put this trash in, Midas?

MIDAS: What is it?

LOFTIS: Tin cans, papers.

MIDAS: Any one, it doesn't make any difference. It's all trash.

LOFTIS: There used to be a time we had to separate things —garbage in one can, cans in another, like that.

MIDAS: Don't do that any more. All rubbish goes together now.

LOFTIS (*Going to can into which* MRS. LISTMAN *threw the wood*): I guess that's right. Trash is trash. (*Sees wood*) Hey, who threw all this good wood away?

MIDAS: Mrs. Listman, up on three. She said it was just junk.

LOFTIS: Women don't have any sense about some things. I could sure use some blocks of wood like these.

MIDAS: Help yourself. (LOFTIS *goes to another trash barrel and empties tin cans out of bag, then returns, and starts putting wood into his bag.*)

LOFTIS: I don't understand how anyone could throw away good wood like this. (*Holds up small block*) That's good walnut. I could carve a nice little figure out of that. (*Holds up another*) And that's real cypress. That's good wood.

PAGE: One man's trash is another man's treasure.

LOFTIS: This is not trash. Why, I could carve a set of checkers out of this wood that would be a lot better than that five-and-ten-cent stuff you're playing with there.

PAGE: This is good enough for me to play with.

MIDAS: Then why don't you play? You've been sitting there for an hour, just looking at those checkers.

LOFTIS: It's downright criminal to throw away good wood like this. Downright criminal. (*Looks in can*) I guess I have it all.

MIDAS (*To* PAGE): Are you going to move?

PAGE: Don't rush me. (*Moves checker*)

LOFTIS (*As he exits*): It's just downright foolish to throw away wood like this. Someday we won't have any more wood left if people don't get better sense.

PAGE: He really thinks he found a treasure.

MIDAS: He did.

PAGE: Just some scraps of wood.

MIDAS: To you and to me. But to old Henry Loftis, they're the raw materials for practical dreams. Have you ever seen the head of Lincoln he carved?

PAGE: I take nothing away from Henry and his woodwork. But if he can do things like that with trash, just think what he could do if he'd get some decent materials.

MIDAS: Trash or jewels, who's to say?

PAGE: Why, any sensible man can look at a piece of trash and know it's trash—no matter what use is made of it.

MIDAS: Do you know that perfume—the best perfume in the world—comes from the diseased innards of a whale? And mankind itself, some say, was scooped up from the mud.

PAGE: If you think trash is so great, why don't you keep it for yourself?

MIDAS: I might just do that from now on. Now stop your talking and move.

PAGE: Did you change the board? (JUNE *enters, looking about as though she has lost something and is most unhappy.*)

MIDAS: No, I didn't change the board.

PAGE: It looks different somehow.

JUNE: Mr. O'Brien, what barrel did I put my trash in?

MIDAS: You mean today?

JUNE: Yes, this afternoon. I did throw out my trash today, didn't I?

MIDAS: Not today, June.

JUNE: Are you sure, Mr. O'Brien?

MIDAS: I'm sure, June. Sure, life down here is too grim for a pretty young thing like you to flit in without lighting up the whole place. You can look around if you like. Did you lose something again?

JUNE (*Looking in barrels*): Yes, and I just have to find it.

MIDAS: You didn't lose your wedding ring again, did you?

JUNE: Worse than that. I lost a letter that came for Bob.

MIDAS: Don't worry about it. Worse things have happened.

JUNE: *Nothing* worse could happen. In all my life . . .

MIDAS: Now that would be all of twenty years, I'd guess.

PAGE: Ah, to be twenty again—and filled with the joys of youth. To bend without creaking, to go up stairs two steps at a time, to wonder what's new in the world just around the corner.

MIDAS: Stop your snorting and move, Page.

JUNE (*Sitting on bench up center*): Oh, I'll never find it.

MIDAS: Has it been a bad day, June?

JUNE: A terrible day. First, I burned the dinner.

PAGE: I like a piece of meat well done myself.

JUNE: And then I lost Bob's letter.

PAGE: That's one he won't have to answer.

JUNE: Poor Bob. Everything's going wrong for him right now, and if I were the right kind of wife for him . . .

MIDAS: You'll find the letter in time, don't worry.

JUNE: I'm not sure. (*Pauses*) I may have thrown it away.

MIDAS: Oh, I don't think you would do that.

JUNE: I think it was a letter about his play.

MIDAS: Then maybe it's good news.

JUNE: I don't think it's good news.

MIDAS: You didn't read the letter, did you? So how would you know that?

JUNE: I know. It was a big letter—a letter in a large brown envelope.

PAGE: That sounds good to me. They probably needed a large envelope to hold all the good things they had to say about Bob's play.

JUNE: It's the kind of envelope they use to send back manuscripts they don't want.

PAGE: Ah, you're just borrowing trouble.

JUNE: I've seen a lot of envelopes like it before. Poor Bob.

PAGE: Maybe the next time.

JUNE: If Bob did get his play back, there may not be a next time. He may stop writing. He's been talking about it.

MIDAS: Lots of playwrights talk that way.

PAGE: One successful play, and he'll whistle another tone.

MIDAS: *Tune,* not *tone.* And you're talking too much, Page. Play checkers.

JUNE (*Rising*): I can't just sit here.

MIDAS: Maybe Bob has found the letter by now.

PAGE: Maybe it's good news.

JUNE: I'm afraid not. Oh, if there were just something that I could do.

MIDAS: You could go back up to your apartment and help Bob look.

JUNE: I'd rather look down here.

MIDAS: You're not likely to find it here.

JUNE: That's one of the reasons I'd rather look here.

MIDAS: You might try in the back. I moved some stuff back there this morning.

JUNE: The letter didn't come till this noon. Or, maybe, it did come this morning. It seems as if it came about three years ago. I'll go look.

MIDAS: Do you want me to help you?

JUNE: No, I'll find it alone. (JUNE *exits in back of large trash can.*)

PAGE (*Almost whispering*): Poor little thing, I hope she finds that letter.

MIDAS: You poor old thing, she's not looking for anything. She's just staying away from Bob. So he can get his disappointment swallowed alone.

PAGE: I would think she'd want to be with Bob . . . if it's bad news.

MIDAS: She's a smart young woman. She'd rather be with him, but she knows he'd rather be alone. Now, would you mind paying attention to the game?

PAGE (*Staring at the board*): Ah-ha, Midas, I see your plan. (*Makes move*) There, now let me see you do something. (GEORGE *enters, looking downcast.*)

MIDAS: Evening, George. How's the spy business?

GEORGE: Hello, Uncle Midas. I've quit the spy business.

PAGE: Going West? Or maybe you've decided to be a pirate?

GEORGE: I've decided to be nothing. (*Pauses*) Uncle Midas, do you know how I could earn about five dollars?

MIDAS: The supermarket needs bag boys. That pays well.

GEORGE: You have to be sixteen.

MIDAS: That's true. What about peddling newspapers?

GEORGE: You have to be twelve.

MIDAS: And you're a bit young for Medicare. What do you need money for, George?

GEORGE: I need a walkie-talkie. I can't be a private detective or spy or anything unless I have a walkie-talkie.

MIDAS: Is that a fact?

GEORGE: It sure is. Charles told me, and he ought to know. He has two walkie-talkies.

MIDAS: Two! Well now, that is something.

PAGE: Why don't you make your own, George? All the professional spies make their own.

GEORGE: Make one? I never heard of that.

PAGE: You just need a couple of tin cans and a piece of string or wire.

GEORGE: I have lots of string upstairs.

MIDAS: Then go to work.

GEORGE: I don't have any tin cans.

MIDAS: I think you might find some in that trash barrel over there.

GEORGE: I never thought of that. (*Goes to barrel with* HENRY's *tin cans in it. They have been cut carefully so they have no ragged edges and are smooth and shiny.*) Hey, look at these.

PAGE: All you have to do is punch a little hole in the top

of each can, knot your string through it, and you have a first-class walkie-talkie.

GEORGE: I'll do it. (*Starts off*) And then I'll find someone I can talk to. (*Exits*)

PAGE: Even Henry's trash ends up a gem. It's an amazing view of life I'm getting here, Midas.

MIDAS: Stop sight-seeing for a moment and move.

PAGE (*Moving*): Amazing. Utterly amazing.

MIDAS (*Staring at board*): Page, did you move the checkers when my back was turned?

PAGE: No, Midas, and it's your move. Don't take all day. (ALVIN FOOTE *enters left as* PATTY MILLER *enters right. Each carries a wastebasket filled with papers.*)

ALVIN: Good evening, Mr. O'Brien. Just in to throw away my trash.

MIDAS: Good evening, Mr. Foote. Just help yourself to any of the barrels.

ALVIN: I've finished reading the paper, and I like to get rid of it as soon as I finish. I don't like to clutter up my apartment.

PATTY: Good evening, Mr. O'Brien. Where shall I put my trash?

MIDAS: Good evening, Miss Miller. Any can will do. They're mostly empty.

PATTY: I don't have much. I just finished reading the paper, and I like to get rid of it as soon as I finish.

PAGE: That's just what Mr. Foote was saying.

PATTY: Mr. Foote? I don't believe I know Mr. Foote.

MIDAS: You two don't know each other? Now that's strange. You've been practically neighbors for the past five years. Miss Miller, may I present Mr. Foote? There, now you know each other.

PATTY: How do you do, Mr. Foote. I've seen you—in

front of the building. But I didn't know we were neighbors.

ALVIN: I've seen you many times, Miss Miller. And I knew we were neighbors, but I didn't know you were *Miss* Miller.

PATTY: Oh, yes. I'm Miss Miller.

ALVIN: It's funny, isn't it, Miss Miller, about both of us throwing out papers as soon as we read them. I mean, it's a kind of coincidence, wouldn't you say, Miss Miller?

PATTY: Indeed it is, Mr. Foote. But since we are neighbors, I wish that you would call me Patty.

ALVIN: I would like that very much. My name is Alvin.

PATTY: Oh, that's a nice name.

ALVIN: My friends call me Alvin. Not Al. Just Alvin.

PATTY: I think that's better. My name is really Patty. Not Patricia or anything like that.

ALVIN: I think Patty is a pretty name.

PATTY: Well, I guess I'll empty my trash.

ALVIN: Oh, yes. I must empty mine, too. (*They go to trash barrels next to each other, each one self-consciously concerned with emptying the trash.*)

PATTY: That's that.

ALVIN: Yes, it is. (*They both turn and start off; then both turn back.*)

PATTY: I forgot something. I have this one earring. (*Takes earring from pocket*) And one earring isn't any good. So I thought I'd just throw it away.

ALVIN: Now that is a coincidence. (*Takes earring from pocket*) I was about to throw away one earring that belonged to my mother. She must have lost one a long time ago. I don't even remember ever seeing the mate. (*They both go to same barrel to throw away earrings.*) That's odd. Our earrings match.

PATTY: They do, indeed. My father gave me a set almost twenty years ago. I don't know when I lost one. I should have thrown the other away a long time ago.

ALVIN: Me, too. One earring isn't much good.

PATTY: No, it isn't.

ALVIN: Not unless you just have one ear.

PATTY (*Laughing*): I know. But I've always had two.

ALVIN: I know.

PATTY: I beg your pardon?

ALVIN: I know you have two ears. They are very attractive.

PATTY (*Flustered, but pleased*): Why, thank you. (*Pauses*) I teach school. Fourth grade.

ALVIN: You do? That's interesting. I teach, too. Tenth grade. Civics. Eleventh grade. History. History's what I like best.

PATTY: I like history, too. Well, I guess I'll just throw my earring away and go grade some papers.

ALVIN: Wait a minute, Patty. You don't have to throw your earring away now. I'll give you this one, and then you'll have a pair.

PATTY: That doesn't seem right—my taking your earring. You must let me pay you for it.

ALVIN (*Handing her earring*): I couldn't do that. Just take it. I was going to throw it away.

PATTY: Thank you. (*Turns and starts off, then turns back*) Thank you very much. And it was nice to have met you.

ALVIN: I am pleased to have met you. (PATTY *turns and starts off.* ALVIN *calls after her.*) Patty.

PATTY: Yes?

ALVIN: Don't you think you should have dinner with me tonight? At Kolb's Restaurant. It's right around the corner.

PATTY: Well, I don't . . . I probably . . .

ALVIN: To celebrate getting the earrings paired up?

PATTY: If you put it that way, I just don't see how I can refuse. I'll just get my coat.

ALVIN: I'll be waiting in the lobby for you.

PATTY: I'll just be five minutes.

ALVIN: I'll be waiting. (*They exit.* MIDAS *and* PAGE *have been playing silently, occasionally removing a jumped checker.*)

PAGE: They had me worried there for a moment. I thought they were going to miss again.

MIDAS: You interfere too much in other people's business, Page.

PAGE: I didn't do anything. But I've heard you say a dozen times that it's too bad those two didn't meet—they're both lonely.

MIDAS: But I never interfere. (BOB *enters with a large brown envelope in his hand.*)

BOB: Is Cinderella back with the ashes, Mr. O'Brien?

MIDAS: I believe she is, Bob. Did you find the lost letter?

BOB: I found it. It was right in plain view, but I thought we were looking for a special-delivery letter. (*Waves envelope*) It's my play. Dick Fallon sent it back again.

MIDAS: Better luck next time, maybe.

BOB: No, no more next times. (*Throws envelope in can*) I'm through. For two years now, I've tried to get my play on the stage, and all I've done is bore my friends and make my wife miserable.

JUNE (*Coming in from back*): That's not true. You never made me miserable.

BOB: You didn't want to tell me I got the play back, did you, June?

JUNE: I didn't know it was the play.

BOB: You didn't want to tell me I got the play back, did you, June? You might as well answer.

JUNE: I didn't know it was the play. I just . . .

BOB: You just lost it "accidentally."

JUNE: Bob, I hate it when you're so disappointed.

BOB: I won't be any more. No more plays for me. From now on, I'll just keep my nose to business and forget all about the theatre.

PAGE: I had an aunt who was in the theatre. She traveled with a tent show and was sawed in half in one of those magic acts. She liked the theatre.

MIDAS: I think it's your move, Page.

PAGE: Well, excuse me.

BOB: Let's go back home, June. I've fixed dinner for us, and from now on, no more depressions, no more temper, no more . . . no more plays.

JUNE: I like your play, Bob. It's a good play. It's a great play. Why, I read it to Miss Warren, and she said that it was just the kind of play that she would like to do. And she was once a great actress, so she should know.

BOB: She's a kind woman, and you are, too. But from now on, no more plays, no more theatre, no more . . .

JUNE: You'll feel differently after you've eaten.

BOB: Not the supper that I've fixed. I think it's a little overdone.

PAGE: I like meat well done.

MIDAS: It's your move again, Page. Don't take all night.

JUNE: We'll look at the play again after we eat.

BOB: Not tonight. (*Takes her arm and leads her off*) Not tomorrow night. Not ever. The play has gone to its proper resting place—the trash barrel. Ashes to ashes and trash to trash.

JUNE: No, Bob, you can't do that. (*Tries to go back*)

BOB (*Leading her off*): Come on, June. Let's stop playing with trash. Let's go eat. (*They exit.*)

PAGE: I know how he feels. A man can have all sorts of

ambition but there comes a time when he has to face facts.

MIDAS: You don't know anything, Page. Bob has a great talent. Miss Warren told me.

PAGE: Then why didn't you do something? At least speak up.

MIDAS: I don't interfere. People bring their trash here and I send it out. I don't make judgments. And it's your move.

PAGE: Midas, you're a smart man, but you don't know everything. (PAULINE WARREN *enters and goes to* MIDAS, *obviously excited.*)

MIDAS (*Rising*): Miss Warren, is something the matter?

PAULINE: I just saw Mrs. Listman and she told me about my costumes.

MIDAS: Oh. I hope you don't mind. I figured you wouldn't care what happened to them, since you were throwing them away.

PAULINE: Care? Of course, I care. I just didn't know anyone else could care. You have no idea, Mr. O'Brien, how pleased I am that someone would want them—that someone would think something of mine worth pulling out of a trash barrel. And she's making a costume for her little girl. To use in a school play. I'm just silly, I know, but I feel . . . well, I feel as though someone has pulled *me* out of a trash barrel. (*Walks toward barrel into which* BOB *threw his manuscript.*) Right now, Mr. O'Brien, I feel as though I could go back on the stage again. Not just pretend as we do, but really do it.

MIDAS: I'm sure you could, Miss Warren.

PAULINE: No, I really mean it. I saw my old director just a few months ago and he said to me, "Pauline, if you ever want to go back on the stage—really go back—

just call me." That's what he said. And it wasn't just talk either. But I'd have to be really willing to work— (*Stops and shrugs*) Of course, I don't suppose I ever will. There's no reason. It wouldn't mean anything to anyone else, even if I really succeeded. (*Pauses*) I guess maybe I really do belong in this barrel. (*Laughs, bends over and looks in barrel*) What's this? (*Brings out manuscript*) It's an envelope, addressed to Bob. I wonder if he lost it. It looks new.

PAGE: No, he threw it away. It's his play.

PAULINE (*Opening envelope and taking out manuscript*): His play? Why, I've read this play. He *must* have lost it. He wouldn't throw this away. He worked on it too long, and it's too good.

PAGE: He threw it away. Somebody sent it back to him, and he says he's all through writing plays. Going to stick to business.

PAULINE: But that's insane. I've read this play. It's a fine play.

PAGE: Maybe so, but he's quitting.

PAULINE: No, he's not. This play will get on the stage if I have to do it myself. People have no business treating treasure like trash. I'll see him right now and give him a piece of my mind. (*Exits*)

PAGE: I'll bet she does more than that.

MIDAS: Perhaps. (*Sits down and looks at checkers*)

PAGE: She'll see the play gets on. And she'll be in it, too. It's a great thing we've seen, Midas, a thing to make a man believe in joy once more. Things thrown away and things found.

MIDAS: Ah-ha. (*Jumps all over board, collecting checkers*) And I win another game, Page. Let's see you save that with your new joy.

PAGE (*Smiling*): I may win the next one.

MIDAS: You won't until you stop minding other people's business and start paying attention to the game.

PAGE: Ah, Midas, there are many ways of winning a game. You may have taken my checkers, but I got something a lot better in exchange.

MIDAS: Page, my friend, you're getting to be a bit of a philosopher. What will it be this time, the reds or the blacks?

PAGE: I think I'll stick with the reds. They bring me luck. (*Curtain*)

THE END

The Whole City's Down Below

Characters

MR. BONS, *an elderly man*
MRS. BONS, *his wife*
JOE, *a young man*
EMILY, *his wife*
ROMEO
JULIET } *from Shakespeare's play*
CYRANO DE BERGERAC
ROXANE } *from Rostand's play*
HELEN OF TROY
PARIS } *from Homer's epic*

SETTING: *The living room of the Bons' apartment, as seen through an apartment window that overlooks the city below. Only the down center section of the stage is lighted; the background and sides are in shadow.*

AT RISE: *Soft music is heard in the background, then fades as the action begins.* MR. BONS *is seated in a wheelchair down center, a blanket over his knees. A game of chess is set up on a small table in front of him.* MR. BONS *moves a chessman, sighs, and looks out over audience. Then he sweeps chessmen off board angrily.* MRS. BONS *enters from the shadows upstage, picks up chessmen and replaces them on table.*

MRS. BONS: Would you like me to play a game of chess with you, Marvin? (*She waits, but he doesn't answer.*) Would you like me to get a book and read to you? (*Again there is no answer. She goes to sofa at right and sits, talking to him but looking out over audience.*) Would you like to talk?

MR. BONS (*Very slowly*): I would like to . . . fly (*Pointing out over audience*) . . . to fly right out that window and zoom down on the city. That's what I would like to do.

MRS. BONS: Yes, dear. (*Pauses*) Are you feeling bad tonight?

MR. BONS: I don't know. I don't know if I'm feeling good or bad. For a while tonight, I thought if I tried, I could get right up and walk around if I wanted to. And then I thought I might just try. (*He stops abruptly.*)

MRS. BONS: Why didn't you, dear?

MR. BONS: I didn't want to. I didn't want to do anything. I just wanted to sit here and look out (*Gesturing toward audience*) at the city.

MRS. BONS (*Patiently*): What were you looking at, dear?

MR. BONS: Life. Yes, that's what I was looking at. Dreams. Hope. Fear. Life. The whole city's down below.

MRS. BONS: Would you like to go down, Marvin? We could go to the park and watch the young people go by. You used to like that.

MR. BONS: I don't want to go.

MRS. BONS: We met Peter and Polly in the park. Remember?

MR. BONS: I don't remember.

MRS. BONS: Polly was crying that afternoon.

MR. BONS: I don't want to remember Polly or Peter.

MRS. BONS (*Rising and coming down center to look out over audience*): Such a nice young couple. I wonder what would have happened if you hadn't been there that day. If you hadn't helped them. (*Turns toward him*) Do you ever wonder about that, dear?

MR. BONS: They didn't need my help. Nobody needs me. If I hadn't been there, things would have been the same. Lovers don't need help. Young people don't need old people. (*Pauses*) I couldn't even help our own son. (*Sadly*) I couldn't even help Jim.

MRS. BONS: Peter and Polly sent us a card last Christmas. You didn't look at it then. Would you like to see it now?

MR. BONS: No.

MRS. BONS: They have a new baby. (*Pauses*) They named the baby for you.

MR. BONS: Lots of babies are named Marvin. I don't know that it was named for me. Besides, I don't care.

MRS. BONS (*Returning to sofa*): John and Joan sent you a package today. It's a sweater. Would you like to try it on?

MR. BONS: No, I don't want it. Send it to the Salvation Army.

MRS. BONS: They wanted to know if they could come and see you.

MR. BONS: I don't want to see anyone.

MRS. BONS: They would like to come very much. You once helped them, too, remember, and they're grateful.

MR. BONS: They don't owe me anything.

MRS. BONS: They think they do. Besides, they love you.

MR. BONS: I don't want to see anyone.

MRS. BONS: The Hospital League called today. Mr. Meriwether. He wants to know if you will help with the fund drive.

MR. BONS: No.

MRS. BONS: It's for the children. It will help save lives.

MR. BONS: Send them a check. It's all I can do. I didn't even know how to save my own son.

MRS. BONS (*Quietly*): Jim was my son, too.

MR. BONS: It was my responsibility. *I* bought him the car.

MRS. BONS: Yes, you did buy him the car. And he was killed in that car. But you didn't buy the rain and the fog that night, and you didn't buy the train that hit the car. And you didn't buy the way life is. You are not responsible because you were not there to stop the train. But you *are* responsible for just sitting here, thinking about the past, refusing to live.

MR. BONS: I don't want to talk anymore.

MRS. BONS (*Rising*): Yes, dear. (*She exits upstage into the shadows. Music is heard again, then fades.* MR. BONS *stares at the chessmen in front of him, starts to move them, and again sweeps them onto floor. Then he sinks back into his chair.* JULIET *comes in down left and picks up chessmen.* ROMEO *comes in down right and joins her. He holds her hand for a moment, as she puts the last chessman in place.*)

ROMEO (*To* JULIET):
If I profane with my unworthiest hand
This holy shrine, the gentle fine is this:
My lips, two blushing pilgrims, ready stand
To smooth that rough touch with a tender kiss.
(ROMEO *lifts her hand to his lips.*)

JULIET (*Slowly withdrawing her hand and putting her hands together as in prayer*):
Good pilgrim, you do wrong your hand too much,
Which mannerly devotion shows in this;
For saints have hands that pilgrims' hands do touch,
And palm to palm is holy palmers' kiss.

MR. BONS (*Quoting as if he were slowly remembering*):
Have not saints lips, and holy palmers, too?
(*Changing voice for answering line*)
Ay, pilgrim, lips that they must use in prayer.

ROMEO (*To* MR. BONS): Excuse us. I forgot myself.

JULIET: You are Mr. Bons, aren't you?

MR. BONS: Yes, and you are Juliet, of course.

ROMEO: I am Romeo.

JULIET: Do you remember us?

MR. BONS: Yes. I remember you. Somewhat.

ROMEO: We need your help, Mr. Bons.

MR. BONS: I can't help you. I'm sorry. I just can't.

JULIET: But we heard some people talking—a young couple. Peter and Polly, I think they were named. They
said you helped them once, when they needed your
help.

MR. BONS: I don't remember any Peter and Polly. I can't
help you.

JULIET: But you said you remembered us.

ROMEO: You must know what is going to happen to us and
what we should do.

JULIET: Should we go to our parents and tell them we are
married?

ROMEO: Should we go to Friar Lawrence?

JULIET: Will Nurse help us?

ROMEO: Would the Prince understand?

JULIET: Should I fly tonight with Romeo to Mantua?

ROMEO: Should I stay here with Juliet in Verona?

MR. BONS: Stop questioning me. I can tell you nothing.

JULIET: We're sorry. We thought . . . we heard so many
people say how much you had helped them in the past.

ROMEO: And then, of course, since you know all about us,
we thought you would help us, too.

MR. BONS: I don't know *all* about you. I just know a little.
I recognized who you were, that's all. But I can't help
you. (*More kindly*) I am truly sorry. I would *like* to
help you, believe me. But I can't. I don't know how.
I can't help anyone.

ROMEO: You do know what is going to happen to us, though, don't you?

MR. BONS: I know that. Yes, I think I know that.

ROMEO: Would you do this much for us? Would you tell me what you know?

MR. BONS: I'd rather not.

JULIET: Romeo, please, let's go. He can't help us, and we are just making him sad.

MR. BONS: I'd like to help you. Why, anyone in the world today would want to help Romeo and Juliet. Just ask anybody else. Anyone else will help you.

ROMEO: We are only allowed to ask once. From what we had heard, we thought you were the one person who might help.

MR. BONS: Maybe once, but not now.

ROMEO: It will be all right, Mr. Bons. Whatever happens to us (*Looks at* JULIET), it will be worth it.

JULIET: Goodbye, Mr. Bons. I'm sorry. I truly am. Good night. (*They exit upstage into shadows.*)

MR. BONS: Good night. (*Pauses, then quotes dreamily*) "Good night, good night! Parting is such sweet sorrow, That I shall say good night till it be morrow." (MR. BONS *rests his face in his hands, as if he were sleeping. Music plays softly in background, then fades.* CYRANO DE BERGERAC *sweeps in from up left,* ROXANE *from up right, and they flank* MR. BONS. CYRANO *makes an elaborate gesture for* ROXANE *to speak first.*)

ROXANE (*To* MR. BONS): Sir, I am a maiden in distress, and I have come to you to be my champion.

MR. BONS (*Looking up suddenly*): Me? Good heavens, I am no champion. I can't even win a chess match with myself.

CYRANO: Roxane, Roxane, it's all in vain. I have lost the game. But smile, pretty lady, it has been a lovely life.

ROXANE (*To* MR. BONS): Mr. Bons, I want you to speak

to this madman Cyrano, this man I madly love. You know him well and love him, too. I remember one night —here in this very room—when your lady read to you from a book about my Cyrano. And you wept real tears. This is your chance to help him. He needs your help so much.

CYRANO: There is no help for me, Roxane.

ROXANE: Speak to him, Mr. Bons. Tell him he will not die. Tell him how much I love him, how much I loved him even before I knew that it was he I loved.

MR. BONS: She did love you, Cyrano. The night you spoke to her beneath her balcony, wooing her for your friend, Christian—

CYRANO: Yes, that has been my life . . . that night Christian spoke (*To* ROXANE) under your window. It was always so! While I stood in the darkness underneath, others climbed to the window to win the applause—the kiss!

ROXANE: You shall not die. I love you.

CYRANO: No, this is not the story. You remember when Beauty said, "I love you," to the Beast that was a fairy prince, his ugliness changed and dissolved, like magic. But you see (*Pointing to his long nose*), I am still the same.

ROXANE: I have done this to you. It's all my fault—mine.

CYRANO: You? Why, no, on the contrary. I would never have known womanhood and its sweetness but for you. Because of you, I have had one friend—not quite only a friend—across my life, one whispering silken gown.

MR. BONS: You have millions of friends. Ask any man in the street what he thinks of Cyrano de Bergerac. Why, even the moon is your friend. Have you forgotten?

CYRANO (*Looking out over audience*): It is true, old Moon. You have been my friend.

ROXANE: I never loved but one man in my life, and I have

lost him—again and again and again. Mr. Bons, you must do something. You must change the ending. Cyrano must not be allowed to die.

CYRANO: Mr. Bons (*Pointing out over audience*), I shall be up there presently—in the moon—without having to invent any flying machines.

ROXANE: Don't leave me, Cyrano.

CYRANO: The moon—yes, that would be the place for me—my kind of paradise. I shall find there those other souls who should be friends of mine—Socrates, Galileo . . .

MR. BONS: Cyrano, I have a son . . . I *had* a son. He was such a man as might be on the moon, too. If you should see him, tell him, tell him I am sorry that I failed him. Tell him . . .

ROXANE: No! No! This is idiotic—too unfair. Such a friend, such a poet, such a man to die so . . . to die so.

CYRANO:
Philosopher and scientist,
Poet, musician, duelist—
He flew high, and fell back again!
A lover—but not like other men.
Here lies Cyrano de Bergerac—
Who was all things—and all in vain.
Well, I must go. Pardon me—I cannot stay. (*He sits down on floor and looks up over audience.*) My Moonbeam comes to carry me away.

ROXANE (*Going to him and kneeling beside him*): Cyrano, stay with me. (*Standing and pleading with* MR. BONS) Mr. Bons, you have helped others in the past. You know what to do. Change this ending.

MR. BONS: I cannot help you. I . . . I don't know how. (*Turning away from her*)

CYRANO: Dear Roxane. Dearer Roxane. Dearest Roxane.

(*Taking her hand*) I would not have you mourn any less that good, brave, noble Christian, who loved you. I ask only this—when the great cold gathers around my bones, that you may give a double meaning to your widow's weeds and the tears you let fall for him may be—for a little—my tears, too.

ROXANE: Mr. Bons, save him.

CYRANO (*Rising; drawing his sword and holding it aloft*): But not sitting down. Not here. Let that old fellow, Death, find me on my feet—my sword in hand.

MR. BONS: Cyrano, stop for a moment. There must be something one can do. What good is man if he cannot change what he knows?

CYRANO (*Speaking to invisible enemies*): I see him there, that rascal Death. He is looking at my nose—that skeleton. What's that you say, Monsieur Death? It is hopeless? Why, very well. It is hopeless. But a man does not fight merely to win. No, no, it's better to know one fights in vain! You there—who are you? A hundred against one—I know them now, my ancient enemies! (*He lunges with sword at the empty air.*) Falsehood! Prejudice! Compromise! Cowardice! What's that? Surrender? No, no, never. (ROMEO *comes in up left. His sword is in his hand, and he is looking about wildly.* CYRANO *sees him.*) Who are you? What phantom from my past?

ROMEO: Do not attempt to stop me, sir. I mean no harm to anyone but myself, but I swear I'll kill the man who keeps me from my Juliet.

MR. BONS: Romeo, stop. This man doesn't belong in your time. He is no Capulet, no citizen of Verona. He is Cyrano de Bergerac.

ROMEO: I do not know the name or care for the man. If he does not stop me, I'll do him no harm.

CYRANO: You do *me* harm? You young pup! Did you think

that because the wolf is dying all the pups may bark
without fear?

ROXANE: Cyrano, wait. This is Romeo. You know his story.

CYRANO: Romeo? Juliet's Romeo?

ROMEO: You have seen Juliet? My man told me that she
has been taken to her tomb, and I will join her if all
Verona stands in my way.

CYRANO: And I will join you.

MR. BONS: But you can't win. It's all been written down,
and there's no changing it.

CYRANO: But a man does not fight merely to win. Come,
Romeo, we go to Verona and immortality. (*Together*
ROMEO *and* CYRANO *disappear up right.*)

MR. BONS (*Shouting after them*): Wait, wait. There is
something I must tell you. Juliet is not dead. Come
back, Romeo. I'll help you.

ROXANE: They can't hear you, Mr. Bons.

MR. BONS: Run after them and tell them. They will listen
to you.

ROXANE: I can't tell them, Mr. Bons. I know now that it
was foolish to come to you about Cyrano.

MR. BONS (*Wildly*): There is still time. Run. Juliet is
merely sleeping. If Romeo will wait—wait until the rain
stops and the fog clears.

ROXANE: There is no rain and no fog. It's a clear night.

MR. BON (*More quietly*): I had forgotten. I was thinking of
another night. Roxane, listen to me. There's no reason
for Romeo's story to end this way. If you will run and
catch them, Romeo and Juliet can be saved . . . and
then maybe even Cyrano. You want that, don't you?

ROXANE: Yes, I want that. Cyrano and Roxane sitting
quietly in old age by the river, remembering. Romeo
and Juliet with children and grandchildren, walking
through the streets of Verona, safely. Yes, I want that,
too.

MR. BONS: Then, stop them.

ROXANE (*Shaking her head sadly*): They can't be stopped. None of us can be stopped, Mr. Bons. None of us whose stories are already told.

MR. BONS: Then what's the sense of the past? What use is my knowledge of what is to happen to you all, if I can do nothing about it?

ROXANE: I don't know, Mr. Bons. But do not be too sad. Romeo and Juliet and Cyrano and I have lived a long time, and we shall live again and again and again.

MR. BONS: But only to die again, again, and again. What's the sense of that?

ROXANE: I don't know, Mr. Bons. Ask Cyrano's moon. He's a funny fellow who waxes fat and wanes and, on occasion, disappears, only to wax fat, wane, and disappear again. Ask the flowers that you used to plant in the spring that died in the fall and came back again when April came around.

MR. BONS: It's different with people. There's only one Romeo and Juliet.

ROXANE: I thought Romeo looked like Peter. But you are probably right. When Romeo and Juliet died, all love died, too. I shall complain to Cyrano about that. I believed him when he said he loved me, but I know that it can't be so. Goodbye, Mr. Bons, I must go.

MR. BONS: No, wait. There is something I almost know. Stay a moment, Roxane. Let me think. Something can be done.

ROXANE: I must go, Mr. Bons. I have an engagement with my Cyrano—in the Park of the Convent of the Ladies of the Cross. I can't be late, for my Cyrano has to fly to the moon. I wouldn't want him to leave until I had said goodbye. (*She disappears up right.*)

MR. BONS (*Shouting after her*): Wait! Wait, I'll go with you. (*Trying to rise from chair slowly*) Wait for me.

We'll find them. We'll make people listen. I have friends. I can do something, if you'll just wait. (*He looks around room and then shouts.*) Wait, I *can* help. I want to help! (*He sinks back into chair as* MRS. BONS *comes into the light from up center. She is followed by* JOE *and* EMILY, *who hang back on the edge of the shadows.*)

MRS. BONS (*Going to* MR. BONS): What is it, dear?

MR. BONS: Stop them. Run after them and stop them.

MRS. BONS: There's no one here, dear, no one except . . . (*She turns and looks at* JOE *and* EMILY.) I thought you were sleeping.

MR. BONS: You have to stop them. Things are not the way she said they were. The people in Verona are not bad people. If someone would explain to them, make them see.

MRS. BONS (*Putting blanket over his knees*): Whom are you talking about? Who is "she"? What people from Verona?

MR. BONS: Oh, I . . . I was talking to . . . I thought I was talking to . . . (*He laughs softly*) I thought I was talking to Romeo and Juliet. Yes, and Cyrano and Roxane, too.

MRS. BONS: Did you have a bad dream, dear?

MR. BONS: I must have. But it seemed so real. Juliet picked up the chess pieces from the floor. (*Points to chess set*) And then she and Romeo met, right here in front of me. "If I profane with my unworthiest hand . . ." That's what he said, I heard him. (JOE *and* EMILY *move closer to* MRS. BONS.)

JOE: Mrs. Bons, maybe we should leave.

EMILY: We didn't know Mr. Bons had been sick.

MR. BONS (*Gazing out over the audience*): And Cyrano looked right out my window and saw his moon. Just as big as you please. There is a moon, isn't there?

MRS. BONS: Yes, there's a moon. (*She looks out over audience and up.*)

JOE: Is there anything we can do to help, Mrs. Bons?

MR. BONS: They were all just as I imagined them. Peter does look a little like Romeo, you know. It wasn't just my imagination. And Polly looks a little like . . . no, not Juliet. Roxane. That's funny, isn't it? I would have thought that Polly would have looked like Juliet.

EMILY: Maybe we could get something. His medicine or something.

MR. BONS: Cyrano looked like Carl. You remember Carl. He had a garage and a wife named Claudette, and about six kids. No—seven kids. They all looked just like her. I guess that was a blessing. Even Carl said so.

JOE: We'll leave, Mrs. Bons. We're sorry that we disturbed you.

MR. BONS (*Suddenly looking at* EMILY *and* JOE): Well, who are you? I don't know you, do I?

JOE: No, sir, you don't know us.

MRS. BONS: Marvin, this is Joe and his wife, Emily. They were friends of Jim's. They didn't know you'd been sick.

MR. BONS: Friends of my son? Well, sit down. Sit down. (JOE *and* EMILY *sit down uneasily on sofa.*)

JOE: We were just passing in the neighborhood—

MR. BONS: Did you know Jim at college?

JOE: Yes, sir. I had a room across the hall. We weren't close friends. I was a freshman when he was a senior. He— well—he helped me once.

MR. BONS: Joe? I think I remember you.

JOE: We've never met. Jim probably never even remembered helping me. We played piano duets together . . . well, once or twice.

MR. BONS: Joe Roppolo! Is that right?

JOE: Why, yes, sir!

MR. BONS: Jim told me a lot about you. (*Smiles*) You really shouldn't have put all those cats in the choir loft. Not right before the Commencement Exercises. (*Sadly*) I was certainly sorry to have missed that.

MRS. BONS: Joe and Emily came to see you for help.

EMILY: It's really not very serious.

JOE: We didn't know you were sick, Mr. Bons.

MR. BONS: Help? (*Shrinks a little in his chair*) I . . . I'm not very good at helping people.

JOE (*Starting to rise*): I'm sorry, sir. We wouldn't have bothered you if we had known.

MR. BONS: There is no real way of helping people. The moon gets fat, wanes, and disappears. And there's nothing anyone can do, except just watch it.

MRS. BONS: Don't you think it might be a little different with people, dear?

MR. BONS: That's what I thought. But it's not so. Romeo and Juliet died, and Cyrano is on his moon, leaving Roxane in the Park all alone.

JOE: We'll leave, Mrs. Bons. We shouldn't have come.

MR. BONS: I'd like to help you. I'd like to help anyone if I knew how.

JOE: We'll just let ourselves out.

EMILY: I hope you are feeling better soon, Mr. Bons.

MR. BONS: Wait. Just wait a minute, you two. Let me think. I don't know why young people are always rushing off. Let me think.

MRS. BONS: Wouldn't you like to know what their trouble is?

MR. BONS: What? Oh. (*Laughs*) I think that would probably be a good place to start thinking. What is the trouble?

JOE: We're going to lose our business unless we can do something.

Mr. Bons: Do you need money? A loan or something?

Joe: No, sir. It's our location. The Municipal Trust Company is going to take the land, and we don't know how to stop them.

Mr. Bons: Oh? What right do they have to your land?

Joe: It's not really *our* land. We just leased it.

Emily: And the lease will run out in three months. They have told us we will have to find a new location.

Joe: But there isn't another location for our business that's right, in that area. All our customers are in that neighborhood, so we don't want to move to another part of the city. But I guess there's no way to stop the Municipal Trust Company. We only came to you because Jim told me one time that if anyone could do anything to help someone, his father was the man.

Mr. Bons: I'm afraid Jim was wrong. I couldn't even do anything to help him, my own son.

Joe: I didn't really think that any one man could stop the whole Municipal Trust Company.

Mr. Bons: That's one thing you're wrong about, Joe. I happen to be a man of some importance in that company. As a matter of fact, I own that blasted company. I remember the case now. The company wants to build a warehouse on the land we leased to you.

Joe: Yes, sir. That's it.

Mr. Bons (*Rising from chair; speaking forcefully*): I told Cassidy at the time that we had a verbal understanding with your company. Besides, the location's no good for us, anyway. Joe, you come down to the office in the morning. Not before ten. We'll straighten this all out. And I don't want you two to worry any more.

Joe: I don't know what to say, Mr. Bons.

Mr. Bons: It's all right, Joe. It's something I should have done . . . would have done anyway if . . . (*He puts his hand to his head*) I feel a little dizzy. (*Suddenly stops and looks about him.*) I'm standing up! (*To* Mrs. Bons) Did you know that I am standing up?

Mrs. Bons: Yes, dear, but perhaps you had better sit down again. It takes a bit of getting used to if you haven't been doing it for a long time. (*She helps him to his wheelchair.*)

Mr. Bons (*Returning to chair*): Perhaps I should. (*Feels head again*) I do feel woozy. Fine, you understand, but woozy. Perhaps I should exercise more.

Mrs. Bons: Yes, dear.

Emily: I guess maybe we should go. (Joe *and* Emily *stand.*) We left the baby with a sitter.

Mr. Bons: A baby? That's nice. Boy or girl?

Joe: A boy.

Emily (*Proudly*): Jimmy will be a year old tomorrow.

Mr. Bons: Jimmy. That's what we called our Jim until he was six. He wouldn't let us after that. (*Pulling himself back to the present*) Well, then, Joe, I'll see you in the morning. About ten. I'll need some time to get my office dusted so that I can receive my clients properly. It's been collecting dust too long.

Emily: Good night, Mr. Bons. And thank you.

Mr. Bons: Good night, Emily.

Joe: Thank you, Mr. Bons.

Mr. Bons: Thank *you,* Joe.

Mrs. Bons: I'll see you to the door. (Mrs. Bons, Emily, *and* Joe *disappear up left into the darkness.* Mr. Bons *picks up a chessman and looks at it. Soft music is heard.* Helen of Troy *and* Paris *run in from up right.*)

Helen: Mr. Bons, Paris and I need your help. Desperately.

Paris: All of Greece is against Helen and me. Help us back to Troy.

Mr. Bons (*Looking up*): Help you? I'm afraid not. Sorry.

Helen: I'm disappointed. We spoke to a young couple who were just leaving and they told us not to worry, because Mr. Bons would help us. We are going to be famous, you know.

MR. BONS: Oh, I know all about Helen of Troy and Paris. But I am not getting involved in the Trojan War. I have other things to do, a few wars of my own to fight.

PARIS: I was certain, Mr. Bons, that you were a man with a little romance in your soul.

MR. BONS: I hope I am, Paris. I hope I am. And I'm not spending it on the past anymore. But the future—that's another thing. If you should see someone from tomorrow—some brave young couple (*Gesturing toward audience*) making their way down there in the city—or maybe in a settlement on the moon—if they need help, you may give them my name.

HELEN: Come, Paris, let's fly. We'll get no help here. Mr. Bons has turned practical on us. (HELEN *and* PARIS *start off up left.*)

MR. BONS: Good luck, young lovers. Give Hector my regards. (PARIS *and* HELEN *exit.* MRS. BONS *re-enters.*)

MRS. BONS: Did I hear you speak to someone, Marvin?

MR. BONS (*Looking off*): Just saying goodbye to living in the past. (*Turns to her and smiles*) There was no one here, really.

MRS. BONS: Marvin, I'm so pleased. . . . Well, you know.

MR. BONS: Pleased that I've started to live again? I am, too, my dear. I've spent so much time trying to hear the voices of the past that I couldn't hear the present shouting in my ear. (*Laughs*) You'd be surprised at the voices from the past I've heard tonight, asking me to help change the past. (*Shaking head*) It can't be done.

MRS. BONS (*Laughing nervously*): I'm afraid whatever you had must be catching. Do you know what I thought I heard just now when I came into the room? You won't laugh if I tell you?

MR. BONS: I may, but I won't laugh *at* you.

MRS. BONS: Well . . . I thought I heard a woman's voice saying that you had turned practical. Now, isn't that odd? (MR. BONS *rubs his chin and looks off*) Marvin, what's the matter? You're all right, aren't you, dear?

MR. BONS (*Smiling*): Yes, I'm all right. Just a little twitch from an old war wound—when I fought with Hector at the Battle of Troy. (*Laughs cheerfully*)

MRS. BONS: Oh, Marvin—you promised you wouldn't laugh. (*She laughs, and puts her arm around his shoulder as the curtain closes.*)

THE END

A Young Man of Considerable Value

Characters

MR. JONES, *the richest man in the world*
HARRISON P. DANGERFORTH, *his adviser*
OPAL, *Mr. Jones' daughter*
RUTH, *Opal's tall friend*
DOT, *Opal's in-between friend*
HARRIET, *Opal's short friend*
DUSTIN HUDSON, *a young man in oil*
CHAUNCEY LODGEWORTH, *a young man in plastics*
NICK MARAT, *a young man with money*
SMITHY, *a young man*

SETTING: *Mr. Jones' treasury room. Up center is a huge gold-colored sack covered with dollar signs, and arranged about the stage are smaller versions of the sack, as well as treasure chests, huge precious stones, etc. At center stand a chair and a table with stacks of coins on it. Three small sacks are lined up on one side of table, and money trees, with stage money for leaves, are right and left of table.*

AT RISE: MR. JONES *is sitting at the table writing in an account book with a pen as* HARRISON P. DANGERFORTH *walks about the room calling off sums for each item.*

DANGERFORTH (*Pointing to one small bag*): Four billion, three hundred million, twenty-two thousand, and forty-three dollars in bag 63.

JONES (*Writing*): Four billion, three hundred million, twenty-two thousand, and forty-three dollars in bag 63. Right.

DANGERFORTH (*Pointing to precious stone*): The last quoted price on the Star of Asia Ruby, three billion dollars.

JONES: Three billion dollars. Right. You know, I don't think that's a fair price.

DANGERFORTH: If we were shrewd, we might be able to get three billion dollars and forty-five cents.

JONES: Don't sneer, Dangerforth. It's the cents that add up to the dollars.

DANGERFORTH: I never sneer at money, Mr. Jones. It's not good manners. (*Points to another stone*) The last quoted price on the Nome Nugget, two billion, three hundred million.

JONES: I wish that it were three billion even. It's much easier to keep the total straight when the figures are even.

DANGERFORTH: To be sure. To be sure. But as you say, it's the pennies that make up the dollars.

JONES: I did say that, didn't I? It was rather clever of me, too. I wonder if I could write that down or something and sell it as a practical guide to young men who want to get on in the world.

DANGERFORTH: I'm sure you could, Mr. Jones.

JONES: But on the other hand, if I blabbed about how I've become the richest man in the world, everyone could become the richest man in the world. It wouldn't be much fun being the richest man in the world if everyone were that rich.

DANGERFORTH: There is much in what you say, Mr. Jones, perhaps too much.

JONES: Hm. That's enough philosophy. Let's get back to the business of life—counting my money.

DANGERFORTH (*Pointing to another small bag*): Four billion, three hundred million, twenty-two thousand, and forty-four dollars and fourteen cents in bag 64.

JONES (*Writing*): Four billion, three hundred million, twenty-two thousand. . . . (OPAL *comes running in at left.*)

OPAL: Daddy, Daddy.

JONES: Yes, my jewel?

DANGERFORTH: Hello, Opal.

OPAL: Hello, Mr. Dangerforth.

JONES: How is my little jewel today?

OPAL: Very fine today, Daddy, especially fine. Today is the day.

JONES: Indeed it is.

DANGERFORTH: In fact, every day is the day, isn't it?

OPAL: No, this is *the* day.

JONES: Oh?

OPAL: You haven't forgotten, have you?

JONES: Indeed I have not. Whatever it is I am supposed to remember, I remember. I have an excellent memory. For example, just as you burst in here, Mr. Dangerforth gave me the figures for bag 64. Four billion, three hundred million, twenty-two thousand, and forty-four dollars and fourteen cents. Right, Dangerforth?

DANGERFORTH: Right, Mr. Jones.

JONES: So it is absolutely absurd to speak of my forgetting anything. Now, just what is it you think I've forgotten?

OPAL (*Turning away*): You *have* forgotten.

JONES: Dangerforth, will you please tell my daughter, my jewel, my precious one, my Opal, that I have not forgotten whatever it is that she thinks I've forgotten.

DANGERFORTH: Opal, your father has not forgotten that this is the day on which you and he will select a husband for you.

JONES: So, you see, my jewel, I have not. . . . Is *this* the day?

OPAL (*Going to him*): Daddy, you promised.

JONES: Very well. But I tell you, quite frankly, that I set very high standards for your husband. I don't intend that my daughter shall be the wife of just anyone.

OPAL: There are some very nice young men waiting to see you right now, Daddy.

JONES: I hope for something better than just a nice young man. I want a *very rich* nice young man for my son-in-law.

DANGERFORTH: Some of this year's candidates are quite well-to-do.

JONES: Don't be snobbish, Dangerforth. If you mean rich, say so. "Well-to-do," indeed. Filthy rich not only sounds better; it is better. And I'll have none for my son-in-law but one who is filthy rich.

OPAL: You already have more money than you can count.

JONES: I can hire another assistant.

OPAL: I don't care if my husband is rich or not. I just want to be happy.

JONES: I care. I want your husband to be a man of considerable value. Happiness won't buy money, you know, Opal.

OPAL: But I want to marry for love.

JONES: I have always found that it is easier to love the rich than the poor, and it's much more selective. Now, not another word. If you want a husband, you'll have my consent only if he is a man of considerable value.

DANGERFORTH: How much is "considerable value," Mr. Jones?

JONES: More than can be reckoned by one of those cheap computers, I can tell you that. All right, bring in the candidates so that we can get this business over with. I need to get back to counting my treasures. And show them in one at a time. I can't stand young men in bunches.

DANGERFORTH: Yes, sir. (*He exits.*)

OPAL: There is one young man I really love. His name is . . .

JONES: Don't tell me. I don't want to know. A man's name is just so much air—a hiss between the teeth. Our name is Jones, a very common name. Dangerforth has a most distinguished name—Harrison P. Dangerforth. But which one of us has the money, huh? Answer me that.

OPAL: But my young man is the most handsome young man in all the world. He has beautiful hair.

JONES: A peacock has fine feathers.

OPAL: Pearly white teeth.

JONES: So does a shark.

OPAL: The loveliest eyes.

JONES: So does every mongrel puppy.

OPAL: And he's so kind.

JONES: That means he must be very poor. I tell you, Opal, if you cannot marry to improve yourself, you shall not marry. (RUTH, DOT, *and* HARRIET *come running in down right, giggling and whispering.* JONES *looks up annoyed.*) I said one at a time. Good heavens, has the husband market come to this? They are going to have to be even richer than I said.

OPAL: Daddy, these aren't the candidates.

JONES: Thank heavens for that. Don't you young men think you should get haircuts?

OPAL: These aren't men.

JONES: I'm glad you realize that, Opal. Now, I'm not one

of those old-fashioned parents who think that young people should dress like their parents, but this is ridiculous.

OPAL: These are Ruth, Dot, and Harriet.

JONES: With names like that, they never will be men.

OPAL: They are my girl friends.

JONES: Oh. What are they doing here? You won't need
bridesmaids until you have a groom, and, frankly, my
jewel, I have grave doubts . . .

RUTH: We don't want to be bridesmaids.

DOT: We want to be brides.

HARRIET: Indeed we do.

RUTH: We thought that Opal can't marry all the young
men who come here.

DOT: So there might be one left over.

HARRIET: Or two.

RUTH: Or three.

ALL: For *us*.

JONES: Oh. That seems reasonable. Sit down somewhere
and look your fill. I am not against marriage. I'm just
not going to give my Opal to some pauper. You girls can
understand that?

RUTH (*Sitting on small money bag down right*): Yes, indeed.

DOT: Especially if he should be very handsome. (*Sits on
next bag*)

HARRIET: And short. (*Sits on next bag*)

RUTH: Or tall.

DOT: Or in-between. (DANGERFORTH *enters*.)

DANGERFORTH: The first candidate is ready. A Mr. Dustin
Hudson, a young oil millionaire.

JONES: Oil is so dirty. It'll make my gold look just terrible.
(DUSTIN, *the tallest of the suitors, enters. He looks about
and smiles*.)

DUSTIN: Howdy, folks.

HARRIET: Isn't he handsome? And so nice and short.

DUSTIN (*To* HARRIET): Hi there, pretty girl. Are you Miss Opal Jones?

HARRIET: No. (*Sighs and points to* OPAL) She is.

DUSTIN: Oh. She's kind of cute, too. Even if she is a little big. (*Goes to* JONES) Mr. Jones, I'm Dustin Hudson of the Hudson Oil Company.

JONES: So?

DUSTIN: I've come here, sir, to ask for the hand of your daughter in marriage.

JONES: Let's not mince words, young man. Are you rich?

DUSTIN: Doggone it, yes. I light my cigars with fifty-dollar bills.

JONES: I don't approve of smoking.

DUSTIN: I don't smoke, sir. I just like to light the cigars.

JONES: *Exactly* how much money do you have, Mr. Hudson?

DUSTIN: I don't know exactly.

DANGERFORTH: That's a good sign.

JONES: It's a sign of supreme carelessness. It's like not knowing how many toes one has.

DUSTIN: I can make a rough guess.

JONES: That's not good enough, but go ahead.

DUSTIN: I have oil wells in Texas, Oklahoma, and Louisiana. I have some cattle in New Mexico, Arizona, and Nevada. I have hotels and motels in Utah, Oregon, and California. And I own the whole state of Montana.

DANGERFORTH: That comes, sir, to approximately fourteen billion, thirty-two million, fourteen thousand, six hundred and thirty-two dollars, and twenty-five cents.

DUSTIN: Golly, that's a pretty good sum, isn't it? I'll have to start lighting cigars with hundred-dollar bills. Or maybe I could just start the fire for barbecues with thousand-dollar bills. (*To* JONES) Well, Mr. Jones, what do you say? Do I get your daughter or don't I?

JONES: Dangerforth, what was that figure again?

DANGERFORTH: Approximately fourteen billion, thirty-two million, fourteen thousand, six hundred and thirty-two dollars and twenty-five cents. Of course, if there's a drought in Montana this summer, he'll lose that thirty-two dollars and twenty-five cents.

JONES: That's not very much, is it, Dangerforth?

DANGERFORTH: Not in terms of your fortune, sir. Your janitor sweeps out that much in gold dust every day.

JONES: Mr. Hudson, I like you. You're a fine young man. Someday—if you give up your bad habits—you may be quite successful, even. . . . What was that term you used, Dangerforth?

DANGERFORTH: Well-to-do, Mr. Jones.

JONES: Thank you, Dangerforth. (*To* DUSTIN) You might even be well-to-do. Some day.

DUSTIN: Some day! Well now, Mr. Jones, I think for a young man of my tender years, it's really something to be worth fourteen . . . fourteen. . . . whatever it was that Mr. Dangerforth said I was worth.

JONES (*Shaking his head*): That's the trouble with the poor, Dangerforth. They have no ambition. (*To* DUSTIN) In brief, Mr. Hudson, you may *not* marry my daughter.

DUSTIN: Sir, you have no sympathy for young love.

JONES: Flattery will get you nowhere.

DUSTIN: Sir, my heart is very likely to break because of your cruelty.

JONES: I shall survive your loss, Mr. Hudson.

DUSTIN: I'll probably never get over it.

JONES: I should hope not.

DUSTIN: Would you do me one favor?

JONES: Probably not, but you may ask before you leave.

DUSTIN (*Going to* HARRIET): Sir, may I have your permission to wed this little miss?

JONES: Certainly. Blessings on you, young people.

DUSTIN (*Rushing to* JONES *and shaking his hand*): Thank you, sir. Thank you. You've made me the happiest man in the world. (*Rushes back to* HARRIET, *takes her by the hand as she rises*) Come on, little girl. You and I are going to be married. Mr. Jones just gave his permission.

HARRIET: I want to go to Niagara Falls on our honeymoon. Can we?

DUSTIN: We sure can. Why, little girl, I'll just buy Niagara Falls for you. (DUSTIN *and* HARRIET *rush offstage*)

JONES: He thinks he'll buy Niagara Falls. I won't sell it to him. He's entirely too fresh. Oh, this is going to be a wearing day. I can see that already.

DANGERFORTH: Shall I bring in the next candidate, sir?

JONES: Opal, my jewel, do we have to go through with this?

OPAL: You promised.

JONES: I suppose I did. But I didn't know it was going to be so wearing. All right, Dangerforth, bring in the next young man.

DANGERFORTH: Very well, Mr. Jones. (*Exits*)

RUTH: Mr. Jones, why did Dustin Hudson ask you if he could marry Harriet?

JONES: I wouldn't know, my dear. No man my age knows what any young man sees in any young woman.

RUTH: But why you? You don't have anything to say about whom Harriet marries.

JONES: That's why I gave my permission.

RUTH: If anyone should ask your permission to marry *me* . . .

DOT: Or me.

RUTH *and* DOT: Don't take so long to say yes. (DANGERFORTH *re-enters, followed by* CHAUNCEY LODGEWORTH, *the shortest of the suitors.*)

DANGERFORTH: Mr. Chauncey Lodgeworth, of the Universal Plastics Corporation.

LODGEWORTH: How do you do.

DOT: Chauncey Lodgeworth. Isn't that a pretty name?

RUTH: And he's so handsome and tall.

LODGEWORTH: Rather. (*To* RUTH) But I'm not as handsome as you are, Miss Jones.

RUTH (*Giggling*): I'm Ruth.

LODGEWORTH: Why, thank you, Miss Jones, but I haven't known you long enough to call you by your first name. Perhaps after we have been married several years, I will call you Ruth, and you may call me Chauncey.

RUTH: I'm not Miss Jones. (*Sighs and points to* OPAL) She is.

LODGEWORTH: Oh. (*Turns to* OPAL) How do you do, Miss Jones.

OPAL: How do you do, Mr. Lodgeworth.

LODGEWORTH: Frightfully pleasant weather we've been having.

OPAL: Frightfully.

LODGEWORTH: Well, then, now that the courtship is taken care of, shall we get down to business?

JONES: Just what *is* your business, young man?

LODGEWORTH: Why, I've come to ask for the hand of your daughter, Ruth, in marriage.

JONES: My daughter's name is Opal, and that's not the business I'm talking about. I mean your business.

LODGEWORTH: I'm in plastics.

JONES: So are jelly beans, dried fish, and ten-cent rings in a gumball machine. Just what do you do in plastics?

LODGEWORTH: I own them. I own the Universal Plastics Corporation, the American Plastics Company, the European International Plastics Plant, Inc., the African Plastics Company, and the Arkansas Do-It-Yourself Tool Company.

JONES: Is that all?

LODGEWORTH: I also have a home in Longmeadow, a cottage on Green Bay, a yacht off Charleston, a 1933 Essex parked in front of your home, three suits of clothes, and two books—both practically new.

JONES: Is that everything?

LODGEWORTH: Everything, except an old Jimmy Dorsey record, which I don't count because it is cracked.

JONES: I must say, Mr. Lodgeworth, I am more pleased with you than the last fellow who was here.

RUTH: Me, too.

JONES: Quiet, please. He was a reckless young man. Didn't even know how much he had and did all sorts of reckless things with money. Do you do reckless things with money, Mr. Lodgeworth?

LODGEWORTH: I'm afraid so, Mr. Jones. Occasionally I throw away money weighing myself on public scales.

JONES: That's wasteful to be sure, but it doesn't sound serious.

LODGEWORTH: I do it to get my fortune told.

JONES: Fortunes are not told, Mr. Lodgeworth. They tell. Money speaks and everyone else listens. Now, exactly, in dollars and cents, what are you worth, Mr. Lodgeworth? I do not intend to have my daughter marry anyone except a young man of considerable value.

LODGEWORTH: I'm not exactly sure . . . to the penny.

JONES: Oh, Mr. Lodgeworth. And I had some hopes for you. What is this young man worth, Mr. Dangerforth?

DANGERFORTH: Twenty-three billion, fourteen million, eight thousand and twenty-two dollars and fourteen cents. I allowed him four cents for the Dorsey record.

LODGEWORTH: Thank you. Would you like to buy it?

DANGERFORTH: Certainly not. It's cracked.

JONES: Then take off that four cents.

DANGERFORTH: Yes, sir. Would you like the revised total?

JONES: It's not necessary. Young man, you just aren't worth enough to marry my daughter. On the other hand, if you would like to marry Ruth there, I shall be happy to give my permission.

LODGEWORTH: Why, thank you, sir. That will be very nice.

RUTH: Golly, yes. (*Rises, goes to him and takes his arm*)

LODGEWORTH: There's just one thing, Mr. Jones.

JONES: You're not trying to back out of your engagement, are you, Mr. Lodgeworth?

LODGEWORTH: Certainly not, sir. I'm an honorable man.

RUTH: He certainly is. And so cute.

LODGEWORTH: It's just that . . . well, I don't know her last name. I just can't start calling her Ruth.

RUTH: That's no problem, Chauncey dear. You can just call me Mrs. Lodgeworth. (*They turn and start off down right arm-in-arm*)

LODGEWORTH: Oh, that's splendid. And it will be so easy to remember. It's the same as mine.

RUTH: That's right, dear. What's yours is mine.

JONES (*Watching them exit*): Dangerforth, do we have any money in plastics?

DANGERFORTH: Yes, sir.

JONES: Sell our stock. I think that young man has just learned to spend money, and I don't want it to be mine. (*Stands and stretches*) Now that this business is over, maybe we can get back to work.

OPAL: Not yet, Daddy, there's still. . . .

JONES: Not another one?

DOT: I hope that he's handsome and in-between.

JONES (*Sitting again*): All right, Dangerforth, bring him in. But let's be quick about it. (DANGERFORTH *runs off and immediately runs back with* NICK MARAT.)

DANGERFORTH (*Quickly*): This is Nick Marat, Mr. Jones. His money is in money.

DOT: Oh, he's so cute and just the right height.

JONES: I'm not interested in his bone and muscle, but his money. How much money do you have?

OPAL: Daddy, that sounds vulgar.

JONES: We mustn't be vulgar. I'll ask in a more refined manner. Mr. Marat, how much are you worth?

NICK: Fourteen billion even.

JONES: That's not enough.

NICK: In British pounds. Six billion more. . . .

JONES: That's still not enough.

NICK: In French francs. And thirty-three billion in American dollars.

JONES: I'm waiting.

NICK: That's all.

JONES: Mr. Marat, how would you like to marry Dot here?

NICK: I'd love to. I think she's cute.

DOT: Me, too.

JONES: Then take her, young man.

NICK: Gee, thanks, Dad. You don't mind if I call you Dad, do you?

JONES: What for? She's not my daughter. My daughter will marry no one except a man of considerable value.

NICK: I also have twenty-three dollars in Mexican money.

DOT: Wonderful, Nicky. We can go there on our honeymoon.

NICK: Why not? (DOT *and* NICK *start down right arm-in-arm.*) You know, I'm glad it came out this way. I never did want to marry Mr. Jones' daughter anyway.

DOT: She's really a very nice girl.

NICK: But "Miss Jones"—who could remember a name like that?

DOT: That's true.

NICK: Incidentally, you never did say what your name is.

DOT: Dot.

NICK: Gee, that's keen. (*They exit.*)

JONES: Was that the last one, Dangerforth?

DANGERFORTH: I think so.

JONES (*To* OPAL): I'm sorry, my dear. But you must agree that none of them would do.

OPAL: I do agree.

JONES: They weren't worth enough.

OPAL: That's true.

JONES: I must say that I am pleased that you are being so sensible about this whole matter.

OPAL: I'm very sensible, Daddy. Ever since I started reading books in the public library.

JONES: Yes, I noticed the change. From the moment, almost, that you started going to the public library every night, you seem to have become more . . . more . . .

OPAL: More sensible?

JONES: Yes, but not only that. To be honest, my dear jewel, I was a little surprised that you wanted to have the examination of candidates at this time.

OPAL: That's my right, Daddy. Every year at this time, you have to consider all my suitors.

JONES: True. But ever since you have started going to the public library, you haven't seemed as interested in young men.

OPAL: I wouldn't say that.

JONES: Today, for example, you were really most disinterested in them.

OPAL: Not really disinterested, Daddy, just not very interested.

JONES: In fact, my dear jewel, I had the feeling that I was being shown these young men just to prepare me for someone else. (*To* DANGERFORTH) Dangerforth, are you sure there isn't another young man lurking in the shadows out there?

DANGERFORTH: Reasonably sure, Mr. Jones. Shall I look again?

JONES: Please do. I have the funniest feeling in the back of my neck, and whenever I get that feeling I know somebody is up to something.

DANGERFORTH: I shall look again. (*Exits*)

OPAL: Daddy, you're so suspicious.

JONES: I'm too tired from this whole business to be even properly suspicious, but I am cautious.

OPAL: Of course, I do have the right to have another candidate examined.

JONES: You do, my dear, but I hope you won't. I'm really too tired to do a proper job.

DANGERFORTH (*Re-entering*): There is no one there, Mr. Jones.

JONES: Good. Now I can relax completely. (SMITHY *enters up center. He is carrying a load of books that reaches almost to his nose.*)

DANGERFORTH: Good heavens, what's that?

OPAL: Hello, Smithy. I'm glad you got here.

SMITHY: Me, too. Are you ready to go to the library?

OPAL: Put those books down this instant, Smithy. Today is the day.

SMITHY: I can't put them down. These books are all due today.

OPAL: Put the books down, Smithy.

SMITHY (*Setting books on floor*): All right, Opal. They're down.

OPAL: Now, I want you to meet my father. Mr. Jones, this is Mr. Smith. Mr. Smith, this is Mr. Jones.

DANGERFORTH: Humph. It comes out even.

SMITHY: How do you do, Mr. Jones.

JONES: How do you do, Mr. Smith.

SMITHY (*Starting to pick up books*): We'd better go to the library now.

OPAL: Leave those books alone, Smithy. I told you today is the day.

SMITHY: Couldn't we wait until tomorrow?

JONES: Or the day after, perhaps?

OPAL: No, today. Daddy, Smithy—Mr. Smith to you— wants to ask you for my hand in marriage.

JONES: I was afraid of that.

SMITHY: I would just as soon wait until tomorrow, sir.

JONES: Don't you want to marry my Opal?

SMITHY: Why, yes, sir, I certainly do. But I have these books, you see, and I should get them back to the library.

JONES: I'm glad to learn that you are a responsible young man.

SMITHY: Oh, yes, sir, I am responsible. (*To* OPAL) Do you want to go to the library now?

OPAL: No, I want you to ask Daddy for my hand in marriage.

SMITHY: It won't do any good.

JONES: It certainly won't. I'm too tired to go through another investigation.

OPAL: You promised, Daddy.

DANGERFORTH: You certainly did, Mr. Jones.

JONES: All right, then, Dangerforth, you examine this candidate. I can't go through it again.

DANGERFORTH: If you insist.

JONES: But I want it clearly understood that if this candidate is not a young man of considerable worth, my answer is no, no, absolutely no. Do you understand, Dangerforth?

DANGERFORTH: Yes, yes, absolutely yes, sir.

JONES: Good. Now, I am going into my gold vault and run through piles of gold coins in my bare feet. It feels so good that it relaxes me. When I return, I'll ask just the one question: Is he a young man of considerable value? If the answer is yes, he may marry Opal. If it is no, however—and I am sure it will be—I want to hear no more talk of marriage for at least three years. Do you all agree?

DANGERFORTH: I agree.

OPAL: I agree.

SMITHY: Could I come back tomorrow?

DANGERFORTH: No.

OPAL: It's now.

JONES: Or never.

OPAL: But let it be now.

JONES: Dangerforth, I am putting you in charge. I trust you completely. Take your responsibility seriously.

DANGERFORTH: I shall, sir.

JONES: Remember, he must be a young man of considerable value.

DANGERFORTH: I will remember.

JONES: Be sure you do, Dangerforth. (JONES *exits up left.* DANGERFORTH *sits in chair behind table and assumes* JONES' *attitude and mannerisms.*)

DANGERFORTH: I must tell you to start with, Mr. Smith, that I set very high standards for Opal's husband. I might add that my standards are even higher than her father's. I do not intend that my employer's daughter shall be the wife of just anyone.

OPAL: Oh, Mr. Dangerforth, I thought you would be more understanding. You were always so sympathetic.

DANGERFORTH: That was when I was only your father's assistant. Now that I am in charge, I have different ideas.

SMITHY: I am not going to pass, Opal.

OPAL: Oh, Smithy, and I do so love you.

DANGERFORTH: Now, Mr. Smith, how much oil do you have?

SMITH: I have a little salad oil in a bottle. If I had some lettuce and carrots, I would make a salad.

DANGERFORTH: Hm-m. A little salad oil. I'll allow fourteen cents on that. Do you own any property?

SMITHY: Just the shoes I'm standing in.

DANGERFORTH: Do you have any money?

SMITHY: No. That's the reason I have to get back to the library—I don't have even enough money to pay any fines.

DANGERFORTH: Plastics?

SMITHY: No.

DANGERFORTH: Yachts, planes, cars?

SMITHY: No, no, no. Opal, it's hopeless. I told you it was. I am not a man of considerable wealth.

DANGERFORTH: You're not even poor-to-do. You're just plain poor.

OPAL: He has my love. That should be worth something.

DANGERFORTH: Young man, Mr. Jones gave me the power to act for him; so I'm going to make you an offer. I'll give you ten thousand dollars if you'll give up Opal. What do you say?

SMITHY: I don't have Opal to give up.

DANGERFORTH: Her love, then. Will you give up her love for ten thousand dollars?

SMITHY: No, not for a million.

DANGERFORTH: For a billion?

SMITHY: Not for ten billion.

DANGERFORTH: For a hundred billion?

SMITHY: Not for all the money in the world.

DANGERFORTH: Am I to assume that you would rather have Opal's love and stay poor than have all the money in the world and give up that love?

SMITHY: If I willingly gave up Opal's love—no matter what else I had—I should be the poorest man in the world.

OPAL: And if I can't marry Smithy, I'll marry no one.

DANGERFORTH: Well, now, this is a pretty pass.

OPAL: Can't you help us, Mr. Dangerforth?

DANGERFORTH: Certainly not. I am not here to help or hurt, but just to report the facts. (JONES *re-enters, carrying one shoe.*)

JONES: And what are the facts, Dangerforth?

DANGERFORTH: Rather grim, sir, I'm afraid.

JONES (*Sitting down and putting on shoe*): I thought as much.

DANGERFORTH: He has fourteen cents worth of oil.

JONES: Oh, that's pitiful.

DANGERFORTH: And it's only salad oil at that.

JONES: More pitiful yet.

DANGERFORTH: And he has the shoes he is standing in.

JONES: And?

DANGERFORTH: And that's all.

JONES: Then there's no problem here. Surely, Opal, even you can see that he is not a young man of considerable value.

OPAL: But, Daddy. . . .

JONES: An agreement is an agreement, and we have all agreed that you shall marry only a young man. . . .

OPAL: "Of considerable value." How I hate that phrase.

DANGERFORTH: However, Mr. Jones, young Smith does have one small jewel.

JONES: A *small* jewel?

DANGERFORTH: *Petite,* I would say.

JONES: I do want to be fair about this. I want to count everything. What value has been placed on the stone?

DANGERFORTH: I heard a hundred billion offered.

JONES: A hundred billion! Now that's a nice round sum. But, still, I am not sure that is quite enough.

DANGERFORTH: And it wasn't enough.

JONES: It wasn't enough? It must be a very fine jewel.

DANGERFORTH: It is, sir. In fact, it is priced—if I recall the expression exactly—at more than "all the money in the world."

JONES: Then he is obviously the young man we have waited for—truly a young man of considerable value.

DANGERFORTH: I must warn you, sir, that Smith has no money.

JONES: Money, Dangerforth, is the cheapest kind of wealth. This jewel that Smith owns—I must have it in my family. I must, you understand. Mr. Smith, you have my permission to marry my daughter. Opal, I command that you marry this young man. The wedding will be tomorrow. Are we all agreed?

DANGERFORTH: I agree.

JONES: I didn't mean you, Dangerforth.

OPAL: I always obey your commands, Daddy.

SMITHY: Me, too, Daddy.

OPAL (*Turning to* SMITHY *and taking both his hands in hers*): Ah, Smithy.

SMITHY: Ah, Jonesy.

DANGERFORTH: Ah, young love.

JONES: Ah, me. This has been a long but profitable day. (*Curtain*)

THE END

Take It from the Beginning

Characters

JANE FROST, *a young actress*
JIM BARK, *a young actor*
MR. WAGNER, *the director*
MARGARET, *his assistant*
RALPH WILLIAMS, *another actor*
LAVERNE BROWN, *another actress*
HARRY, *a character actor*
BETH, *a young may-be actress*
ANDY, *a young may-be actor*

SETTING: *A theatre stage during try-outs. Part of the stage is being used for furniture storage and flats, which lean against the walls. Down center is a stool, and to the left of it, a small table and chair.*

AT RISE: JANE FROST *and* JIM BARK *are acting out their parts. Although they carry scripts, for a moment the illusion should be given that they are the characters they represent. They are, however, overacting, turning a simple scene into heightened soap-opera melodrama. Sitting at the small table, in semi-darkness, is* MR. WAGNER. *He keeps his head bowed and says nothing the early part of this scene. Thus until an interruption comes, the audience should feel that they are watching a play, not a reading for parts in a play.*

JANE: I don't really know why I do these things. (*She puts her hands on the stool and looks at it for a moment.*) It's just that I grow tired of being alone all the time. (*Turns to* JIM) Do you know what I mean?

JIM: Yes. Yes, I know what you mean.

JANE: I just want to be around other people.

JIM: I know.

JANE: And I want them to know that I'm there.

JIM: I know.

JANE: I don't mean I want to stand on my head or anything. I'm not an exhibitionist.

JIM: It's just that you want somebody to see you as a person. That's it, isn't it?

JANE: That's exactly it. (*Pauses*) How do you know how I feel?

JIM: I feel that way, too. At work, you're just . . . well, just somebody who works.

JANE: And at home you're just somebody who lives there.

JIM: Somebody that has to be fed.

JANE: And told to be happy even when you don't feel like being happy.

JIM: It just causes trouble when you're unhappy.

JANE: Even when being unhappy is the happiest thing you can do.

JIM: I know.

JANE: At any rate, that's why I'm here. I don't really know anything about art. And I don't really care very much either. (*Moves away from stool and gestures up right center, as though pointing out a painting hanging on the wall*) That painting, for example, that one there.

JIM: Botticelli's *Primavera*!

JANE: Yes. Painted in 1477, according to the folder I was given at the door.

JIM: One is supposed to note the detail as he looks at it.

JANE: The ripe oranges on the trees.

JIM: The iris, the larkspurs, the daisies, the wild orchid.

JANE: The wood strawberry daintily balancing in the grass tells us that it is early springtime.

JIM: That's what it says in my folder, too.

JANE: But it doesn't mean anything to me.

JIM: I can barely pronounce the artist's name.

JANE: Or the name of the painting.

MARGARET (*Calling from offstage up right*): Mr. Wagner! Mr. Wagner, telephone. (*Comes onstage from up right*) You're wanted on the phone, Mr. Wagner. I think it's your wife.

WAGNER (*Rising*): I've told her a thousand times not to call me when I am working.

MARGARET: It doesn't do any good to tell amateurs about show business, Mr. Wagner.

MR. WAGNER: I know. They think putting on a play is fun.

JANE (*No longer acting*): I thought so, too. Until I tried out for this one.

MR. WAGNER: I'm sorry, Miss Frost. But after all my wife does have the right to call me if she wants to.

JIM: I don't see why, when we are right in the midst of a scene.

WAGNER: A scene for which Mrs. Wagner has put up the money.

JIM: I see why.

WAGNER: Besides, now that we have been interrupted, I might as well tell you that you are doing it all wrong.

JANE: I felt that about your interpretation, too, Jim.

JIM: Oh, you did? Well, I can tell you that I thought you hammed up the scene from start to finish.

JANE: Look who's talking.

WAGNER: There's no need to leap at each other's throats. You're both hamming it up. Look, this is really a very simple scene.

MARGARET: What about the telephone, Mr. Wagner?

WAGNER: Tell my wife that I'm out trying to find some properties. After all, it's not easy to set a scene that's supposed to look like the Museum of Art. You might ask her if she knows anyone who would let us borrow Botticelli's *Primavera*. It will cost $400,000 if we have to buy it.

JANE: And it's not for sale.

MARGARET: All right, I'll tell her. (*Starts off up right*)

WAGNER: And turn on some stage lights, will you, Margaret. I can't read the notes that I take in the dark.

MARGARET: O.K. I'll lie to your wife, and I'll turn on the lights. The glamour of show business! (*Exits.* JANE *sits on the stool;* JIM *sits on the floor beside her.* WAGNER *picks up a sheaf of papers and goes into area of spotlight to try to read them.*)

WAGNER: I can't read a thing that I've written down. It's all just a scribble. (*Returns to table*)

JANE: That's the way I find this script, too. Just a scribble.

JIM: Let's face it. It's a dumb play.

WAGNER: Look, let's take it from the beginning. I think once you see what the point of this play is, you'll like it.

JANE: Why can't we do Chekhov?

JIM: Or Eugene O'Neill?

JANE: Or even Shakespeare? He's old-fashioned, but he's better than this.

WAGNER: Chekhov is not my wife's brother. O'Neill is not my wife's brother. Even Shakespeare is not my wife's brother. Marvin is my wife's brother, and Marvin wrote this play. My wife loves her brother, Marvin.

JANE: And your wife is putting up the money for the play. We know.

JIM: But it's a lousy play.

WAGNER: Marvin's a lousy brother-in-law, true; but this is not a lousy play. It's a good play. I don't know how a guy like my brother-in-law could do it, but *Work of Art* is a fine play—full of hope and love and the quiet pleasure of being alive.

JIM: People get tired of hope and love and quiet pleasure. That's why they are willing to shell out real money to go to the theatre.

JANE: Where they go to see violence, crime, and wild passion.

JIM: Let's do *Hamlet.*

JANE: Or *Blood Wedding.* That has a great role in it for an actress with my sensitivity.

WAGNER: We are going to do *Work of Art.*

JANE: I'm not. I'm quitting.

JIM: Now wait a minute, Jane. Let's try it once more. (*The stage lights come on.*)

WAGNER: Give the play a chance. Let's take it from the beginning. You have this young couple. They don't know each other when the play opens, but they are very much alike. They are leading dull lives—not unhappy, but dull. And they both try to do something about it. They come to this museum in the hope that the great art of the past will do something for them. It doesn't, of course. Great art only means something when you are ready for it. You have to bring excitement to it, and that they don't have yet. But they meet and fall in love.

JANE (*Sarcastically*): Now, that will be different.

WAGNER: But they don't really know it. At first, I mean. Then they discover they are in love, but by then they have parted. What can they do? New York is a big city.

How do you find someone when you don't even know his name?

JIM: How about those computer dating services? I signed up with one of them, and I met a girl I used to know back in Iowa. We hated each other as kids, and even after ten years, we still hated each other.

WAGNER (*Ignoring him*): So what do they do?

JANE: The man could join the Green Berets, fight John Wayne, and then when John Wayne is dying, our hero could discover—from a picture in John Wayne's wallet— that the man he has killed is really the father of the girl he loves. It would be better than *The Cid*.

WAGNER: You two aren't even going to give the play a chance, are you?

JANE: *Work of Art* doesn't have a chance.

JIM: It's old-fashioned, slow, stupid.

WAGNER: Then, there's no sense in my wasting your time any further. Thank you, Miss Frost, Mr. Bark.

JANE (*Handing him the script*): I'm sorry, Mr. Wagner, I just can't do it. The play doesn't grab me.

WAGNER: I guess you're right. It's not the kind of thing that you can do—any more. You've been around the theatre too long. You've forgotten what it means to have your whole world hang on the smile of one rather shy young man.

JANE: You don't have to be nasty about it. I'm not sweet sixteen, I'll admit; but I'm not. . . . Oh, what's the use. There never was a time in my life when my whole world hung on the grin of a dumb kid. (*She stalks off down left.*)

JIM (*Handing script to* WAGNER): There's something in what she says, Mr. Wagner. It isn't just the play. It's life. People don't believe in all that sweet young love hokum anymore.

WAGNER: O.K. I think you're going to be sorry, but O.K.

JIM: No offense meant.

WAGNER: Mr. Bark, if you're right about life, there's no offense possible. If youth and love and . . . yes, even sweetness are dead, can theatre be far behind? Or the fun of being alive anywhere?

JIM: I think I'll leave before you start quoting Longfellow. So long, Mr. Wagner. (*He exits down left.* WAGNER *rises and looks off after* JIM, *quoting "Twelfth Night."*)

WAGNER:

Enough! No more!

'Tis not so sweet now as it was before.

O spirit of love, how quick and fresh art thou,

That, notwithstanding thy capacity

Receiveth as the sea, nought enters there

Of . . . Of what validity and. . . . (*Hesitates.* RALPH WILLIAMS *and* LAVERNE BROWN *enter up right, stopping to hear* WAGNER *recite. When* WAGNER *pauses,* RALPH *continues.* RALPH *and* LAVERNE *contrast with* JANE *and* JIM *in their method of acting.* RALPH *and* LAVERNE, *who are in their mid-fifties, play their roles in an old-fashioned rhetorical manner.*)

RALPH (*Reciting almost pompously*):

Of what validity and pitch soe'er,

But falls into abatement and low price,

Even in a minute! (*Changing tone*) Shakespeare's *Twelfth Night; or, What You Will,* Act I, Scene 1.

LAVERNE: What country, friend, is this?

RALPH: This is Illyria, lady.

WAGNER: All right, all right. You know your Shakespeare. What can I do for you?

RALPH: I, sir, am Ralph Williams. You've heard of me, of course. And my fair partner is Laverne Brown.

LAVERNE: And if you've heard of Ralph, you've heard of me. I do Juliet.

RALPH: To my Romeo.

LAVERNE: Portia.

RALPH: To my Bassanio.

LAVERNE: Cleopatra.

RALPH: To my Antony.

WAGNER: I'm sorry. I've never heard of you.

RALPH: Oh? It's not surprising. We don't do the things that make one popular today.

LAVERNE: We wouldn't do such things.

RALPH: Cheap, vulgar. . . .

LAVERNE: Noisy, angry.

WAGNER: I'm glad to hear it, but you still haven't told me what I can do for you.

RALPH: We have come to try out for the play.

WAGNER: I'm sorry, but I'm not doing Shakespeare.

RALPH: No, no, the modern thing you're doing.

LAVERNE: It's called *Work of Art*. We've read it. We want to try out for the leads.

RALPH: It's a light thing, to be sure—hardly enough for a man who has given his life to doing Hamlet, Lear, Macbeth.

LAVERNE: But maybe worth doing.

RALPH: It has some hope in it.

LAVERNE: Some love. Even some sweetness.

RALPH: It's not Shakespeare to be sure.

LAVERNE: But still it is something that one may do without total disgrace.

WAGNER: You want to try out for parts in *Work of Art*; is that right?

RALPH: Not just parts, the leads.

WAGNER: Well . . . you said you'd read the play.

LAVERNE: Read it and liked it. Rather like Sir James Barrie, I thought. In parts.

WAGNER: The leads are . . . young people. Late teens, early twenties, and you. . . .

RALPH: Are more mature, that's true. But we are performers, sir. We can create illusions. We are actors. I did the aged Lear when I was twenty.

LAVERNE: And I did the child Juliet when I was . . . just last year.

WAGNER: Well, why not? Maybe young people today don't know how to play young people anymore. Maybe it will take people of . . . of our generation to show them what fun it is to be young and in love and full of hope.

RALPH: Very well put, sir.

WAGNER (*Taking scripts and giving one to each*): Here, let's just see how it works. Start on Act I, Scene 2. The lovers have gone to the Museum of Art. They have just met. They don't know each other's names. They don't even know they are interested in each other. But they just know that they can talk to each other, although they are strangers. They can talk to each other in a way they can't talk to friends or family. Turn to page 10 and take it from the beginning.

RALPH (*Turning pages*): Page 10. (*He peers at page; then takes out glasses and puts them on.*) Oh, yes. A nice little scene. Are you ready, Laverne?

LAVERNE (*Who also has put on glasses to read the script*): Ready.

WAGNER (*Sitting down at table*): Go ahead. Start. It's a simple scene, but I know that as soon as I find people who do this scene right, I'll have my leads.

RALPH: Rather like the "To be or not to be" scene in *Hamlet*.

LAVERNE: Or the sleep-walking scene in *Macbeth*.

WAGNER (*Prepared to be disappointed*): I guess so. (*Pauses*) Would you like to begin?

RALPH (*In manner of a Shakespearian actor*): Would you begin, my dear?

LAVERNE (*Reading script in a grand manner*): I don't really know why I do these things. It's just that I grow tired of being alone all the time. Do you know what I mean? (*She turns to him, almost as if pleading.*)

RALPH (*Going to her and taking her hand*): Yes! Yes, by heaven, I know what you mean.

WAGNER: Wait a minute. There's no "by heaven" in the script.

RALPH: I know. I added it. It sounds rather bleak without something.

WAGNER: Just read it as it is.

RALPH: All right. (*Reads*) Yes, yes, I know what you mean.

LAVERNE: I just . . . just have to be around other people.

RALPH: I know. Oh, how I know.

WAGNER: And there's no "Oh, how I know" in there either.

RALPH: True, but these lines are bleak to the point of starvation. They need vitamins, old boy.

LAVERNE: And I want them to know that I'm there.

RALPH: I know. But break my heart for I must hold my tongue.

WAGNER: There's no. . . .

RALPH: I know. It's from *Hamlet,* and if it's good enough for Shakespeare, it should do something for this little piece of fluff. (WAGNER *buries his face in his hands.*)

LAVERNE: I don't mean I want to stand on my head or anything. I'm not an exhibitionist. (*Breaks*) Do you think it would pick up the action if I were to stand on my head at this point?

RALPH: Laverne used to be an acrobat, you know, before she joined me on the legitimate stage. Quite good.

WAGNER (*Rising*): Wait a minute. This just isn't going to

work. You two are great. I can see that, but this play just isn't for you. You're too . . . too grand . . . too magnificent.

RALPH: Does this mean that you are willing to scrap this silly thing and do Shakespeare? My Hamlet is very good, I have been told.

LAVERNE: I could do Ophelia.

WAGNER: No. I really couldn't. I'm committed to doing *Work of Art.*

RALPH: Why, pray tell, when you could be directing me as Hamlet?

LAVERNE: And me as Ophelia?

WAGNER: I've promised the playwright.

RALPH: You're not the kind of man who would sacrifice artistic principle to mere friendship, are you, Mr. Wagner?

WAGNER: Besides, I like *Work of Art,* and that's the play I'm going to do.

RALPH: If you'll make a few small changes, I might consent.

WAGNER: No, I'm afraid that you two just won't do for the parts. It's not that you're not great, you understand, but I'm sure you understand. (HARRY, *an older character actor, enters up left.*)

HARRY: Mr. Wagner, you're wanted on the phone. It's your wife, I think.

WAGNER: Oh, thank you, Harry. (*To* RALPH *and* LAVERNE) If you two will excuse me. It's been very fine meeting both of you, and if I ever do Shakespeare, I'll give you a call.

RALPH: Now, wait a minute. We'd like to discuss the matter of our doing *Work of Art.*

WAGNER: I'm sorry. The parts just aren't right for you.

LAVERNE: You could change the parts.

WAGNER: Oh, the playwright wouldn't like that.

RALPH: Then we could change playwrights.

WAGNER: We couldn't do that. The playwright's my wife's brother, and my wife is putting up the money for the production.

HARRY: You'd better hurry, Mr. Wagner. Mrs. Wagner sounded a little impatient.

WAGNER: Yes, thank you, Harry. I have to run. (*He runs offstage up right.*)

RALPH (*Shouting after him*): You'll be sorry. (*To* LAVERNE) Well, my dear, you blew it again.

LAVERNE: I blew it? It was you and those "by heavens."

RALPH: My dear, let's not quarrel. Somewhere in this city there's a director who still has taste. We shall find him.

LAVERNE: And in the meantime, we'd better get back to the restaurant. That girl at the register makes so many mistakes, we'll go broke if I'm not there to watch her all the time.

HARRY: Are you two in the restaurant business?

RALPH: Only between shows.

LAVERNE: We're the owners of A Little Bit of Stratford. Surely, you've heard of us. We've been in business twenty-three years.

HARRY: Of course. On 37th Street.

RALPH: Come in some time. We have special rates for those in the profession. Shall we depart, my dear?

LAVERNE (*Taking his arm*): Maybe, Ralph, we should produce our own play. Then we could do what we want— *Romeo and Juliet,* perhaps.

RALPH: Produce our own play? You mean put our own money into a Shakespearian production?

LAVERNE: Forgive me, Ralph, I was carried away. When I see the commercialism of someone like Wagner, it offends my artistic taste.

RALPH: Mine, too, but not to the point of putting our own money into something that risky.

LAVERNE: True, dear, true. (*They exit down left. *HARRY* watches them, grinning. *MARGARET* comes running in from down right.*)

MARGARET: Mr. Wagner, your wife wants you on the phone.

HARRY (*Laughing*): He's already on the phone, talking to his wife.

MARGARET: Oh, was I too late?

HARRY: It was kind of tight for Wagner. You know how he hates to turn anyone down for a part.

MARGARET: Yes, but I wish that he would come up with a better dodge.

HARRY: Oh, I don't know. It's a good story. He's producing his brother-in-law's play with his wife's money. No one can try to get him to change that.

MARGARET: Except that he isn't married, and *Work of Art* is his own play.

HARRY: True. But if people knew that he was producing his own play with his own money, every fast-talking actor in New York would be in here to get him to do something else.

MARGARET: I know. Maybe this business of theatre requires a thicker skin than Wagner has. I think he's going to have trouble.

HARRY: I don't know. He does some good things.

MARGARET: Do you think *Work of Art* is any good?

HARRY: This may surprise you, from an old cynic like me, but I do. I think it's a very decent play.

MARGARET: Maybe so, but he's certainly having his troubles casting those leads.

HARRY: Sweet kids with theatre experience are hard to come by.

MARGARET: I thought that Jane Frost and Jim Bark were the right types.

HARRY: So did Wagner, but not the way they were doing the roles.

MARGARET: Hm-m. I'd better get back to work. I just thought he was probably being pressured by those old Shakespearian hams, and he'd need a call from his "wife" so he could get away.

HARRY: Don't knock them. They make a very good beef stew.

MARGARET: Oh?

HARRY: And inexpensive, too.

MARGARET: Speaking of expenses, I'm going to turn some of these lights off. If it's going to take Mr. Wagner five years to find the leads for *Work of Art,* we'd better start economizing on the popcorn and lights. (*Exits down left.* HARRY *goes to table and arranges papers on it.* BETH *enters down right.*)

BETH (*Going to* HARRY): Excuse me, sir, are you the director?

HARRY: No, I'm just one of the flunkies. Wagner's the director. He'll be back in a few minutes.

BETH: Thank you. (*Pauses*) I wanted to see him about a position.

HARRY: A position? You mean you want a job?

BETH: Yes, a job. I want to be in theatre.

HARRY (*Appraising her*): Are you an actress?

BETH: I was in a high school play once, but I only had two lines. I said, "Excuse me, madam," and then I said, "It's the Master. He wishes to speak to you in the study."

HARRY: One play, two lines. That's not much experience for someone trying out for a professional play.

BETH: I wasn't going to try for a part. I type. I take short-hand, too. And I'm a good file clerk. I thought something like that.

HARRY: Oh, a stenographer. Why here? Theatre doesn't pay as much as other businesses in town.

BETH: I know, but I thought it might be more interesting.

HARRY: Mr. Wagner will be here in a minute. (*Turns back to papers, and* BETH *walks upstage a little to stand.* ANDY *enters down left and goes to* HARRY.)

ANDY: Excuse me, Mr. Wagner. A fellow told me you might need somebody to work as a stagehand. I've worked with electricity, and I can paint pretty well. I don't mean pictures, but things like. . . .

HARRY: Whoa, son. I'm not Mr. Wagner.

ANDY: You're not?

HARRY: No. He'll be here in a minute, though, so you'll have to go through that whole memorized speech again.

ANDY: You knew I memorized it, eh?

HARRY: I suspected it. But it's all right. You can't tell when we'll need stagehands who can memorize speeches. (*The lights go out and a spot goes on.*)

ANDY: Golly, what was that?

HARRY: The beginning of the economy drive, I guess. Well, amuse yourself. Mr. Wagner will be here in a minute.

ANDY: Thank you, sir. (HARRY *exits.* ANDY *and* BETH *become nervously aware of each other, clearing their throats, and walking about until they are approximately in the positions that* JANE *and* JIM *were in for the opening scene.*) Hi, are you an actress?

BETH: No. No, I'm not.

ANDY: I'd like to be an actor, but right now I'm trying to get a job working with scenery and stuff.

BETH: I'd like to be an actress, but right now I'm trying to get a job typing and stuff.

ANDY: I've applied to about a dozen directors.

BETH: Me, too.

ANDY: They all told me no. I don't have much hope.

BETH: Me, neither.

ANDY: I have another job . . . with a company that makes furniture.

BETH: I have another job, too. In insurance.

ANDY: I just thought it might be interesting to have a job around actors and, well, you know, people who are doing things . . . like acting. (WAGNER *enters up center, but stops when he sees them. They are not aware of him.*)

BETH: I don't really know why I do these things. (*Laughs nervously*) It's just that I grow tired of being alone all the time. Do you know what I mean?

ANDY: Yes. Yes, I know what you mean.

BETH: I just (*Shrugs*) want to be around other people.

ANDY: I know.

BETH: And I'd like them to know that I'm there.

ANDY: I know.

BETH: I don't want to do anything odd, you know, like standing on my head.

ANDY: It's just that you want somebody to see you as a person. That's it, isn't it?

BETH: That's exactly it. (*Looks at him*) How do you know how I feel?

ANDY: I kind of feel that way, too. Sometimes.

BETH: That's the reason I thought that if I could get a job here at a theatre. . . .

ANDY: I know. This must be a wonderful place to work.

WAGNER (*Coming down to them*): Wait a minute. Wait a minute. That's not in the play.

ANDY: I beg your pardon, sir.

WAGNER: Those lines about the theatre. They're not in the play. You're supposed to be in a museum.

BETH: A museum? I thought this was a theatre. I came to see a man named Mr. Wagner about a job.

ANDY: I did, too.

WAGNER: I'm Wagner; and if you can do the rest of the

play the way you did that scene, the parts are yours.
Perfect, just perfect. But I don't want any fooling around
with the lines. I want them done exactly as they're
written.

BETH: There must be some mistake, Mr. Wagner. I came
to see you about a job as a typist. I don't know anything
about a play.

WAGNER: What were you doing when I came in?

ANDY: We were just talking. We weren't doing anything
wrong.

WAGNER: You were just talking! You mean you weren't
doing the scene? Ha, ha, a joke. It doesn't make any difference. You were doing it just the way I wanted it.
(HARRY *comes in from right.*)

HARRY: You're wanted on the phone, Mr. Wagner. Your
wife.

WAGNER: Never mind that now, Harry. Listen, I've found
my leads.

HARRY: You have? Where?

WAGNER (*Points to* ANDY *and* BETH): Right here. I caught
them rehearsing a scene, and it was just perfect.

HARRY: Mr. Wagner, they're not actors. They just came
to see about other jobs here. She's a typist, and he. . . .

WAGNER: I know. I know. They can say whatever they
want, but they are my leads. Look, you'll see. All right,
now, you two, let's take it from the beginning.

ANDY: Take what?

WAGNER: The scene. The scene.

BETH: We don't know any scene.

WAGNER: All right, I'll go along with you. (*Goes to table,
takes scripts and gives one to each.*) Start at the top of
page 10. Just read the lines the way you were when I
came in. (*To* HARRY) Wait until you hear this, Harry.
Perfect, just perfect.

ANDY: You want us to read these parts?

WAGNER: That's right. Now go ahead.

ANDY: Well . . . (*To* BETH) I'll take the man's part, I guess.

BETH: I'll take the woman's.

ANDY: You're first.

BETH: O.K. (*She reads part in high voice, stiff and a little frightened.*) I don't really know why I do these things. It's just that I grow tired of being alone all the time. Do you know what I mean?

ANDY (*Stiff and formal*): Yes. Yes. I know what you mean.

BETH: I just want to be around other people.

ANDY: I know.

WAGNER: Wait a minute. Wait a minute. What are you doing? That's not the way you were reading those lines when I came in.

ANDY: We weren't reading any lines. We were just talking.

BETH: Honestly. I don't know how to read lines.

HARRY: It must have been just a coincidence that they were saying something like the play.

WAGNER: But they were saying it so well. It was perfect, Harry, just perfect. (*To* HARRY) Do you think there's a chance we could train them?

HARRY (*Shaking his head*): Mr. Wagner, you heard them.

WAGNER: I finally find just the perfect couple, and they can't act. It's enough to make me give up the theatre. (*To* ANDY *and* BETH) I guess if you can't act, you can't.

ANDY: I wanted to talk to you about a job, sir.

BETH: Me, too, Mr. Wagner.

WAGNER: Jobs? (*Shrugs*) Come back tomorrow and tell Harry to put you to work

ANDY: You mean we have jobs?

WAGNER: Yes, you have jobs. Now come back tomorrow. (*Turns to* HARRY) They were perfect, Harry. Just perfect.

BETH: I want to thank you, Mr. Wagner.

ANDY: Me, too.

WAGNER: It's all right. See Harry in the morning. (BETH *and* ANDY *walk off down left together.*)

HARRY: What am I supposed to do with them?

WAGNER: I don't know. Find something for them to do. They're nice kids.

HARRY: Rotten actors, but nice kids.

WAGNER (*Smiling*): If that Jane Frost was a kid like that, with her talent and what that kid's got, I'd have my lead.

HARRY: Look at it this way, Mr. Wagner, maybe you don't have your leads, but now you have some proof that people like your characters do exist in real life.

WAGNER: There *is* that, I suppose. And that's something. (JANE *and* JIM *enter from down left.*)

JANE: Mr. Wagner?

WAGNER: Oh, you? What can I do for you?

JANE: Jim and I have been thinking about it, and we decided you might be right.

JIM: About the characters in the play.

JANE: And about the play, too. Now, mind you, I personally was never that young, but. . . .

JIM: When we were leaving here, a girl came up and asked for you. She told us that she was looking for a job as a typist and wanted to work in a theatre for the chance to be around people.

JANE: And then a boy came up. Practically the same story.

JIM: And Jane and I got to thinking about it. These two could have been the characters in your play.

JANE: They were nice kids. So, we figured maybe we'd better think about the play again. Maybe . . . they were nice kids. I don't know why, but they got to me.

JIM: What do you say, Mr. Wagner? Do you want to try us again?

WAGNER (*Giving scripts to* JIM *and* JANE): Well, I'll be!

What do I say? I say, all right, let's give it a whirl. Take it from the beginning of the scene on page 10. (JIM *and* JANE *walk to upstage position, looking at scripts, reading as they go.*)

JANE: I don't really know why I do these things. (*Smiles*) It's just that I grow tired of being alone all the time. Do you know what I mean?

JIM: Yes. Yes, I know what you mean.

WAGNER: Perfect. Just perfect. (*Curtain*)

THE END

Hi Down There

Characters

HOWARD, *a young man*
ANNE, *a young lady*
JOEY, *another young man, their friend*
MR. WILKINS, *a salesman*
CLARISSA } *young girls*
HELEN
VINCENT, *a poet*
BETTY, *a young lady admired by Joey*

SETTING: *A vacant lot between two high buildings. At right and left are tall stepladders, about six feet high. A smaller ladder, about four feet high, is in the middle. A large trash can is down left, and down right are three soap boxes, painted with alternating blue and white stripes. A spotlight shines on each ladder.*

AT RISE: HOWARD *is sitting on ladder at left, reading a newspaper. He is calling out. He experiments with inflections as he calls.*

HOWARD: Hi down there. Hi down there. One, two, three, testing. Hi down there. Hi down there. Four, five, six, testing. Hi down there. Hi down there. Six and one-quarter, six and one-half, six and three-quarters. Testing. Hi down there. Hi down there.

ANNE (*Entering from down right, carrying rolled-up banner and knitting*): I could hear you as far as Wagner's Meat Market, Howard.

HOWARD (*Turning toward left and increasing volume*): Hi down there. Hi down there. Seven, eight, nine, testing.

ANNE: At least I think I heard you. Mrs. Wagner was yelling at Mr. Wagner, so I can't be sure. Mrs. Wagner yells quite loudly at times. Especially when she's happy.

HOWARD: Hi down there. Hi down there. Nine, eight, seven.

JOEY (*Entering from down left*): O.K., Howdie, I could hear you as far as Wissner's Shoe Store.

HOWARD (*Not noticing them*): Hi down there. Hi down there.

ANNE: We're here, Howdie. You can come down now.

JOEY: Yoo-hoo, Howdie, Anne and I are here.

HOWARD (*Looking down at them*): Oh, hi down there.

JOEY: Please don't say that and mean it. I really think this whole business is very stupid.

HOWARD (*Coming down from ladder*): You want a date with Betty, don't you, Joey?

JOEY: Yes, but there must be an easier way than this. Maybe I should just go over to her house and talk to her.

HOWARD: You called her on the phone. A lot of good that did you. What did she say to you?

JOEY: You know what she said to me.

HOWARD: I'll tell you what she said to you.

JOEY: I know what she said to me. You don't need to tell me.

HOWARD: You said, "Hello, Betty, this is Joey."

ANNE (*Pantomiming speaking on phone*): Hi, Joey.

HOWARD (*Pantomiming phoning*): And then you said,

"Betty, how about going to the dance with me Saturday night?"

ANNE: And she said, "Joey, I don't want to go to the dance with you Saturday night."

HOWARD: And you said, "Why not?"

ANNE: And she said, "Because it's dull going to a dance with you. That's why."

HOWARD: And you said. . . .

JOEY: All right, hang up, both of you. I mean, just don't say anything else. I know what she said, and I know what I said.

HOWARD (*Pantomiming hanging up phone*): And that's why you'd better listen to my plan.

ANNE (*Pantomiming putting phone down*): And when it comes to making plans, little old Howdie is the world's best.

HOWARD: Because I have imagination.

ANNE: Because he has imagination.

HOWARD: And originality.

ANNE: And originality.

HOWARD: And creativity.

ANNE: And creativity. And if you think you had a problem before Howdie started to help you, Joey, you haven't seen anything yet.

JOEY: That's exactly what I'm afraid of.

HOWARD (*To* ANNE): Now, what did you have to say that for?

ANNE: You know little old me. I just go around blurting out the truth whenever I think of it.

HOWARD: Never mind the truth. Joey tried that, and look how much good it did him.

JOEY: I think there's some kind of mistake. Betty isn't the kind of girl that would just tell a guy he's dull. Besides, how would she know? We've never had a date before.

HOWARD: Some girls have an instinct for that kind of thing.

JOEY: Anne, I ask you, do you think I'm dull?

ANNE: Joey, I think. . . . Well, let's put it this way, Joey. . . . On the other hand, Joey. . . . Now, look, Joey, I like you. You're a good friend, you know what I mean?

JOEY: Yeah, you mean I'm dull. Go ahead and say it.

ANNE: I never could keep a secret.

HOWARD: Joey, you're too sensitive. So, you're a little dull? Is that a crime? Lots of great men were dull.

JOEY: Name one.

HOWARD: Miles Standish. King Arthur. Arvel Smith.

JOEY: Who was Arvel Smith?

HOWARD: Well, he wasn't so great. But, boy, was he dull.

ANNE: Yeah, Joey, if you think you're dull, you should meet Arvel Smith. He's really dull.

JOEY: I don't want to meet Arvel Smith. I see all the dull people I ever want to meet when I look in the mirror.

HOWARD: Joey, we're joking.

ANNE: Sure, Joey, there's no such person as Arvel Smith.

HOWARD: Joey, you're not really dull. You just lack color.

ANNE: And imagination, and inventiveness, and creativity. Now that I think about it, you're very much like Arvel Smith.

HOWARD: Anne, please don't talk You are destroying Joey's self-confidence, and self-confidence is one thing that a man needs when he is trying to get a date with something as luscious as Betty Johnson.

ANNE: I won't say a word.

HOWARD: Good.

ANNE: But didn't Arvel Smith have a lot of self-confidence?

HOWARD: There's no such person as Arvel Smith.

ANNE: But for somebody who is nobody, didn't Arvel have a lot of self-confidence?

HOWARD: Anne, please be quiet. Please.

ANNE: I'm quiet.

HOWARD: Joey, all you have to do is show Betty that you have imagination, and she'll be knocking herself out to go to the dance with you.

JOEY: I still think I should just go to her house and talk to her.

HOWARD: You did talk to her. On the phone. You want us to play that record again?

JOEY: No, not again. All right, I'll do what you say.

HOWARD: Fine.

JOEY: But I'll feel silly.

HOWARD: As long as you do what I tell you, you can feel any way you want.

JOEY: You want the three of us to sit on those ladders, right?

HOWARD: We're not going to just *sit* there. We are going to perch there, like three eagles.

ANNE: Or maybe like two vultures and one turtle dove?

HOWARD: Quiet, Anne. (*To* JOEY) Soon a crowd will gather.

JOEY: Why will a crowd gather?

HOWARD: Because people will want to know why we are sitting on ladders, that's why. It's just natural human curiosity to want to know why three people are sitting on ladders in the middle of Main Street.

JOEY: How will they even know we are here?

HOWARD: They will hear us. That's why I had you test how far my voice will carry. We will call out to the world, and it will respond.

ANNE: I hope nobody throws eggs. Eggs are very hard to get out of one's hair. Especially if they are not fresh eggs.

HOWARD: Quiet, Anne. (*To* JOEY) Soon a crowd will gather. People will talk. Word-of-mouth advertising will

carry your name from one end of our fair town to another. Someone will say, "That's Joey." Someone else
will say, "I thought he was dull." Then someone will
say . . .

ANNE: "He may be dull, but he's also a little nuts."

HOWARD: Please, Anne! Soon, word will reach the fair
Betty. She will come to see for herself, and there you
will be perched against the heavens. How can she resist
you?

ANNE: She could knock the ladder down.

HOWARD: Then, we unfold our banner. You have the banner ready, haven't you, Anne?

ANNE: I have indeed.

HOWARD: She sees that banner. Bingo! Immediately she
knows that you are a man of imagination. Naturally
she will go to the dance with you.

ANNE: Or she may never speak to you again.

HOWARD: That's a possibility. I admit it.

JOEY: I've thought about it. I'm not going to do it. Maybe
she doesn't like me well enough to go to the dance with
me, but she doesn't positively hate me.

HOWARD: So what do you have to lose? You want to go
through life being the guy that Betty doesn't hate, only
because she can't remember his name? You can do what
you want, Joey, but I would rather be hated than ig-
nored.

JOEY: She didn't exactly ignore me. She just said it would
be dull going to a dance with me. She recognized me
immediately. She said, "Hi, Joey," and sounded very
friendly. I don't think I'd better do this, Howdie.

HOWARD: All right, Joey. I won't try to force you.

ANNE: You might as well do it, Joey. Howdie will find
some way to force you.

HOWARD: No, I won't. Joey's my good friend, but if he

wants to be the forgotten man, that's his business. And there're no hard feelings, Joey. When I see Betty at the dance with Someone Else, I'll dance with her and think about you.

JOEY: All right, I'll do it. But I want to go on record, right now, that I think this whole business is insane.

HOWARD: All right, then, troops, to your battle stations.

ANNE: What about the banner?

HOWARD: Not until Betty appears. That will be our big surprise.

JOEY: Some surprise. If Betty doesn't kill me, her father probably will. (*They climb up the ladders*—HOWARD *on the right;* JOEY *in the middle; and* ANNE *on the left. They sit rigidly.* HOWARD *reads newspaper;* ANNE *has the banner and some knitting in her lap;* JOEY *twiddles his thumbs and looks ill-at-ease.*)

HOWARD: All right, testing. One-third, two-thirds, one.

ANNE: Hi down there. Hi down there.

JOEY: I feel like a fool.

ANNE: Testing. Two, three, four.

HOWARD: Testing. Five, six, seven.

ANNE: Hi down there. Hi down there.

JOEY: Maybe I could just run away .

HOWARD: All right, Joey. You're either going to do it or you're not. Anne and I are giving all our time to helping you, but you have to help yourself. Now, what do you say?

JOEY: All right, I'll cooperate.

HOWARD: Testing. One, two, three.

JOEY (*Almost whispering*): Hi.

HOWARD: Louder, Joey.

JOEY (*Louder*): Hi.

HOWARD: All of it, Joey.

JOEY: Hi down there.

HOWARD: O.K., then let's go. Hi down there.

ANNE: Hi down there.

JOEY: Hi down there.

HOWARD (*Louder*): Hi down there.

ANNE (*Louder*): Hi down there.

JOEY (*Louder*): Hi down there.

ALL: Hi down there. Hi down there. Hi down there. (MR. WILKINS, *a salesman, enters from down left as they continue to call "Hi down there." WILKINS sets the suitcase he is carrying down, takes one of the soap boxes and sits on it. He looks up at them.*)

WILKINS: Hi up there.

HOWARD (*Not noticing WILKINS*): Hi down there.

ANNE: Hi down there.

JOEY (*Waving his fingers timidly at WILKINS*): Hi down there.

WILKINS: What time's the show?

HOWARD (*Sternly*): Hi down there.

ANNE: Hi down there.

JOEY: Hi. . . .

HOWARD (*Shouting*): *Hi down there!*

WILKINS: You don't like me, do you?

JOEY (*Almost whispering again*): Hi down there.

WILKINS: Don't feel bad about it. Nobody likes me. I mean people don't hate me or anything, they just don't like me. I—mean, I'm not well liked, you know what I mean?

JOEY: I like you, Mr. Wilkins.

WILKINS (*Laughing and standing up; to HOWARD*): You have a good show here, Howdie. But you have to get rid of that guy in the middle. He has no sense of theatre.

HOWARD (*Angrily*): Hi down there.

ANNE: Hi down there.

WILKINS: He's a nice boy, I guess. A little dull maybe, but

probably a very good boy. But he has no sense of theatre. And I know, Howdie. Man and boy, I've been in sales for thirty years, and one thing I have is a sense of theatre. You have to have it to be a good salesman. And believe me, Howdie, that kid (*Points at* JOEY) doesn't have it. He doesn't have it at all. (*Exits right*)

JOEY: Even Mr. Wilkins knows I'm dull. This isn't going to do any good, Howdie. I just can't do it right. Let's face it, I'm a dull kid.

HOWARD: You have to work at it, Joey.

ANNE: Sure, Joey. It's too bad Mr. Wilkins was our first customer. He's had a lot of experience with things like this, being a salesman and all.

HOWARD: Sure. He goes to the big sales conventions in Little Rock. . . .

ANNE: And Boise. . . .

HOWARD: And Slippery Rock.

ANNE: So he's seen a lot of big sales promotions, but you'll be just fine with the home folk, like Betty.

HOWARD: Let's start again.

JOEY: All right, I'll try.

HOWARD: Testing, one, two, three. Hi down there.

JOEY (*With determination*): Hi down there.

ANNE: Hi down there.

HOWARD (*Faster*): Hi down there.

ALL: Hi down there, hi down there, hi down there. (CLARISSA *and* HELEN *enter right. They arrange the three boxes to form a kind of tunnel, two on their sides and the third for the roof. They crawl through on their knees.* HOWARD *looks over paper at them, then hides behind paper.*)

HOWARD: Hi down there.

ANNE (*Starting to knit*): Hi down there.

JOEY: Hi down there. (*The two girls rearrange boxes so*

they are piled on top of each other. They join hands and dance around boxes.) What? (HOWARD *reaches over and hits him with the newspaper.*) Oh. Hi down there.

HOWARD: Hi down there.

ANNE: Hi down there. (*The girls stop dancing and look up at them.*)

HOWARD: Hi down there.

CLARISSA: Hi up there.

ANNE: Hi down there.

HELEN: Hi up there.

JOEY: Hi down there.

CLARISSA: My name's Clarissa. What's yours?

HOWARD (*With determination*): Hi down there.

HELEN: My name's Helen.

ANNE: Hi down there.

JOEY: Hi down there.

HELEN: It's Greek. My name I mean. I'm not Greek. I'm Irish. Helen O'Brien. (*To* JOEY) What's your name?

HOWARD: Hi down there.

ANNE: Hi down there.

JOEY: Hi down there.

CLARISSA: My name is English. Clarissa, I mean. I don't know what my last name is—it might be English, or German, or just anything. It's Smith, and I guess every country has Smiths. It's kind of international. (*To* JOEY) What did you say your name is?

HOWARD: Hi down there.

ANNE: Hi down there.

JOEY: Hi down there.

HELEN (*Pointing to* ANNE): I'll bet her name is Madame Defarge. You know, because she's knitting, like Madame Defarge in *A Tale of Two Cities.*

CLARISSA: I had to read that in English.

HELEN: It was very sad. If I hadn't had to read it, I would

have liked it. Because it was very sad. (*To* JOEY) Did
you tell us your name?

HOWARD: Hi down there.

ANNE: Hi down there.

JOEY: Hi down there.

CLARISSA: I'll bet it's Smith. Smith is a nice dull name,
and you look like a nice dull boy. I'll bet your name is
Smith. Of course, my name is Smith, and I'm not dull.
But my name won't always be Smith. If I marry, I mean.
But you'll always be Smith.

HOWARD: Hi down there.

ANNE: Hi down there.

JOEY: Hi down there.

CLARISSA: I have a cousin. His name is Smith, too. One's
cousin doesn't always have the same name, you know.
But this cousin is named Smith. (*Looks at* JOEY *carefully*) He looks like my cousin, doesn't he, Helen?

HELEN: Which cousin is that, Clarissa?

CLARISSA: You know, my dull cousin.

JOEY: Is his name Arvel? (*Both girls laugh and again dance
around boxes.*) Howard, you said there was no such
person as Arvel Smith.

HOWARD: Hi down there.

ANNE: Hi down there.

JOEY: You lied to me, Howdie. There is so an Arvel Smith.
He's very dull and he's her cousin. (*The girls, still giggling, put boxes back in their original position.*)

HOWARD (*Almost in despair*): Hi down there.

ANNE: Hi down there.

JOEY: I don't like being fooled, Howdie. You tried to fool
me.

CLARISSA: My cousin's not named Arvel Smith.

HELEN: In fact, her name isn't even Smith. It's Jones.

JOEY: Why did you girls make up that story, then?

CLARISSA: Because you wouldn't talk to us.

HELEN: Boys should talk to girls.

CLARISSA: If anyone is not going to talk to anyone, it should be the girl.

HOWARD: Hi down there.

ANNE: Hi down there.

CLARISSA (*To* HOWARD): We don't care if you talk to us or not, because he (*Points at* JOEY) talked to us.

HELEN: But we're not going to talk to you anymore.

CLARISSA: Because we think all of this is very stupid.

HELEN: And childish.

CLARISSA: And dull. (CLARISSA *and* HELEN *skip off down left.*)

JOEY (*To* HOWARD): I goofed again, didn't I?

HOWARD: Well. . . .

ANNE: You goofed.

JOEY: I tried.

HOWARD: I know you did, Joey. You did very well there for a few minutes. They were just lucky on that Smith business.

ANNE: It was just a coincidence. It wouldn't happen again in a million years.

JOEY: Coincidences happen to me every day. I'm that kind of guy. I just go around bumping into coincidences. Maybe I'm coincidence-prone.

HOWARD: You have to think positively, Joey. You just have to say, "I can do it."

JOEY: Wouldn't that be lying, when I know I can't?

HOWARD: You have to believe it, too, Joey. Look, it's not very hard. All you have to do is sit here, look straight ahead and say, "Hi down there." That's all you have to do.

ANNE: Just don't think about it, Joey. Just don't look at anything.

JOEY: Maybe if I closed my eyes.

HOWARD: No, Joey, you have to keep your eyes open. You want to see Betty when she comes, don't you?

JOEY: I don't think she'll come. We haven't gotten much of a crowd yet.

HOWARD: We will, if you'll just work at this.

ANNE: Sure, Joey. If you hadn't spoken to Mr. Wilkins, he'd still be here.

HOWARD: And those two kooks—Clarissa and Helen— they'd have stayed all day to try to make you talk.

ANNE: But once you pay any attention to people out there, they're going to leave. Because that's the whole point.

HOWARD: They see us sitting up here, aloof.

ANNE: Above the world.

HOWARD: Indifferent like the clouds.

ANNE: Silent like the moon.

HOWARD: Removed like the sun.

ANNE: Mysterious like the wind.

HOWARD: Uh, uh . . . well, you get the idea.

JOEY: I get the idea, I guess. But I don't do very well.

HOWARD: Let's try it again. And this time, don't listen to what anyone says.

JOEY: I'll try, but I hope Betty appreciates all the suffering I'm going through for her sake.

HOWARD: All right, then, let's start again. Testing, one, two, three. Hi down there.

ANNE: Hi down there.

JOEY: Hi down there.

HOWARD: Hi down there. (VINCENT, *the poet, enters up center. He reads a book as he walks down center, past the ladders, without looking up. He sits on a box, reading all the while. The three continue their routine.*)

VINCENT (*To himself*): There is no rhyme for orange.

JOEY: Hi down there. (*He looks to* HOWARD *for approval.*)

VINCENT: It's strange. There are lots of rhymes for *strange* —*range, grange, mange;* but there is no rhyme for *orange.* And yet there are more *oranges* in this world than *stranges.*

HOWARD: Hi down there.

VINCENT: Now that I think upon it, I don't think I've ever seen a *strange.* (*Thinking*) Of all the wonders that I yet have seen, it seems most strange to me that I have never seen a strange.

ANNE: Hi down there.

VINCENT: I have seen oranges, apples, pears, plums, and even peaches, grapes, melons, coconuts, and once I saw a pomegranate. But a strange—never.

JOEY: Hi down there.

VINCENT: If I weren't a poet, these things would not bother me.

HOWARD: Hi down there.

VINCENT: If I weren't a poet, I could wander through the world blind to all such mysteries, unconcerned with the plight of a world that does not have a single strange in it.

ANNE: Hi down there.

VINCENT: If I weren't a poet, I could walk right through this life without a single thought.

JOEY: Hi down there.

VINCENT: It would not matter to me what time the Gray-fly winds her sultry horn. . . .

HOWARD: Hi down there.

VINCENT: Or that the Evening Star has sloped his westering wheel.

ANNE: Hi down there.

VINCENT: If I were not a poet, I would be content to walk about like dull, ordinary people. . . .

JOEY: Hi down there.

VINCENT (*Rising*): But I *am* a poet, and I have no rhyme for *orange*.

HOWARD: Hi down there.

JOEY: Hi down there.

VINCENT: And yet if I were not a poet, but a dull, ordinary person, then the world would be a friendly place—and I would not be lonely. I would greet each dull, ordinary person I met with a "hi" or a "hi there," if I knew him particularly well.

HOWARD: Hi down there.

VINCENT: But I would rather be a poet, loneliness and all.

JOEY: Hi down there.

VINCENT: And I would rather be a poet someplace else. (VINCENT *exits, down left.*)

JOEY: I did everything you told me, and it still didn't work.

HOWARD: What can you expect? That guy was a poet.

ANNE: Poets do not make very good audiences.

JOEY: He said dull, ordinary people say "hi."

HOWARD: So?

JOEY: That's what we've been saying.

HOWARD: We've been saying, "Hi down there." It's different. Tell me, Joey, have you ever heard anyone else in your whole life say, "Hi down there"?

JOEY: No, and that's another thing. It's kooky to say it's hi down there. It's hi up here; it's low down there.

HOWARD (*Sighing*): You have no imagination, Joey.

JOEY: Maybe not, but this isn't going to work. Big crowd we've gathered. One salesman on his way to the bus. Two kooky girls, and a poet. And we couldn't even keep them interested. If Betty did come this way, she'd cross the street to avoid us. I'm quitting.

HOWARD: Wait a minute, Joey. You've forgotten the banner.

ANNE: Yes, Joey, the banner. (*She starts unfolding it.*)

HOWARD (*Getting down from ladder to help her*): Just wait until you see how it looks, Joey. You'll be impressed. (HOWARD *and* ANNE *unfold a banner that reads* BETTY, PLEASE GO TO THE DANCE WITH JOEY. *They spread it from the two tall ladders so that it faces the audience.* JOEY *sits on small ladder, in the pose of "The Thinker.")*

ANNE: It's really a great banner, Joey.

HOWARD: Using billboards for courting has proved successful all over the country.

ANNE: There was a man in Albuquerque who proposed to his girl with a huge billboard sign.

HOWARD: And she accepted him.

ANNE: There was a man in Baltimore who used a billboard sign to tell his wife he was sorry he forgot their anniversary.

HOWARD: And she forgave him.

ANNE: There was a man in Seattle who used a billboard to tell his mother-in-law what he thought of her.

HOWARD: And she sued him. (*The banner is now in place, and* HOWARD *and* ANNE *move down center to admire their work.*)

ANNE: Just look at it, Joey.

JOEY: I don't want to.

HOWARD: It looks great, Joey. When Betty sees it. . . .

JOEY: She's not going to see it. She won't even come by here.

ANNE: Sure she will, Joey. (*She goes to* JOEY.) Aw, Joey, don't feel so bad. We'll think of something else.

HOWARD: Sure, Joey, maybe this didn't work. But I have lots of other ideas.

ANNE: Maybe we could call Betty and tell her that you've been hit by a train. Play on her sympathy.

HOWARD: That's it! You're delirious. You've been calling for her.

JOEY: No.

HOWARD: The doctor says your only chance for survival is if she'll go to the dance with you this Saturday.

JOEY: No, no, no. No more schemes, no more publicity stunts.

HOWARD: No more Betty.

JOEY: That's all right. I'll never see her again anyway. And maybe it's just as well.

HOWARD (*Looking off left*): Then you'd better close your eyes, because here she comes.

JOEY: You're joking.

ANNE (*Going down left*): No, he's not.

JOEY (*Starting to get off ladder*): We have to get this sign down.

HOWARD: Sit down. It's too late.

JOEY (*Sitting down and covering his face with his hands*): I wish I were dead. (BETTY *enters down left.*)

ANNE: Hi, Betty.

BETTY: Hi, Anne.

HOWARD: Hi, Betty.

BETTY: Hello, Howard.

HOWARD: Nice day, isn't it?

BETTY: I suppose. (*She looks up at* JOEY.) Hello, Joseph.

JOEY (*Without uncovering his face*): Hi down there.

BETTY: What are you doing on that ladder?

ANNE: He's putting up that banner.

BETTY: That's nice. How have you been, Joseph?

JOEY: Pretty well, I guess, except that I'm kind of sick now.

HOWARD: How do you like Joey's banner?

BETTY: It's very nice.

JOEY: Hi down there.

BETTY: I thought you must have been sick, Joseph. I haven't seen you much this fall.

HOWARD: You really do like Joey's sign, Betty?

BETTY: It's very nice.

ANNE: Well, what's your answer?

BETTY: My answer to what?

ANNE: To the question on the sign.

BETTY: I . . . (*Looks at sign carefully*) I. . . .

JOEY: You don't have to answer, Betty.

BETTY: I don't mind answering. I just can't read the sign without my glasses.

HOWARD: The sign says. . . .

JOEY (*Yelling*): Hi down there. (*He hurries off the ladder*) It just says, CAN WE BEAT CENTRAL SATURDAY NIGHT?

BETTY: Oh. I hope so. It won't be much of a dance if we don't win.

JOEY: Are you going to the dance, Betty?

BETTY: I don't know. Joey wants me to go with *her*.

JOEY: Joey? *Her?*

BETTY: Yes, you know, Josephine Moore. She's with me all the time. You must know her.

JOEY: And you call her *Joey?*

BETTY: Sometimes. I'd rather call her *Josephine* because I don't see any sense in having a name if people call you something else, do you, Joseph?

ANNE: Joseph?

JOEY (*Quickly*): I certainly do not, Betty.

BETTY: Josephine likes to be called Joey. She really does. She called me yesterday and asked me to go to the dance with her, and she said, "This is Joey." I heard her.

JOEY: Betty, has anyone else asked you to go to the dance?

BETTY (*Looking at him shyly*): Not yet. Just Joey.

JOEY: Would you go to the dance with me?

BETTY: I would love to, Joseph.

JOEY: Betty, may I walk home with you?

BETTY: I think that would be very nice. (BETTY *and* JOEY *start off right together.*)

JOEY (*Turning*): Oh, goodbye, Howard. Goodbye, Anne.

HOWARD: So long, *Jo*-seph.

ANNE: Goodbye, *Jo*-seph.

BETTY: Goodbye. I hope to see you two at the dance.

HOWARD: Goodbye, Betty. (JOEY *and* BETTY *exit.* HOWARD *climbs up ladder and sits.*) She thought it was Josephine Moore who asked her to the dance.

ANNE: Josephine must have a very deep voice.

HOWARD: Or maybe Joey's voice squeaks when he gets nervous.

ANNE: Well, Joey has his date for the dance.

HOWARD: And my whole campaign went down the drain. I hope Madison Avenue doesn't hear about this, or I'm washed up in public relations before I even start.

ANNE: That's life.

HOWARD: Hi down there.

ANNE: Hi down there.

HOWARD: Hi down there. (*Sadly*) Isn't anyone listening? (*As the curtain falls*) *Hi down there!*

THE END

Tree to the Sky

Characters

PETER QUINCE, *the builder*
MRS. MERIWETHER, *the owner*
MRS. MAUER, *the widow*
EILEEN
IRENE } *her daughters*
JUDGE CASSIDY, *a retired jurist*
DICK WAGNER, *a young businessman*
JOHN MOORE, *a young artist*

SETTING: *A bare stage, under bright, stark lights. A little mound of earth is at center.*

AT RISE: *A lonesome sound (a single horn or soft music) is heard for a moment, and then* PETER QUINCE, *carrying a bag and a folded canvas chair, comes onstage and looks around. He looks up, and for a moment the song of a bird is heard. He looks down and the sound stops. He looks out at the audience, and for a moment the sound of waves is heard. He looks away and the sound stops. He looks offstage and a sound suggesting a breeze is heard. He looks onstage, and the sound stops. He goes over to the little mound of earth, pats it, and steps back to examine it. He sets down chair, opens bag, and takes*

*out a little shovel, a watering can, and a small fence. He
looks about cautiously, takes a little box from his pocket,
opens it, takes out a small object, and starts to dig a
little hole in the earth. He buries the small object, puts
his little fence in position around the mound, and sets up
his chair. He steps back and admires his work. The
lights dim a little and pick up color. PETER takes his
watering can and waters the earth. He sets up his chair,
as though he were finding a shady spot, and sits. MRS.
MERIWETHER enters.*

MRS. MERIWETHER: Who are you? What are you doing here
on this land?

PETER: I'm Peter Quince. I didn't know anyone owned
this property.

MRS. MERIWETHER: You're wrong. You're wrong, wrong,
wrong. I own this property. I am Mrs. Meriwether.

PETER: I'm sorry, Mrs. Meriwether. (*Standing*) I'll get my
things together and leave.

MRS. MERIWETHER: That's not what I mean. I do own all
this property between the two ridges, but to be honest,
I wish I didn't. It's a bare, bleak place, a mean land, to
tell the truth. No birds sing here, and no one wants to
live here. I wish I could get rid of the place.

PETER: Would you sell it to me?

MRS. MERIWETHER (*Shaking her head*): My conscience
would bother me if I did.

PETER: Please. I should like this place. I'll give you a dollar
for it.

MRS. MERIWETHER: In cash?

PETER: In four quarters.

MRS. MERIWETHER: I can't do it. It isn't worth a dollar.

PETER: Please.

MRS. MERIWETHER: Well, maybe for fifty cents.

PETER: I'd rather pay a dollar. And in cash—four quarters.

MRS. MERIWETHER: Very well. (*Taking a paper from her handbag.*) Here's the deed to all this barren land that lies between the two ridges, from the bleak horizon to the silent sea. I tell you again, it's no bargain.

PETER (*Taking the paper and giving her coins*): It will be. I will make it so.

MRS. MERIWETHER (*Biting one of the quarters to be sure it isn't counterfeit*): Nothing will make this place *anything* but nothing.

PETER: I've planted a tree.

MRS. MERIWETHER: There? (*Pointing to mound*)

PETER: Yes, I just planted the seed. One day, there will be a tree there.

MRS. MERIWETHER: That, of course, will make a difference.

PETER: It will reach the sky. Birds will come and sing in it. Little squirrels will run through its branches. Children will play under its shady limbs.

MRS. MERIWETHER: It does sound rather pleasant. Lovely, in fact.

PETER (*Gesturing*): Homes will spring up, with gardens. (*Pointing out at audience*) We do have a lovely view of the sea here, too—the quiet, beautiful, silent sea.

MRS. MERIWETHER (*Shading eyes and looking out over audience*): We do indeed. I never observed it before, but it is a lovely sea.

PETER: And, thanks to you, I will have a home right here in the center of all this loveliness, right here beneath the tree that will reach the sky.

MRS. MERIWETHER: You wouldn't like to sell me a lot here, would you? Say that spot up there (*Points up left*), near the ridge. The brightest star shines there every night. I never paid much attention to it before, but now I remember. It is a truly remarkable, lovely star, and I would like to have it right outside my bedroom window.

PETER: Then I will give you that lot.

MRS. MERIWETHER: Oh, no, I would rather pay for it. Does a quarter seem about right to you?

PETER: I would say so, yes. Here, I'll give you a deed. That's the northwest corner, isn't it?

MRS. MERIWETHER: Yes, I think so. (*Hands him coin*) Here's your quarter. (PETER *tears a corner from the deed she gave him, and hands it to her.*)

PETER: And here's your deed.

MRS. MERIWETHER (*Looking at deed closely*): I don't have my glasses with me. There's no small print on the bottom, is there?

PETER: Of course not. (*He bites the quarter she has given him.*) Certainly, we can trust each other. We're going to be neighbors.

MRS. MERIWETHER: You're so right, Peter. (*She puts deed in handbag*) Now I must see about building my home. I'd like to get the work done before the star comes out. Now that it's mine, I don't want to waste the shine.

PETER: That seems sensible. (*She starts to exit down left, then stops and turns to* PETER.)

MRS. MERIWETHER: Will the tree reach the sky soon?

PETER: I think it may. I'll water it again.

MRS. MERIWETHER: Then I'll get to work on my house. (*She exits down left.* PETER *again waters the mound.* MRS. MAUER, EILEEN, *and* IRENE *enter up right.*)

MRS. MAUER (*Waving and calling*): Yoo-hoo, young man.

PETER (*Looking up*): Are you calling me?

MRS. MAUER (*Coming down center with* IRENE *and* EILEEN): Yes. Is this the way to the city?

PETER: What city?

MRS. MAUER: Any city. I am a widow with two lovely daughters, Irene and Eileen. Say hello to the nice young man, daughters. (*The girls giggle and curtsy.*)

PETER: Hello, Irene and Eileen. I am Peter.

MRS. MAUER: We are glad to meet you, Peter. I am Mrs. Mauer.

PETER: Pleased to meet you, Mrs. Mauer. I am Mr. Quince.

MRS. MAUER: Peter Quince. What a lovely name. Don't you think it's a lovely name, daughters, a name a girl could wear with pride? (*The girls again giggle and curtsy.*)

PETER: You mean a name a *man* could wear with pride, don't you?

MRS. MAUER: If you insist, that's what I mean. It's not easy being a widow with two lovely daughters. That's why we now are moving to the city—to be near things.

PETER: I lived in the city once, but I like it here.

MRS. MAUER: Here? There's nothing here, except (*Indicating chair*) your little house, of course. Nothing but two ridges, bare sky, and the silent sea.

IRENE (*Looking up center*): And the horizon, Mama.

EILEEN: Yes, Mama, it's a lovely horizon.

MRS. MAUER (*Looking up center*): Indeed it is. A lovely horizon. (MRS. MERIWETHER *enters down left, followed by* DICK WAGNER *and* JOHN MOORE, *who carry a beach umbrella and a chair.*)

MRS. MERIWETHER: Well, Peter Quince, I'm ready to build my house with the help of these two fine boys, Dick Wagner and John Moore. (*Pointing up left*) Get to work, boys.

WAGNER (*To* PETER): We are not really boys, Mr. Quince. We were just passing strangers.

PETER: I see.

MOORE: But she took us in. Now we are carpenters.

WAGNER: And electricians.

MOORE: And plumbers.

WAGNER: And bricklayers.

MOORE: And landscapers.

MRS. MERIWETHER: If you two will hurry and build my house, you may retire.

WAGNER: Let's get to work.

MOORE: I suppose. But I'm really an artist.

WAGNER: And I'm a businessman.

MRS. MAUER: Are you boys married?

WAGNER: We're not boys.

MOORE: And we're not married.

MRS. MAUER: Then you're boys. Meet my lovely daughters, Irene and Eileen. I'm Mrs. Mauer.

WAGNER: My name is Dick, Irene and Eileen. (*Turns to* MRS. MAUER) Mr. Wagner to you, Mrs. Mauer.

MRS. MAUER: That's a nice name, isn't it, Irene?

IRENE (*Giggling*): Yes, Mama.

MOORE: I'm John Moore.

EILEEN: I like that name, Mama.

MRS. MAUER: Then it's all settled. Peter Quince, we would like to build a house here, too. Who owns this land?

PETER: I do. That is, I own all of it except the northwest corner. I just sold that to Mrs. Meriwether. This is Mrs. Meriwether. Mrs. Meriwether, this is Mrs. Mauer.

MRS. MAUER: How do you do? Do you have any daughters, Mrs. Meriwether?

MRS. MERIWETHER: No, no daughters, and no sons either.

MRS. MAUER: We shall be good friends.

MRS. MERIWETHER: That may well be so, but right now I have a house to build. Come along, boys. (*She goes up left, followed by* MOORE *and* WAGNER, *who set up the chair and umbrella, as the lights grow softer.*)

MRS. MAUER: You have convinced me, Peter Quince. I will settle here and make this my home. (*Looking about*) Of course, it is very barren here. One would almost say stark.

PETER: But I've planted a tree here. (*Pointing to mound*) See. One day soon it will reach the sky. People will come from miles around just to see this tree. It will be famous.

MRS. MAUER: Are there many people around here?

PETER: Not yet, but there will be, once this tree reaches the sky.

MRS. MAUER: That's quite true. A tree will make the difference. I'd like that lot up there (*Pointing up center*) in front of the horizon. It's just lovely. Well, Mr. Quince, what is the price?

PETER: I don't know.

MRS. MAUER: I'll give you fourteen dollars.

PETER: Oh, no, that's too much.

MRS. MAUER: Not for that horizon.

MRS. MERIWETHER (*Coming downstage, followed by* WAGNER *and* MOORE): I paid twenty-five cents for my lot. And I have a star.

PETER: Yes, that is true, Mrs. Mauer. And you don't have a star. How about twelve and a half cents?

MRS. MAUER: But I have an horizon. That's twice as good as a star. I should pay fifty cents.

MRS. MERIWETHER: Then I should pay a dollar. My star is really quite remarkable.

MRS. MAUER: Then I shall pay two dollars.

MRS. MERIWETHER: I shall pay four.

MRS. MAUER: Eight.

MRS. MERIWETHER: Sixteen.

MRS. MAUER: Thirty-two.

PETER (*Interrupting*): Ladies, let's settle this matter calmly. A star is a blessing to be sure, but then so is an horizon. Now, Mrs. Meriwether has given me a quarter for the star; so, Mrs. Mauer, you should give me a quarter for the horizon.

MRS. MAUER: In cash?

PETER: Of course, in cash.

MRS. MAUER: It's a lot to pay—I'm just a poor widow with two lovely daughters. (*Thinks for a moment*) Oh, very well. Here's my quarter. (*She hands* PETER *a quarter and he bites it.*) Now, where's my deed?

PETER (*Tearing off a piece of original deed*): Here you are, and be careful not to smudge it. The ink's not dry yet.

MRS. MAUER: Come, my daughters, let us build our house. (*To* PETER) They don't have husbands, you know, so we must do everything ourselves. (MRS. MAUER, EILEEN, *and* IRENE *go up right and exit.*)

MRS. MERIWETHER (*Indicating her chair and umbrella*): My house is in order. The night star is on its way, so I'd better prepare a little broth. Young men, what do I owe you?

MOORE: There's no charge.

WAGNER: We like you. We were glad to be of service. (MRS. MAUER, EILEEN, *and* IRENE *return with a gaily-painted cardboard house and white picket fence, which they place up center.*)

MRS. MERIWETHER: I insist. Does a quarter sound about right?

WAGNER: For each?

MRS. MERIWETHER: Yes, of course, for each.

MOORE: It sounds right to me.

WAGNER: And to me.

MRS. MERIWETHER (*Giving them quarters which they accept and bite*): You young men should invest this money. Don't just spend it on nonsense. I bought a star for a quarter. Now that was a very good investment.

MRS. MAUER (*Calling from up center*): I bought an horizon for a quarter.

MOORE: I could never live here. I'm an artist. I need a scene.

MRS. MERIWETHER: Stars are very nice.

MRS. MAUER (*Calling from up center*): Horizons are better.

MOORE: Stars and horizons are all very well, but not for an artist. A star is just a corner of a canvas, and an horizon is just a canvas without a star. No, I'm afraid there is no scene here. Not for an artist.

PETER: But there will be soon. I have planted a tree.

MOORE: A tree? Now that would make a scene. What kind of tree?

PETER: What kind of tree would you like?

MOORE (*Shrugging*): Oh, I don't know. A pine, perhaps. Or maybe an oak. Or yet again, perhaps a California redwood. California redwoods are very nice for scenes.

WAGNER: They are also good for building hamburger stands. I am a businessman, you know. (MRS. MAUER, EILEEN *and* IRENE *join others.*)

MRS. MAUER: Is it settled then, John Moore? Will you open your studio here?

MOORE (*Ignoring her*): Or maybe an orange tree. Or a redbud tree. Yes, I think this place will do very nicely. There's the sea. And there's a star.

MRS. MERIWETHER: It's *my* star.

MOORE: But you will allow me to paint it, won't you?

MRS. MERIWETHER: What color?

MOORE: Silver.

MRS. MERIWETHER: Oh, very well. Silver is a nice color, but you must use fast-drying paint. I don't want the star to drip on my house.

MOORE (*To* PETER): Very well. I'll buy one of your lots and build my studio here. I think I like this lot. (*Points down left*) It's the southwest corner.

PETER: You may have that lot.

MOORE: I'll pay for it. I'll pay for it. I have a quarter, you know.

PETER: Very well. (*Tears off corner of deed and gives it to* MOORE) Here's your deed.

MOORE: And here's your quarter. (*Hands* PETER *a coin*)

PETER (*Putting it in his pocket*): Thank you.

MOORE: Aren't you going to test it to see if it's counterfeit?

PETER: Oh, no.

MOORE: You trust me, eh?

PETER: Yes. Besides, this is one of the quarters I gave Mrs. Meriwether, and if it should prove false, I'd be too embarrassed to mention it.

WAGNER: Everyone is moving here. This place will soon be the center of the universe. I should open my business here.

PETER: I think that's wise.

MOORE: If you'll excuse me, I can't stand to hear talk about business. I'll just build my studio while it is being discussed. (*He exits down left.*)

WAGNER (*Looking after* MOORE): Artists may sneer at business if they like, (*To* PETER) but where would they be if they had no hamburger stands? A hungry artist is a bad artist, I say.

IRENE: I quite agree. There's a nice lot left near our house.

WAGNER: No, it's too far away from the center of things.

MRS. MAUER: Young man, where my daughters are *is* the center of things.

WAGNER: Quite true, I'm sure, but I want to build near this fine tree. (*Gesturing toward mound*) It's a California redwood, isn't it?

PETER: I think so.

WAGNER: I must be near the crowds if I am going to be a success in business.

PETER: There are only two lots left. Up there. (*Pointing up right*) And down here. (*Pointing down right*)

WAGNER: You wouldn't want to sell your lot, would you?

PETER: Of course not. I must be near the tree so that I can water it. (*Picks up watering can and waters mound*)

WAGNER: I guess I'll take this lot. (*Stands down right*) It's near the beach. It's near the road. It's not too far from the tree. Yes, this will do very well. All right, I'll take it. (*Returning to* PETER) Here's my quarter.

PETER (*Taking coin*): And here's your deed. (*Tears off another corner of deed.* MOORE *enters, carrying easel, camp chair, canvas frame and palette. He sets up easel and chair down left.*)

MOORE: I think I'll call my studio the Happy Hours Shop.

WAGNER: Excuse me. I am a businessman with no time for arty talk. (*He starts to exit down right.*)

IRENE (*Calling after him*): Wait, Dick, a businessman must have a secretary.

WAGNER: Come along, then. I am a very busy man.

IRENE: Businessmen marry secretaries, don't they, Dick?

WAGNER: That's what I've heard, Irene. (*They exit.*)

MOORE (*To* PETER): Businessmen may sneer at artists if they like, but where would they be if we didn't buy their hamburgers? A businessman without any business is a bad businessman, I say. (*Busies himself arranging easel and chair*)

MRS. MERIWETHER: This is now a very nice community. I think I'll start a garden club.

MRS. MAUER: I'll join.

MRS. MERIWETHER: Good. Shall we have a meeting at my house? I'll be president, of course.

MRS. MAUER: Of course, and I'll be vice-president.

MRS. MERIWETHER: Let's go. (*She and* MRS. MAUER *go up left to* MRS. MERIWETHER'*s "house."*) I shall sit because I am president. (*Sits*) And you must stand because I have only one chair. (*They talk quietly.*)

MOORE: I think I'll start an art club.

EILEEN: I'll join. Shall we have a meeting?

MOORE: Very well. (*They go to his easel and chair, and he sits.*) I shall sit because I am the artist, of course.

EILEEN: And I shall stand because I am the model. Artists marry models, don't they, John?

MOORE: That's what I have heard, Eileen. (JUDGE CASSIDY *enters up right.*)

CASSIDY: Marriage, marriage. Did I hear something about marriage?

MOORE: Perhaps, if you were eavesdropping.

CASSIDY (*Coming downstage*): Don't be fresh with me, young man. I am a judge, Judge Cassidy. If you marry, you will need me.

EILEEN: Be nice to him, John.

PETER: Good evening, Judge. Can you really perform a marriage?

CASSIDY: I can dance a jig, and with a comb and a bit of tissue paper, I can play the entire score of Wagner's *Tristan und Isolde.*

PETER: Yes, but can you perform a marriage?

CASSIDY: Yes . . . and no. I am a judge, and judges can perform marriages. But I do not reside here, and so I am not a judge here. But I *am* a judge. Do I make myself clear?

MRS. MAUER (*Coming downstage*): Your Honor, if you were to settle here, then could you perform a marriage?

CASSIDY: Of course. But why would I settle here? (*He looks about.*)

PETER: Because I have planted a tree.

CASSIDY: Well, now, that does make a difference. But where would I live?

MRS. MAUER: There is a lot available right next door to me. Peter Quince here will gladly let you have it. Are you married, Judge?

CASSIDY: No. No, I'm not.

MRS. MERIWETHER (*Coming downstage*): That's rather odd, isn't it? A marrying judge and not married?

CASSIDY: One doesn't have to lay an egg to judge an omelet.

MRS. MAUER: It's not the same.

MRS. MERIWETHER: Indeed it's not.

CASSIDY: I'll be the judge of that.

MRS. MAUER: You'll like the neighborhood.

MRS. MERIWETHER: You may come and see my star.

MRS. MAUER: I have a very fine horizon.

CASSIDY: I'm sorry. I don't think that a star and an horizon are enough to have a real court.

PETER: You've forgotten the tree.

CASSIDY: I have indeed. This really would be a pleasant place to reside.

EILEEN: And we do need a judge.

CASSIDY: How much does a lot cost here, Mr. Quince?

PETER: Twenty-five cents is the going price at the moment.

CASSIDY: That's a little too high.

PETER: An adjustment could be made. Say, ten cents.

CASSIDY: Just a wee bit too high.

PETER: A nickel?

CASSIDY: You're close.

PETER: Nothing?

CASSIDY: I'll take it. Where's my deed?

PETER: Here you are. (*Tears off another corner of deed*) I think you'll find it all in order.

CASSIDY: It had better be. You don't fool with the law, boy. (WAGNER *enters, followed by* IRENE. *He carries a small, gaily-colored stand.*)

WAGNER: I'm in business. (*Places stand down right.*)

CASSIDY: You don't have a chair.

WAGNER: I'll get one. (*He exits right.*)

CASSIDY: That boy has ambition.

WAGNER (*Coming back with a gaily-painted stool*): I couldn't find a chair.

CASSIDY: I'll take that. It will be just right for my court. (*Takes stool and starts up right*)

WAGNER: Hey, that's mine.

CASSIDY: Don't be pushy, boy. Remember what happened to Macbeth. He was pushy. (CASSIDY *goes up right and sits on stool.* MRS. MERIWETHER *goes up left and sits in her chair;* MRS. MAUER *goes to her house;* WAGNER *stands behind his stand with* IRENE; MOORE *sits before his easel and pretends to paint, and* EILEEN *poses for him.* PETER *waters the mound. Soft music is heard, then stops.*)

MOORE (*Jumping up*): I just happened to think of something!

WAGNER: And I did, too!

MRS. MAUER: And I!

MRS. MERIWETHER: And I!

IRENE *and* EILEEN: And we!

CASSIDY: What kind of tree is that going to be? (*All rush to* PETER *at center.*)

PETER: What kind do you want?

CASSIDY: I don't want any. This place, it seems to me, is just perfect as it is.

MRS. MERIWETHER: A tree that reaches the sky would hide my star. Chop the tree down.

MRS. MAUER: And what would happen to my fine horizon when the leaves started to blow?

WAGNER: And suppose it should be a fruit tree! Who would buy my hamburgers when they could eat free fruit?

MOORE: And if Dick makes no money, how can he buy my paintings?

IRENE *and* EILEEN: And then how can we afford to marry?

PETER: You could live on love.

IRENE *and* EILEEN: No.

MOORE *and* WAGNER: No.

CASSIDY: Young man, that tree has got to go.

PETER: No. No. (*Moving toward mound*)

CASSIDY: Grab him, men, and hold him fast. (MOORE *and* WAGNER *grab* PETER *and hold him.*)

PETER: Don't touch the tree. It's too remarkable. How many trees do you see that reach the sky?

CASSIDY (*Raising hand for silence*): Quiet. (*Pacing back and forth*) That tree is a danger to our community. It must be rooted out before it roots us out. Who is in charge of rooting out here?

MRS. MAUER: Mrs. Meriwether is president of the garden club.

CASSIDY: The very person for the job. All right, Mrs. Meriwether. Get to work and remove the tree.

PETER (*Struggling to escape* MOORE *and* WAGNER): It's just a seed.

CASSIDY: It will be a tree. Dig it out, Mrs. Meriwether.

PETER: It won't be a large tree.

CASSIDY: Root it out, Mrs. Meriwether. (MRS. MERIWETHER *takes small shovel and goes to mound.*)

PETER: Please, Mrs. Meriwether, you remember how desolate it used to be here before I planted the tree. No one lived here at all, and now this place has become a home for us all. Please, Mrs. Meriwether, spare that tree.

MRS. MERIWETHER: Everything is changed now, Peter. This place has become the loveliest spot on the sea, and whether we like it or not, there is no room for the tree.

CASSIDY (*Sternly, to* MRS. MERIWETHER): Remove the seed. (*She starts to dig.*)

MRS. MAUER: I wonder what kind of tree it was going to be.

WAGNER: We'll never know now.

MOORE: Oh, yes, we can tell by the seed.

MRS. MERIWETHER (*Rising and holding up the "seed"*): I have it. I have the seed.

IRENE: What kind of seed is it?

EILEEN: What kind of tree was it going to be?

MRS. MERIWETHER: Well, just as I suspected, the seed is a . . . a (*Looks at it closely*) a button?

CASSIDY: A button tree? I don't think I've ever seen a button tree.

MOORE: Nor have I. But it would have been a disaster, I'm sure.

WAGNER: A horrible tree with thorns.

MRS. MERIWETHER: Oh, no. It's not a *real* seed. It's just a button. Look.

CASSIDY (*Taking button from her*): A button. Just an ordinary button.

MOORE (*Letting PETER go and taking button*): No tree would grow from this.

WAGNER (*Letting PETER go and taking button*): Just an ordinary button.

PETER (*Taking button*): It's not such an ordinary button. It's mine and it made a town grow. But you all dug it up, and now it's an ordinary button again.

WAGNER (*Going to his stand*): There never *was* going to be a tree that reached the sky.

MOORE: It was all a fake. (*Goes to his easel*)

CASSIDY: At least we don't have to worry about a tree. The community is saved.

MRS. MERIWETHER: Yes, my star is safe.

MRS. MAUER: And my horizon.

MOORE: And my art.

WAGNER: And my business.

CASSIDY: And the law. Don't forget the law.

IRENE: It's lovely.

EILEEN: It turned out just lovely.

PETER (*Taking down his fence and putting his things back in his bag*): I guess I'll be moving on. There'll be another lot here now for all of you. Mr. Wagner, you said you liked my lot. You may have it.

WAGNER: I don't want it now. I'm happy where I am.

PETER: Would you like it, Mrs. Meriwether?

MRS. MERIWETHER: No, thank you.

PETER: Judge?

CASSIDY: I can't afford to expand just now.

PETER: I'll just leave it.

MOORE: You're really going, eh?

PETER: I might as well. There's no need for me to stay anymore, since there's no tree.

MOORE: Now there will be a horrible hole in the middle of the town.

PETER: Maybe the town could put a birdbath here.

WAGNER: What for? With no tree, we'll have no birds.

PETER: You'll think of something. (*Puts bag over shoulder*) I guess I'll be going. (*The lights change slightly, losing some of their varied color.*)

MOORE: I just thought of something! If there's to be no tree, I'll have no scene, nothing at all to paint. Would anyone like to buy my lot? (*Pauses*) No? I guess I'll just take the loss. I might as well be leaving, too.

WAGNER: Now, where does that leave my business? The tree is gone, and art is going. (*Starts to push his stand offstage*) I might as well move on, too.

IRENE: But what about me?

EILEEN: And me?

IRENE: Mama, what are we going to do?

EILEEN: Now we'll never get married.

CASSIDY: It can't be helped, young ladies. The town is dying fast. (*Turns his stool upside down.* MOORE *folds his chair and easel.*) This will soon be a barren spot.

EILEEN: Mama, what are we going to do?

MRS. MAUER: Don't worry, dear. Mama will take care of everything. Judge, put your court in order. (CASSIDY *sets stool upright again.*) Dick, get back to work. (WAGNER *puts stand back in position.*) And, John, back to your painting. This is a good town. It will stand.

MOORE: It just won't work, Mrs. Mauer. It won't do any good to just hang on. The heart of the town is dead. If we don't move today, we must tomorrow.

MRS. MAUER: Don't argue. I am a mother. I know what is best.

MOORE: I'll do it, but it won't do any good. (*He unfolds his easel and chair.*)

MRS. MAUER: Now, Peter, plant the button again.

PETER: It won't do any good. It's just a button. I pretended that I had a real seed, but it was just a button, an ordinary button. If you hadn't dug it up today, you would have dug it up next year when no tree grew. It's just an ordinary button.

MRS. MAUER: Do as I tell you. Plant the button.

PETER: I'll do it, but it won't do any good. (*He takes his tools from bag and starts to dig hole in mound.*)

MRS. MAUER: Be sure that you plant it right side up. You won't get a tree unless the seed's planted right side up.

PETER (*Dropping button in hole and covering it with earth*): It's right side up.

MRS. MERIWETHER: It won't do any good. You can't grow an oak from a button.

CASSIDY: Not even a pine.

WAGNER: And certainly not a California redwood.

MRS. MAUER: Now, I'll put the fence around the seed so no one will step on it. (*She puts fence around mound, and pats mound gently.*) All right, now put your house in order, Peter.

PETER (*Setting up chair*): It's not going to do any good.

MRS. MAUER: It did good once. When you first planted that button, this place was only a barren waste, and then it became a town.

PETER: But the town fell apart. It fell apart the moment we looked at it, really looked at it.

MRS. MAUER: Judge, prepare to perform some marriages. Irene, go to your young man. Eileen, go to yours. Get your houses in order. Today you will be married, and tomorrow we will all live happily ever after. (EILEEN *goes to* MOORE, *and* IRENE *goes to* WAGNER.)

MOORE: Mrs. Mauer, I want to marry your daughter, but I can't until I get settled and establish myself.

WAGNER: I can't marry until my business is showing a profit.

MRS. MAUER (*Ignoring them*): Water the button seed, Peter.

PETER (*Sitting down*): No, I won't. I didn't mind watering it when I could pretend it was really a seed, but I can't now—now that everyone knows it isn't.

MRS. MAUER: Water the button, Peter.

PETER (*Stubbornly*): I'm not going to do it. It would be too silly.

MRS. MERIWETHER: It would indeed. I quite agree.

CASSIDY: Ridiculous.

MOORE: Outrageous.

WAGNER: Outlandish.

IRENE: You've gone too far, Mama.

EILEEN: You really have.

MRS. MAUER (*Raising her hands for silence*): Please, I am a mother, and I will be heard.

PETER: None of you even wanted a tree anyhow. You tore it down to nothing. To a button.

MRS. MAUER: That was the trouble. You can't grow a *tree* from a button.

PETER: Then why should I water the button?

MRS. MAUER: To grow a button *bush*.

PETER: A button bush?

MRS. MERIWETHER: I never heard of such a thing.

MRS. MAUER: A button bush is, indeed, unusual. It requires great care. You must water it every day, three times a day, Peter. But it will be worth it. (*Gesturing toward mound*) Imagine a beautiful bush with buttons of all sorts—gold buttons, diamond buttons, pearl buttons, silver buttons. Buttons so small they are used for doll clothing, and buttons large enough to use for boats. And birds will come to our bush. Not just ordinary birds, either. But peacocks and orange and yellow wrens and green and white parrots.

MOORE: Now there's a scene I could paint.

WAGNER: I'll have postcards made from your paintings and sell them to tourists.

MRS. MERIWETHER: I may open a little tourist home.

CASSIDY: And, of course, we'll need more laws.

PETER: But will the button bush really grow?

MRS. MAUER: It will grow, but it must be watered carefully, three times a day.

PETER: For how long?

MRS. MAUER: Seven times seven times two years, I think.

WAGNER: Why that's—that's ninety-eight years!

MRS. MAUER: That's right, Dick. You're very good at numbers. You'll make a good businessman. You have a good man, Irene.

IRENE: Thank you, Mama.

MOORE: But what are we to do while the button bush is growing?

MRS. MAUER: We need to get ready. We need to raise food and catch fish and build roads and paint barns. It will take us years and years to get ready, for once our button bush is grown, thousands—no, millions of people will come here to see it.

WAGNER: I must get another jar of mustard.

MRS. MERIWETHER: I'll need more than one star for so many guests.

CASSIDY: And I shall need a constable, maybe two, to handle the crowd.

PETER (*Standing up*): I don't believe it. I don't believe a button bush will ever grow.

MRS. MAUER: All right. I don't ask you to believe me. Just try it. If after seven times seven times two years, there's no button bush, I'll admit I'm wrong.

PETER: It's just a trick. You're trying to trick us into living useful lives here.

MOORE: Happy lives.

WAGNER: Profitable lives.

PETER: All for something that may never happen.

MRS. MAUER: I shouldn't do this. I should let your doubt blight your lives. People who can't live by faith in the future don't deserve to know what a good life is. But I'm a mother. I'm forgiving. Look at your button, Peter. Look at it now.

PETER (*Bending over and peering at mound*): It is sprouting. Look, it's pushed a little diamond leaf through the ground. (*He holds up a small diamond.*) Oh, Mrs. Mauer, I was wrong. There is a button bush, and we all shall be happy!

WAGNER: And prosperous!

MOORE: And arty!

CASSIDY: And with all this, lawful, I hope.

WAGNER: There's much to be done. I must go and tell the businessmen of the world. Keep the business open, Irene. I'll return tonight and we shall be married. (*Exits down right*)

MOORE: And I must tell the artists of the world. We, too, shall wed tonight, Eileen. (*Exits down left*)

CASSIDY: And I must tell the judges of the world. Keep my court warm, ladies. And I may marry one of you when I return. (*Exits up right*)

PETER: And I need more water. Here, Mrs. Mauer, keep the diamond leaf for me. (*He hands her the diamond and exits left with watering can.*)

MRS. MERIWETHER (*Coming to* MRS. MAUER *and looking at diamond*): It's your diamond, isn't it, Mrs. Mauer?

MRS. MAUER: It was my engagement ring. (IRENE *and* EILEEN *join them.*)

MRS. MERIWETHER: Do you think the men will ever discover there will be no button bush?

MRS. MAUER: They will forget what's planted there. Men need to work for dreams of the future, but, the poor dears, they need women to plant the dreams for them.

MRS. MERIWETHER: It is going to be a lovely town.

MRS. MAUER: Just lovely. (*The lights now become soft. Offstage music is heard, and the curtains close.*)

THE END

An Anton Chekhov Sort of Evening

Characters

ERNEST BLAIR, *an English teacher*
CHARLOTTE, *his college-age daughter*
GRACE, *his wife*
DUKE MANTEE, *a visiting killer, from "The Petrified Forest"*
LENNIE, *his partner in crime, from "Of Mice and Men"*
HAROLD RANDALL, *a young director*
MRS. WINGFIELD, *a neighbor*

TIME: *Eight o'clock in the evening.*
SETTING: *The family room of the Blair home. Down right is a desk, on which are a telephone and piles of books and papers.*
AT RISE: ERNEST BLAIR, *a pleasant-looking, middle-aged man, is speaking on the phone.*

ERNEST: Don't worry about it. . . . Why sure, Grace knows. I wouldn't do something like this without my wife's approval. . . . I know I didn't tell her about that lot until I had bought it. . . . I thought she would talk me out of it. . . . All right, I should have been talked out of it. That land is no good—I admit it. . . . Now, you know what to do? Carl and John have already left.

Good. And don't forget to call. . . . Oh, I guess in fifteen minutes would be fine. O.K. Thanks, Amos. I'll be waiting. (*He hangs up phone, rubs his hands, and sits down at desk, humming happily.* CHARLOTTE, *an attractive, self-assured young woman, enters down left from kitchen. She is carrying a book which she is reading.*)

CHARLOTTE: I've found it, Dad. His exact words.

ERNEST (*Pretending to grade papers*): How do you spell *separate*, Charlotte? With an *a* or an *e*? I used to be a good speller before I started teaching English, but now *everything* looks wrong.

CHARLOTTE: Don't try to change our discussion with that tactic. Harold says . . .

ERNEST: I think it must be an *a*.

CHARLOTTE: You know it's an *a*. Now, back to our discussion.

ERNEST: Not again, Charlie. We've been on that same topic for a week.

CHARLOTTE: Do you want to admit you've been wrong?

ERNEST: Certainly not.

CHARLOTTE: Good. Now, Harold says. . . .

ERNEST: Harold who?

CHARLOTTE: That's a cheap debate trick. Really, Father, I expected better of you.

ERNEST: Harold makes mistakes, too.

CHARLOTTE: Then you admit you've made a mistake?

ERNEST: I wasn't talking about me. I was talking about Harold What's-his-name. You know, the great young director.

CHARLOTTE: Harold was right about those two people you sent to read for parts in his new production. They were terrible.

ERNEST: He didn't even give them a chance. He didn't even look at them.

CHARLOTTE: He did, Father. I should know. I was there.

ERNEST: You didn't look at them, either. You just looked at Harold.

CHARLOTTE: You're just trying to change the subject by not listening.

ERNEST: All right, Charlotte, I'll listen.

CHARLOTTE: Will you really listen and not make jokes?

ERNEST: I'll really listen. Go ahead. It's only fair to tell you, however, that I think you and Harold are all wet.

CHARLOTTE: I know what you think, but listen. (*Finds place in book*) Now, this is what Anton Chekhov says a play should be. Are you listening?

ERNEST: I'm listening. Who's Anton Chekhov?

CHARLOTTE: You promised. No more jokes. (*Reads*) "A play ought to be written in which the people should come and go, dine, talk of the weather, or play cards, not because the author wants it, but because that is what really happens in real life. Life on the stage should be as it really is and the people, too, should be as they are and not stilted." (*She looks up*) Now, that's what Chekhov says, and that's what Harold says, and that's what I say.

ERNEST: Well, naturally, you say whatever Harold says. You're in love with him, but I'm not.

CHARLOTTE: Being in love doesn't mean one has to agree. Mother loves you, but she disagrees with a lot of things you say.

ERNEST: Only since we've been married. After you become Mrs. Harold What's-his-name, I'll be able to count on one of you to be on my side in any argument on any subject. I won't be losing a daughter, I'll be gaining a debating partner.

CHARLOTTE: Well, I just hope you learn something about logic by that time.

ERNEST: Now, don't lose your temper. You always lose the argument when you lose your temper. Why don't you sit down, Charlotte? You make me nervous.

CHARLOTTE (*Sitting*): Will you be logical and objective and not make jokes about Harold?

ERNEST: I, joke about Harold Randall? The man who has volunteered to pay your bills? Would I bite the hand that gives me dog biscuits?

CHARLOTTE: There you go again. You know, Father, I'm not a baby.

ERNEST: You're still my baby, aren't you?

CHARLOTTE: You're afraid to discuss the topic. You really are. That means you have the losing side. I can always tell when you're trying to change sides. You keep trying to change the subject.

ERNEST: What is the subject?

CHARLOTTE: I knew you were going to say that. I just knew you would. But this time it won't work. The subject is: What should plays be about? Harold and *I* say that plays should be about life, the way it really is.

ERNEST: Do I have to debate both of you at once? Couldn't I just debate you now and then take Harold on in the semifinals? It's most annoying to have the ghost of Harold parading through here, especially when he's such a rotten judge of acting talent.

CHARLOTTE: There you go again, trying to make me angry. You'll do anything to win an argument, Father. Especially when you're wrong. I wish you'd be fair.

ERNEST (*Seriously*): All right, Charlie, I'll be fair. I agree with you. Plays should be about life.

CHARLOTTE: But last night, you said. . . .

ERNEST: I said Chekhov was all wet. No, I'll be fair. I did say I didn't think he ever said what you just quoted, but if he did—and I'll admit he did—he was all wet. People in real life don't just come and go, dine, talk of the weather, and play cards. Look at Chekhov's own plays. People plot and intrigue. They lose fortunes, kill themselves and others, fall in love, get married, fall out of love. Chekhov—in his better moments—knew that life is melodramatic.

CHARLOTTE: And how many fortunes have you lost, Father?

ERNEST: I lost two hundred dollars on that stupid lot I bought.

CHARLOTTE: And how many times have you killed yourself?

ERNEST: At least once for every dollar—that's two hundred times. And I've killed George Bardley a hundred times for every dollar for talking me into buying it.

CHARLOTTE: For a man who turns green at the sight of a rare steak, you're very bloodthirsty, Father.

ERNEST: There's a lot you don't know about me, Charlie. For all you know, I might have been a gunfighter in my youth.

CHARLOTTE: A gunfighter! Now I know you're losing the argument, Father.

ERNEST: Oh, am I? All right now, think about this. Everybody is born. Right? That's melodrama. People marry or don't marry. Either way, that's a soap opera. They live a short time or a long time, but they always die. And that's melodrama, too. Why, if Chekhov ever sat down to watch his quiet, unstilted people for one evening— any evening—after two hours, he'd have seen so much melodrama, that he could write *ten* plays from it.

CHARLOTTE: Any evening, Father?

ERNEST: That's what I said. Any *normal* evening when people are gathered in one room for a while. Why, this discussion is the beginning of a melodrama. The next thing you know, you'll lose your temper, and go storming out into the world, then discover that you have been wrong—years later, naturally—and come back to me for forgiveness. I'll forgive you, of course. I can see the scene now—with a little violin music in the background.

CHARLOTTE: I know you can, Father, but we're not talking about your overactive imagination. We're talking about life. Would you call tonight a *normal* evening?

ERNEST: It's a regular Anton Chekhov sort of evening. Why?

CHARLOTTE: I'll tell you why. We'll use tonight as a test. I'll be home all evening. Mother's home. You're home. Harold will be over as soon as he finishes rehearsal. Somebody else will probably drop in. Is that enough of a cast for you?

ERNEST: I might call up a couple of your old boy friends, too. What was that fellow's name—Marvin?

CHARLOTTE: Daddy, don't you *ever* mention his name in front of Harold.

ERNEST: Ah-ha. Melodrama comes creeping into our quiet abode.

CHARLOTTE: You can force melodrama in if you want to, but it's just artificial. Life, mostly, is sort of boring, but happy—cleaning house, eating meals, talking about nothing in particular, doing work. That's what life is, and that's what plays should be about. Normal, routine life.

ERNEST: What play is Harold directing these days?

CHARLOTTE: *Hamlet.* You know that. And that has nothing to do with our discussion.

ERNEST (*Rising, arm outstretched*): "To be or not to be. That is the question." (GRACE *enters down left.*)

GRACE: Are you two still arguing?

CHARLOTTE: We are not arguing, Mother. We are discussing. And your husband is losing.

GRACE: I don't see why he's always *my* husband when he's losing and *your* father when he's winning. Are you going to lose your tempers with each other, or will I be able to sit in here and read?

ERNEST: *I* never lose my temper.

CHARLOTTE: No, Mother, it's going to be a nice quiet Anton Chekhov sort of evening.

GRACE: That's nice. (*Looks about*) I do like a nice quiet evening. Has anyone seen my book?

ERNEST: What are you reading, Grace?

GRACE: It's just a book. With a blue cover.

CHARLOTTE (*Picking up a book from table*): Is this it, Mother?

GRACE: Yes, I think so.

CHARLOTTE (*Reading title*): *Murders for Fun and Profit!* Really, Mother.

GRACE: I have to do something for excitement.

CHARLOTTE: See, Father, I told you. Exhibit One. (*Hands book to* GRACE)

ERNEST: I don't think that exhibits anything, except your mother's homicidal tendencies.

GRACE (*Sitting down and opening book*): Really, Ernest, I don't think that's a bit funny. (*Starts reading*)

CHARLOTTE: Well, here we are at the beginning of our play. Mother is quietly reading. Father is grading papers.

ERNEST: Now, there's melodrama for you.

CHARLOTTE: Daughter might even help Father if he would ask nicely.

ERNEST: No, I'm almost through. Knit or something. I think that would be in character.

CHARLOTTE: No, I'm going to write everything down. (*Finds pad and pencil on desk*) I'm going to write down

everything that happens and then we can see what life
is really about. (*Starts writing.*)

ERNEST: What are you writing?

CHARLOTTE: I'm going to start first with this from Chekhov: "A play ought to be written in which people
should come and go, dine, talk of the weather. . . ."

ERNEST: Don't forget to put in there about your mother's
taste in reading. That will be a very important clue
later. (*Picks up papers*) Did I ask you how to spell *separate?*

CHARLOTTE: With an *a*, Father. (*Reads aloud and writes*)
"Life on the stage should be as it really is and the people, too, should be as they are and not stilted."

ERNEST: And that's another thing. People offstage are more
stilted than they are on. Look at your mother, pretending to read. Now that's stilted.

GRACE (*Rising and closing book*): I knew I wasn't going
to be able to read in here. When you two get in one of
these moods, nobody can do anything. I'm going to bake
a pie.

CHARLOTTE (*Writing*): Mother bakes pie. See, Father, how
commonplace life is. Real life, I mean.

ERNEST: I don't think your mother's pies are commonplace, and even if they are, I don't think it's very nice
of you to say so. I apologize for her, Grace.

GRACE: Don't try to get me into your silly argument.

CHARLOTTE: See, Father, you can't even get a domestic
scene started. That's the way life is on an Anton Chekhov sort of evening—quiet, peaceful, uneventful. (*A
door slams offstage and two men enter up left—*DUKE
MANTEE *and* LENNIE. *They are dressed to look like gang-
sters from a 1930's movie.* DUKE *is waving a gun about,
and* LENNIE *has a rifle.* DUKE *wears a heavy fake mus-
tache.* LENNIE *is husky and strong-looking. The Blairs
look up, startled.*)

DUKE: All right, all of you. Don't open your yaps. Lennie, look outside and see if anything looks suspicious.

LENNIE: O.K., Duke. I'll look. (*He exits up left.*)

GRACE: What are you doing here? In my living room!

DUKE: I told you to keep your yap shut, lady.

ERNEST (*Rising slowly*): Sit down, Grace, and do what he tells you. (GRACE *sits down.*)

CHARLOTTE: Father, who are these men? Do you know them?

ERNEST: I . . .

DUKE: Go on, Pop, tell her. Do you know us?

ERNEST: I think I know who you are. You're Duke Mantee.

DUKE: You're a smart boy, Pop. You read the papers. Now, sit down and shut up.

GRACE: I don't think you look very much like a duke.

DUKE: Royalty has fallen upon evil days, lady. Let's face it. Things are tough all over. (LENNIE *comes back into room.*)

LENNIE: Everything's quiet out there, Duke.

DUKE: Good. Turn off some of these lights. It looks like a party's going on here.

LENNIE: Do I have to? I like the bright lights, Duke. I didn't see much light when they put me in solitary.

DUKE: Don't worry, kid. When we get out West, you'll see lots of lights. Now, turn off some.

LENNIE (*Turning off all lights but one*): Yeah, Duke, when we get out West, things will be wonderful, won't they?

DUKE: Yeah, kid, wonderful.

LENNIE: We'll have rabbits and everything, won't we, Duke?

DUKE: Yeah, kid, rabbits and everything.

LENNIE: Tell me about the rabbits, Duke. Tell me about the rabbits.

DUKE: Later, kid, later. You stay back there now, kid, and watch the door.

CHARLOTTE: What are you going to do with us?

DUKE: That depends on you, sister. You keep your lip buttoned, and maybe nothing. (*Points to door down left*) Where does that door go?

GRACE: That's to my kitchen. (*She rises.*)

DUKE: Good. Go get us something to eat. You go with her, Lennie.

GRACE: Now, you just see here. . . .

ERNEST: Just do what he says, Grace. And don't argue.

DUKE: You'd better listen to your old man, lady. He's a bright boy. (*To* ERNEST) You're a bright boy, aren't you?

ERNEST: We'll do what you say. Go to the kitchen, Grace.

DUKE: Sure you're a bright boy. (*To* LENNIE) Go with her, Lennie. Keep an eye on her. Sometimes these old dames are tricky.

GRACE: Old dames! (*To* DUKE) Sir, you are no gentleman, even if you do call yourself a duke.

LENNIE: Duke doesn't mean any harm, lady. He just talks like that. Now, just go in the kitchen like Duke says, lady, and nobody will hurt you. (GRACE *goes into kitchen, followed by* LENNIE.)

CHARLOTTE: Daddy, aren't you going to do anything?

ERNEST: There's nothing I can do.

CHARLOTTE: But, that man . . . that Lennie . . . he might hurt Mother.

ERNEST: We have to do what they tell us, honey. Just do what they say. (*To* DUKE) Lennie won't hurt her, will he?

DUKE: Not unless you try anything funny. Lennie has a bad reputation, but he's really a simple, good-natured kid, unless somebody panics him. If your old lady behaves herself, she'll be all right.

ERNEST: What do you want us to do?

DUKE: Just what you're doing, Pop. Stay nervous, and you'll stay alive.

ERNEST: What are you going to do to us?

DUKE: Nothing, if we don't have to. We're going to wait here a little while. And then we're going to leave. You got a car?

ERNEST: Yes, it's in the garage.

DUKE: That's good. As soon as we're sure that we've shaken the cops, we'll leave.

CHARLOTTE: They won't leave us here to talk, Daddy. Do something now.

DUKE: Don't try anything, Pop. We don't want to kill anybody—if we don't have to. (*To* CHARLOTTE) And you'd better keep your mouth shut.

ERNEST: She's right, though, isn't she? You're going to kill us all when you leave?

DUKE: Not unless we have to. Course, we'll have to take Big Blue Eyes (*Points to* CHARLOTTE) with us. For insurance.

ERNEST (*Standing*): No, you can't do that. You can take me with you, but she stays.

DUKE: Sit down. (ERNEST *sits.*) Don't try to be a hero, Pop. You're too old for that. (*Telephone on desk rings.*)

ERNEST: I'd better answer it.

DUKE: O.K., but watch it, Pop. (*He holds gun on* CHARLOTTE)

ERNEST (*Picking up phone*): Yes. Yes, this is Mr. Blair. Oh, hello, Sheriff. No, we didn't hear the news. . . . Duke Mantee? . . . No, I never heard of him. . . . No, Sheriff, I don't think he'd come this way. There's nothing out here that an escaped convict would want. Yes, Sheriff, I'll call you if I see or hear anything. . . . Yes, anything at all. Goodbye. (*Hangs up*) The alarm's out, but they think you're headed East.

DUKE: That's lucky for you, Pop. (*Yells toward kitchen*) Hey, what about that food?

LENNIE (*Coming to doorway*): It's going to take a little longer, Duke. Mrs. Blair is baking us a pie.

DUKE: A pie? I don't want pie.

LENNIE: It's going to be an apple pie, Duke. You'll like an apple pie. My mother used to bake apple pies.

DUKE: I don't want an apple pie.

LENNIE: You don't like my mother, Duke?

DUKE: All right, so I like apple pies. But tell her to hurry it up.

LENNIE: You can't hurry an apple pie, Duke, but I'll tell her. (*Exits*)

DUKE: This place is driving me crazy.

ERNEST: You're afraid of Lennie, aren't you, Duke?

DUKE: Don't get too smart, Smart Boy, or you'll end up dead.

ERNEST: Maybe you ought to get out of here now, Duke. The longer you stay, the more chance there is you'll be discovered.

DUKE: You talk too much, Smart Boy.

ERNEST: I just don't want you to get in trouble. Here.

DUKE (*Lifting gun and pointing it at him*): I'll tell you who's got trouble, Smart Boy, and that's you. I've had about all the lip I'm going to take from you.

CHARLOTTE: No. No, don't shoot him. Daddy, don't say anything more. Please, Daddy. (*Phone rings again.*)

DUKE: This is a very busy place, Pop. O.K., pick up the phone. But be careful.

ERNEST (*Picking up phone*): Hello? Oh, hello, George. . . . Now, look, George, I told you after that last speculation, I was through. Two hundred dollars for a sand trap in the middle of the desert. I may be an English teacher, George, but I'm not that stupid. . . . Why, sure I think I was stung. . . . What? . . . Well, I don't know. You'll pay two hundred and fifty for it? Tell me,

George, why are you suddenly so generous? . . . Sure, George, I believe you. I know you wouldn't stick "your best friend." Sure, George, but why two hundred and fifty? . . . And why tonight, George? . . . This *is* George, isn't it? George Bardley? My old friend? What? (*Looks at* DUKE) Yes, you might say we have company. I don't know, George, let me call you back in an hour. . . . Well, I just can't now. I'll call you in forty-five minutes. All right, George. (*Hangs up*) That was George Bardley. You know, that speculator who stuck me with that lot.

CHARLOTTE: What lot?

ERNEST: The one over in Shearer County that I lost two hundred dollars on. (*He scratches his chin.*) Now he wants to buy it back from me for two hundred and fifty.

DUKE (*Out of character*): Hey, that's all right. Fifty dollars profit. (CHARLOTTE *looks at him suspiciously, and* DUKE *goes back to his tough character.*) I mean, Pop, let's face it. You're not the smartest guy in the world. A fifty-dollar profit is a lot better than a total loss.

CHARLOTTE: Why should *you* be concerned?

DUKE: Well, I'll tell you, Blue Eyes. Pop here is likely to lose a lot more than money tonight, so I'd like him to be sure to have enough for burial expenses. (*To* ERNEST) I'd take it, Pop.

ERNEST: I don't know. If George thinks it's worth two hundred and fifty, it's probably worth five thousand. (HAROLD *comes in down right.*)

HAROLD: How come all the lights are out? I thought maybe no one was home. (*Points at* DUKE) Who's that? (*Points to gun*) And what's that?

ERNEST: We're home, Harold. That's Duke Mantee. And that thing he has in his hand is a gun.

HAROLD: Well . . . well . . . what's he doing with it?

ERNEST: He's thinking about shooting me.

HAROLD: But why? Is he a former student?

DUKE: Because I'm Duke Mantee, that's why. You've heard of me, haven't you, Smart Boy?

HAROLD: Duke Mantee! Why, sure, I've heard of you. I . . . (LENNIE *comes to doorway*)

LENNIE: Duke, do you want ice cream or cheese on your pie?

DUKE: Cheese. And hurry it up, Lennie.

LENNIE (*Pointing at* HAROLD): Who's that?

DUKE: That little rabbit's another smart boy, aren't you, Smart Boy?

LENNIE: Oh, I like rabbits. Tell me about the rabbits, Duke. Tell me about the rabbits.

HAROLD: Wait a minute, you guys. This is some kind of joke.

CHARLOTTE: Please, Harold, don't start anything.

HAROLD: I've heard of Duke Mantee. He was the gangster in Robert Sherwood's play, *The Petrified Forest.* Humphrey Bogart played the part.

DUKE: Yeah, and he didn't do a very good job of it, either. If I run into him, I'm going to rough him up a little. I might even bump him off.

LENNIE (*Interrupting*): Tell me about the rabbits, Duke. Tell me about the rabbits.

HAROLD (*Pointing at* LENNIE): And that's Lennie. He's from *Of Mice and Men,* by John Steinbeck. What is this? Amateur night at the Blair House?

DUKE: I don't know what you're talking about, Smart Boy, but I've had it with you. (*To* CHARLOTTE) Get out of the way, Blue Eyes, I'm going to blast Hopeless Harold here right now. I've had it with this jerk and his bum jokes.

CHARLOTTE (*Leaping in front of* HAROLD *to shield him*):

Shoot if you must, but you'll have to kill me first. (*She poses melodramatically. Lights come up.*)

HAROLD: You mean this is real? This is *really* somebody called Duke Mantee? (*Sinks down in chair*) It can't be. Things like this don't happen in real life.

LENNIE: Let me shoot him, Duke. You shot the last one.

CHARLOTTE (*Exasperated*): Oh, stop it. This isn't funny. (*To* ERNEST) And I don't think this proves anything, anyway.

DUKE: You shoot him, and I'll shoot her.

LENNIE: And then you'll tell me about the rabbits, Duke?

DUKE: Then I'll tell you about the rabbits. Ready, when I count three . . . one . . . two . . .

ERNEST (*Standing suddenly behind desk, a gun in his hand*): All right, Duke, drop the gun. I've got you covered.

CHARLOTTE: Oh, Daddy, stop this. This is just silly.

DUKE: Now I know you, Smart Boy. You're Ernie Blair, the Marshal of Tucson.

ERNEST: That's right, Duke. Do you want to try to shoot it out, or do you want to give up?

DUKE: Give up! I've just begun to fight. (DUKE *and* ERNEST *both fire, and* DUKE *drops to floor.*) You got me, kid.

ERNEST (*Going to stand over* DUKE): I'm sorry, Duke, but you wouldn't have it any other way.

DUKE: That's always the way it is. You good guys always win. (*Dies*)

HAROLD (*Still frightened*): Is he . . . is he dead?

LENNIE: And he never did tell me about the rabbits.

ERNEST: I'll tell you about the rabbits, Lennie.

LENNIE: No, you killed my friend, and I'm going to kill you. (*He turns to shoot* ERNEST *who again fires.* LENNIE *staggers across the stage and drops.*) You got me.

ERNEST: I'm sorry, Lennie, you wouldn't have it any other way.

LENNIE: It's all right. I never would have made it out West anyway. Us bad guys always get it in the end.

ERNEST: That's the way it goes. (GRACE *enters from kitchen*.)

GRACE: Anyone who wants pie can come to the kitchen. I'm not going to have crumbs all over my living room. (*To* HAROLD) Hello, Harold. How did rehearsal go?

HAROLD (*Excitedly*): Mrs. Blair, look, everybody's dead.

ERNEST: Not everybody, Harold. Some of us are only half-dead.

CHARLOTTE: Mother! You were in on this stupid plot, too, weren't you? Honestly, Mother, you let Daddy talk you into anything.

ERNEST: It was your mother's idea.

CHARLOTTE: Mother!

HAROLD: Will somebody tell me what is going on?

LENNIE (*Getting up; in an ordinary voice*): Did you say the pie was ready, Mrs. Blair?

GRACE: Yes, Lennie.

LENNIE: Hey, Duke, the pie's ready.

DUKE (*Rising*): Big deal. Pie. I like cake better.

LENNIE (*Using character voice again*): You never did like my mother. (*Laughs. He and* DUKE *exit to kitchen.* GRACE *follows them.*)

HAROLD: Who are these characters and what is going on around here?

ERNEST: These characters—as you call them, Harold—are the two actors I sent over to you to try out for your play. Obviously, they are a good deal more convincing as actors than you thought they would be. And you didn't even recognize them.

CHARLOTTE: It's just Daddy's cheap way of winning an argument, Harold. But he didn't fool me. I knew it all the time.

HAROLD: Then why didn't you tell me? You're already

keeping secrets from me. And you said our marriage was going to be different.

CHARLOTTE: Well, I didn't know it *all* the time. But I was suspicious, and as soon as you reminded me where I had heard those names before. . . . Harold, it was just wonderful the way you could recognize the characters that way.

HAROLD: It was? I mean, so it was. But I still don't know what this is all about. Maybe I was wrong about those two when they read for me. I'll give them another try-out.

CHARLOTTE: That was only a side issue, Harold. Father's just trying to win an argument. (*To* ERNEST) But Chekhov is still right, Father. You may bring all the Duke Mantees in the world in here, but by the end of the night, they'll all just be college boys eating Mother's pie.

ERNEST: Don't talk to me about cheap tricks, Charlie. That was a great one you tried to pull, but that phone call didn't fool me.

CHARLOTTE: Telephone call? (*Sarcastically*) You mean the one from the "sheriff" about Duke Mantee, the escaped convict? (GRACE *enters, unnoticed by others.*)

ERNEST: No—that was one of my friends. I mean the call that was supposed to be from George Bardley. It didn't even sound like George.

CHARLOTTE: I don't know what you're talking about.

GRACE: Ernest, what about George Bardley?

ERNEST: Nothing about George Bardley. One of Charlotte's friends called and pretended to be George. He offered me two hundred and fifty dollars for that lot.

GRACE: Well, I hope you took it.

ERNEST: That's what I'm saying, it wasn't (*Looks at* CHARLOTTE, *who shakes her head*) . . . it wasn't . . .

CHARLOTTE: It wasn't one of my friends, Daddy. You're

the only one in this family with friends who make stupid
phone calls.

ERNEST (*Sitting down, startled*): Oh, no, don't tell me.

CHARLOTTE: This is one time, Daddy, when you were just
too clever for your own good—Smart Boy. And I recognized *that* from Hemingway all on my own.

ERNEST: I can still call George back. He gave me forty-five
minutes to call back and accept. (*Starts for phone. Doorbell rings, but* ERNEST *answers phone.*) Hello? Hello,
George? (*Doorbell rings again.*)

GRACE: It's the doorbell, Ernest. (*She exits up left.*)

ERNEST: The doorbell? Oh, yes, the doorbell. I'll call
George. No, maybe it's George at the door. (GRACE *and*
MRS. WINGFIELD *enter.*)

GRACE: Ernest, it's Mrs. Wingfield.

HAROLD: Not little old Amanda Wingfield from *The Glass
Menagerie!* Well, I'll tell you, Mrs. Wingfield, the play
is over for tonight. We've had *The Petrified Forest, Of
Mice and Men,* and we're right in the midst of *A
Comedy of Errors.*

MRS. WINGFIELD (*With great dignity, pointing at* HAROLD):
Who is that person?

CHARLOTTE: This really *is* Mrs. Wingfield, Harold. She
lives next door. Mrs. Wingfield, this is Harold Randall.

HAROLD: Oh. I . . .

GRACE: You'll have to excuse Harold, Mrs. Wingfield. He's
had a rather trying evening. He's the young man who's
going to marry Charlotte, you know.

MRS. WINGFIELD: Well, now, don't feel too bad about it,
my dear. I'm not pleased with the man my Eileen
brought home, either. (*To* ERNEST) But, congratulations,
Mr. Blair, congratulations.

ERNEST: For Harold? You're kidding.

MRS. WINGFIELD: Then you haven't heard? The government is building a dam.

ERNEST: Well, hooray for the government.

MRS. WINGFIELD: But it's being built in Shearer County. That lot you bought and are always complaining about is in Shearer County.

ERNEST: Oh.

MRS. WINGFIELD: It will be worth thousands.

GRACE: You mean we're rich?

MRS. WINGFIELD: Well, two thousand, maybe three.

GRACE: That's rich for us. Let's celebrate. I have a nice fresh apple pie in the kitchen, Mrs. Wingfield. Won't you join us?

MRS. WINGFIELD: I really shouldn't. But I will.

GRACE: The rest of you come along, too—when you've finished your argument.

HAROLD: I'm finished now.

MRS. WINGFIELD: I do like a nice quiet evening with friends . . . just talking about the weather and things like that. (MRS. WINGFIELD, HAROLD, *and* GRACE *exit into kitchen.*)

ERNEST: Two thousand dollars. Maybe three thousand dollars. We're rich, Charlie, and that should prove something.

CHARLOTTE: Well, it proves something to me. A nice quiet Anton Chekhov sort of evening would never play on the stage. Nobody would believe it. It's too melodramatic.

ERNEST: Now, I agree with that. (*Phone rings.*) Don't answer it. One act of *Life at Blair House* is enough for any evening. Even for Anton Chekhov. (*Phone rings, a horn blares offstage, and the curtain falls.*)

THE END

The Happiest Hat

Characters

MR. WANDIMILLER, *an attorney*
MAGGIE, *his secretary*
MR. THOMPSON, *a husband*
MR. DICKSON, *a doer*
MR. HAROLDSON, *a playboy*
DAISY, *Thompson's wife*
MISS ERNEST, *Dickson's secretary*
BLONDIE, *Haroldson's girlfriend*
GEORGE, *a party-giver*
EMILY, *his wife*

SCENE 1

SETTING: *Mr. Wandimiller's office. Up center is a desk, behind which is a chair. Down right of them are six kitchen chairs in a row, painted alternately red, white, and blue. Down left of desk are six orange crates, also painted alternately red, white, and blue.*

AT RISE: MAGGIE, *carrying a shorthand dictation book and pencil, enters from down left, looks about quickly, then goes off down right.* MR. WANDIMILLER *enters from up right, carrying three large hat boxes, painted red, white, and blue. They are piled one on top of the other*

*and held high so that his face is hidden until he arrives
at his desk. He sets the boxes on the floor, then puts
blue box on top of desk.* MAGGIE *re-enters, starts across
stage, apparently upset. She sees* MR. WANDIMILLER *and
stops.*

MAGGIE: Oh, there you are, Mr. Wandimiller.

WANDIMILLER: That's doubly true. I am here, and I am
Mr. Wandimiller.

MAGGIE: They're here.

WANDIMILLER: That's probably true. Have you seen them?

MAGGIE: Yes, sir, Mr. Wandimiller. I've seen them.

WANDIMILLER: Yes?

MAGGIE: I've seen Mr. Thompson. I've seen Mr. Dickson.
And I've seen Mr. Haroldson.

WANDIMILLER: Then, it follows logically that you have seen
them.

MAGGIE: That's true, Mr. Wandimiller.

WANDIMILLER: And since you are my ever-faithful secretary, and you never make a mistake, it is safe to assume
that they're here.

MAGGIE: That's true, Mr. Wandimiller.

WANDIMILLER: *Now* it's true. When you first said it, it was
merely a theory; but *now* that it has been demonstrated
by experience and logic, we may say that it is true.

MAGGIE: You do like experience and logic, don't you, Mr.
Wandimiller?

WANDIMILLER: Of course. I am a lawyer; and we guardi-
ans of the law know the worth of experience and logic.
Without them, society is nothing.

MAGGIE: That's true, Mr. Wandimiller. (*Quickly*) Well, at
least it's an interesting theory.

WANDIMILLER: It is also true, Maggie, but I have no time
at the moment to demonstrate it. They are ready?

MAGGIE: They are more than ready. They are eager.

WANDIMILLER: I would think so. Most people are eager when they are to receive an inheritance. Do they know what it is yet?

MAGGIE: No, sir, you told me not to tell them. Of course, when I called them, I did suggest they were going to get *something*, but I didn't say *what* it was. I would *like* to have told them *what*, because they asked me *what*. But you told me not to tell them *what*, so I didn't tell them *what*—just that they'd better come and see you because it would be to their advantage. That's what *you* told me to tell them, and that's all I told them. Just that they were going to get *something*, but not *what*.

WANDIMILLER: A wise precaution on my part, for if they knew what their inheritance *was* without knowing what it *is*—if you follow me—they might not stay. And that would be a terrible loss. (*Orating*) This is a moment of historic interest for those three men. Henceforth, they will date their lives from this event. They will take pictures of it and have them bronzed and pass them on from one generation to another, even unto the seventh generation.

MAGGIE (*Applauding*): Oh, Mr. Wandimiller, that was wonderfully expressed.

WANDIMILLER: It probably was, and it was only half the length of the Gettysburg Address. (*Laughs pompously*) Rather like the Gettysburg Address without a ZIP code number so to speak.

MAGGIE (*Giving a little burst of happy applause*): Oh, that was very good, Mr. Wandimiller. The Gettysburg Address without a ZIP code number. I must remember to tell it to Mother.

WANDIMILLER: Now to business. Who is to be first?

MAGGIE: Mr. Thompson is, sir.

WANDIMILLER: He's the married man, right?

MAGGIE: Right.

WANDIMILLER: And he's unhappy?

MAGGIE: Right.

WANDIMILLER: Why is he unhappy? Doesn't his wife love him?

MAGGIE: Wrong.

WANDIMILLER: Miserable children?

MAGGIE: Lovely children.

WANDIMILLER: They hate him?

MAGGIE: No, they love him.

WANDIMILLER: Then why is he unhappy? When a man has so much love. . . . He does have love, doesn't he?

MAGGIE: He is the most loving, loved man in the world. Probably.

WANDIMILLER: Then why is he unhappy?

MAGGIE: He worries about wasting his life. He thinks he should do something important.

WANDIMILLER: Being loved is important.

MAGGIE: He doesn't know that it is *that* important.

WANDIMILLER: Well, send him in, and I'll send him on his way to being the happiest man in the world.

MAGGIE: Right, sir. (*She exits left.* WANDIMILLER *looks in hat box, nods, sits down, scratches his head, then rises and starts downstage.* MAGGIE *enters, followed by* MR. THOMPSON.) Mr. Tom Thompson. (*She turns and exits.*)

WANDIMILLER (*Going to* THOMPSON *and shaking his hand*): Well, well, Mr. Thompson. I am pleased to see you. This is your lucky day, sir. The greatest day in your life.

THOMPSON: I should think so. It isn't every day that a man gets a legacy. I wish I could have brought the wife and children with me. It would have been a proud day for them.

WANDIMILLER: It is better than a proud day, sir. This is a

happy day. (*Turns and goes upstage to desk.*) Come, sir, take a chair.

THOMPSON (*Picking up a blue chair and holding it*): Thank you, sir. (*He stands with the chair in his hands.*)

WANDIMILLER (*Sitting*): What are you doing with that chair, Mr. Thompson?

THOMPSON: You told me to take it.

WANDIMILLER: I meant for you to sit on it.

THOMPSON: You didn't say that.

WANDIMILLER: No, I should have. Please sit down, Mr. Thompson.

THOMPSON (*Setting the chair down and sitting on it*): I think people should say what they mean, especially lawyers, don't you, Mr. Wandimiller?

WANDIMILLER: I certainly do.

THOMPSON: I don't like all that small print and double-talk on the bottom of a legal document, do you, Mr. Wandimiller?

WANDIMILLER: I certainly do not.

THOMPSON: I hope I don't have to sign any document with a lot of small print. With the legacy, I mean.

WANDIMILLER: You don't have to sign a thing, Mr. Thompson.

THOMPSON: I don't?

WANDIMILLER: You certainly do not.

THOMPSON: It can't be much of a legacy without a legal document with a lot of small print.

WANDIMILLER: It's the greatest legacy in the world, sir. This, Mr. Thompson, is a moment of historical interest for you. Henceforth you will date your life from this event. You will take pictures of it and have them bronzed and pass them on from one generation to another, even unto the seventh generation.

THOMPSON: You said that very well, Mr. Wandimiller.

WANDIMILLER: Thank you, and it was shorter than the Gettysburg Address.

THOMPSON (*Smiling smugly*): Rather like the Gettysburg Address without a ZIP code number.

WANDIMILLER: I'm afraid so.

THOMPSON: I read the ZIP code joke in a Boy Scout humor book. I thought it was pretty good. Well, now to business. What is my legacy?

WANDIMILLER (*Opening the box and taking out a blue hat; smiling, confidently*): This, Mr. Thompson!

THOMPSON (*Rising*): That, Mr. Wandimiller? That funny hat?

WANDIMILLER: This funny hat, as you call it, Mr. Thompson, is not just any old hat. It's a magic hat.

THOMPSON: Oh?

WANDIMILLER: It's a happiest hat.

THOMPSON: I knew it was something that ended in "est."

WANDIMILLER: It's the only one of its kind in the world.

THOMPSON: Well, that's something. But really, Mr. Wandimiller, I really don't consider this much of a legacy. (*Almost crying*) In fact, if you must know, Mr. Wandimiller, I feel just downright disappointed.

WANDIMILLER: That's fine, Mr. Thompson. Remember the feeling. It will be the last time in your life that you will be "dis" anything: disappointed, disgusted, disenchanted, dismembered, distrustful, or even distinct. This, Mr. Thompson—and I repeat—is *the* Happiest Hat. (*Hands it to* THOMPSON) Here, put it on.

THOMPSON (*Taking it and putting it on*): I feel silly.

WANDIMILLER: It looks very well on you, and it should. If you wear this hat every day—even for a minute a day—you will be the happiest man in the world. That's your legacy, Mr. Thompson. Happiness.

THOMPSON: I don't know if I believe that.

WANDIMILLER: Do you have a wife, Mr. Thompson?

THOMPSON: I do, the loveliest wife in the world—and fifteen lovely children.

WANDIMILLER: Are you happy, Mr. Thompson?

THOMPSON: Well, yes. I guess so.

WANDIMILLER: Is there anyone happier, Mr. Thompson— anyone with a lovelier wife or lovelier children?

THOMPSON: I should say not.

WANDIMILLER: Then, Mr. Thompson, you are the happiest man in the world. Right?

THOMPSON: Right. And I owe it all to you and this funny hat. I must rush right home and tell my wife and children the good news. (*Pauses*) It is really something to be the happiest man in the world. Now everyone will envy me. (*He rushes off down right.* WANDIMILLER *takes the blue box off up right and returns immediately. He takes the white box and sets it on desk.* MAGGIE *enters down left and stands waiting.*)

WANDIMILLER (*Sitting*): Oh, these affairs weary me, Maggie. Who's next?

MAGGIE: Mr. Dickson, sir.

WANDIMILLER: He's the mover of the universe, right?

MAGGIE: Yes, sir. Mr. Dickson is a doer.

WANDIMILLER: A failure?

MAGGIE: No sir, a success.

WANDIMILLER: Not appreciated?

MAGGIE: No, sir, everyone appreciates him. In fact, they are thinking of changing the name of *that* city to Dickson, D. C.

WANDIMILLER: Then why is he unhappy? Does his conscience bother him because he is a crook?

MAGGIE: No, sir, he is the most honest successful man in the world, or the most successful honest man—depending on how you look at it.

WANDIMILLER: Why isn't he happy?

MAGGIE: He doesn't think he's having any fun.

WANDIMILLER: Good grief. Send him in, and I'll send him on his way to being the happiest man in the world.

MAGGIE: Yes, sir. (*She exits left.* WANDIMILLER *looks in white hat box, nods, sits down, scratches his head, then rises and starts downstage.* MAGGIE *enters, followed by* MR. DICKSON.) Mr. Dick Dickson. (*She turns and exits.*)

WANDIMILLER (*Going to* DICKSON *and shaking his hand*): Well, well, Mr. Dickson. I am pleased to see you. This is your lucky day, sir. The greatest day of your life.

DICKSON: That, sir, remains to be seen. My life has been filled with great days.

WANDIMILLER: This, sir, will be better than a great day. This will be a happy day. (*Turns and goes upstage to desk*) Come, sir, take a chair.

DICKSON (*Picking up a white chair and carrying it forward*): Thank you, sir.

WANDIMILLER: I mean for you to sit on that chair, Mr. Dickson.

DICKSON: I assumed that, sir, although, in truth, you didn't say it. (*Sits*) But let's skip the formalities and get down to business. What is it I am to inherit? If it's money, I don't want it. I have too much now. If it's an honor of some sort, skip it. I am already too honored. (*Starts to rise*) Now that I think about it, I should leave anyway. Obviously you can give me nothing I want. Good day, sir.

WANDIMILLER: Just one minute, sir. This is the greatest legacy in the world. This, Mr. Dickson, is a moment of historical interest for you. Henceforth. . . .

DICKSON: Mr. Wandimiller! I may accept a legacy, but I am not going to listen to an oration.

WANDIMILLER: It's a very small one. (*Pauses*) Do you read Boy Scout joke books?

DICKSON: Of course, doesn't everyone? But I didn't come here to discuss modern literature. I really must go. (*Starts off*)

WANDIMILLER: No, wait. You'll be sorry. (*Grabs box and pulls out white hat*) Look, this is your legacy.

DICKSON (*Stopping and looking at hat*): That stupid hat is my legacy?

WANDIMILLER: That stupid hat, as you call it, Mr. Dickson, is not just any old hat. It's a magic hat.

DICKSON: Yes, I know. It's the happiest hat, isn't it?

WANDIMILLER (*A little disappointed*): You know about it?

DICKSON: Of course.

WANDIMILLER: It's the only one of its kind in the world.

DICKSON: Of course. Is it genuine?

WANDIMILLER: Why, certainly. (*Hands him hat*) Here, try it on.

DICKSON (*Putting hat on*): It is genuine. So, this is how it feels to be the happiest man in the world. Thank you, Mr. Wandimiller, I owe a great deal to you and this stupid hat. I must get back to my work of saving the world. But now it will be fun. And now everyone will envy me. (*Rushes off down right.* WANDIMILLER *takes the white box off up right and returns immediately. He takes the red box and sets it on desk.* MAGGIE *enters down left and stands waiting.*)

WANDIMILLER: Each one gets harder, Maggie. Mr. Dickson wouldn't let me finish my speech and he reads Boy Scout joke books, too. He even tried to walk out on me.

MAGGIE: He did? Well, Mr. Wandimiller, he may be the happiest man in the world, but he's not very nice, I must say.

WANDIMILLER: Well, well, who's left?

MAGGIE: Mr. Haroldson is, sir.

WANDIMILLER: He's the playboy, isn't he?

MAGGIE (*With enthusiasm*): Yes, sir. Handsome and just

full of fun. We've been playing post office while he was waiting. He owns boats and horses and a cabana in Florida, and he can ski and ride and play the zither.

WANDIMILLER (*Indignantly*): He can play the zither? Then why isn't he happy?

MAGGIE: He thinks he's wasting his life, sir. He thinks he would be happier if he were married with sixteen kids . . . or doing Important Things, like saving the world.

WANDIMILLER (*Tired*): All right, Maggie, show Mr. Haroldson in. (MAGGIE *exits down left.* WANDIMILLER *looks in red box, nods, sits down, scratches his head, then rises and starts downstage.* MAGGIE *enters, followed by* MR. HAROLDSON.)

MAGGIE: Mr. Harry Haroldson. (*She turns and exits.*)

WANDIMILLER (*Going to* HAROLDSON *and shaking his hand*): Well, well, Mr. Haroldson. I am pleased to see you. This is your lucky day, sir. The greatest day of your life. (*Blackout and fast curtain*)

* * * * *

SCENE 2

SETTING: *The Happiest Men at home. In Area 1 at right, the Thompson home, a blue chair and a blue crate serve as a chair and footstool, and a little upstage from them is the desk. A blue and white streamer running from the top of the upstage wall, right corner, down to the floor, right center, divides Area 1 from Area 2, at center—the Dickson area. Two white crates and one blue crate are placed together to form a worktable. In back of it is a blue chair, with white chairs at either end. A red and white streamer divides this area from Area 3, the Haroldson home. Two red chairs are placed side by side, with two red crates set on their sides to suggest a couch and coffee table.*

AT RISE: THOMPSON *is seated in Area 1, with his feet on crate.* DAISY *is standing at desk, using it as an ironing board.* DICKSON *is seated in Area 2 behind worktable, holding maps and papers.* MISS ERNEST *is taking dictation.* HAROLDSON *is sitting on the couch in Area 3, a tennis racket in his hand.* BLONDIE *is sitting beside him. The three men wear the hats they were given in Scene 1. Throughout scene, when actors in one area are speaking, the others remain frozen in position.*

BLONDIE: You're happy now, aren't you, Harry?

HAROLDSON: The happiest man in the world.

BLONDIE: You look cute in that crazy hat.

HAROLDSON: I am cute.

BLONDIE (*Laughing*): Oh, Harry, you are the one. (*She and* HAROLDSON *freeze in position.*)

DICKSON: Well, Miss Ernest, we've saved another nation from destruction and made a pretty penny while doing it.

MISS ERNEST: I know, Mr. Dickson. You're just wonderful.

DICKSON: I guess I am.

MISS ERNEST: I know you are.

DICKSON: I won't argue.

MISS ERNEST: I've always thought you were wonderful (*Pauses*) but. . . .

DICKSON: But?

MISS ERNEST: But . . . for a long time I thought you were not very happy. Great, you understand. Wonderful, you understand. But not very happy.

DICKSON: I know, Miss Ernest.

MISS ERNEST: But ever since that day you went to see that Mr. Wandimiller . . . well, you've just been another person.

DICKSON: That's true, Miss Ernest. Quite true. That was

the day I became the happiest man in the world. (*He and* MISS ERNEST *freeze.*)

THOMPSON: Are the children all settled for the night, Daisy?

DAISY: Yes, Tom, dear. The twins are in their cribs; the triplets are in their beds; the quadruplets are studying; the quintuplets are playing with a zither band. They call themselves the Happiness Gang. Isn't that cute?

THOMPSON: Very cute. (*Pauses*) What's Tom, Jr., doing?

DAISY: You know, dear. He's working with Mr. Dickson, learning to do Great Things and save the world.

THOMPSON: A fine man, Mr. Dickson.

DAISY: Oh, yes, a very fine man.

THOMPSON: But do you know, Daisy dear, I don't think Mr. Dickson is very happy.

DAISY: I don't either, dear. And if I weren't so happy, it would make me sad. Why can't everyone be happy the way we are, dear?

THOMPSON (*Laughing tolerantly*): Because, dear, I'm the only happiest man in the world. (*He and* DAISY *freeze.*)

BLONDIE: What party?

HAROLDSON: I told you. *The* party. The one George and Emily are having.

BLONDIE: Oh. (*Pauses*) Did you really tell me about that party, Harry?

HAROLDSON: Of course, I did, Blondie. (*Laughs*) It's really a party for me.

BLONDIE: I didn't know that.

HAROLDSON: That's because I didn't tell you. But the invitation says it. (*Picks up invitation from table in front of davenport and reads*) "George and Emily invite you to their lovely home, Friday evening at seven, to honor The Happiest Man in the World."

BLONDIE: I must get a new dress. (*They freeze in position.*)

DICKSON: I should work, of course. But George and Emily are such old friends. And, of course, since the party is for me, I think we can make it for a few hours, don't you, Miss Ernest?

MISS ERNEST: I certainly do. I'll get a new dress.

DICKSON: Miss Ernest. The party is for *me*. (*They freeze.*)

THOMPSON: And, of course, Daisy, I want you to get a new dress for George and Emily's party.

DAISY: I don't need a new dress. Tom. After all, the party is for you. Not me.

THOMPSON: Whatever you think, dear. Just as long as you're happy.

DAISY: If you really want me to. (*Pauses*) I saw a wonderful one at the Fifth Avenue Shoppe.

BLONDIE: And I can wear my pearls with it.

MISS ERNEST: And it will give me just the chance I've wanted to wear my diamond clips. (*Blackout and fast curtain*)

* * * * *

SCENE 3

SETTING: *George and Emily's party. Streamers are draped on backdrop. Desk is at center, covered with a tablecloth, with a punch bowl on it. Chairs and crates are placed in three conversational groupings.*

AT RISE: GEORGE *is up center, wearing a party hat and blowing a tin whistle for attention.* EMILY *is smiling and standing next to him.* THOMPSON, DICKSON, *and* HAROLDSON *are standing down right in conversation.* DAISY, MISS ERNEST, *and* BLONDIE *are down left, obviously talking about their dresses which they are modeling for each other.*

EMILY: Listen, everyone. Listen. George has an announcement.

GEORGE (*Blowing whistle*): Listen, everyone. Listen. I have an announcement.

HAROLDSON: Do you hear an echo in here?

THOMPSON: Say, Harry, old boy, did I tell you the one about the ZIP code number for the Gettysburg Address?

EMILY: Everyone, please listen to George. (*Pauses*) After all, it's his party. (*Everyone stops and turns slightly upstage to listen to* GEORGE.)

GEORGE (*Full of good humor*): I'm sure all of you are wondering about the occasion for this party.

EMILY: Never mind the introduction, George, just get on with the announcement.

GEORGE: Let me do it *my* way, Emily. No wonder *I'm* not the happiest man in the world.

HAROLDSON: Don't worry about that, George. You are the man who's giving the party for the happiest man in the world.

DICKSON: You certainly are, George.

THOMPSON: That's true, George, and that should make you happy.

GEORGE: It does make me happy to know that my good friend is the happiest man in the world.

EMILY: It really does. He's not just saying that.

GEORGE: But I'm just downright frustrated because I don't really know which one of you is the happiest man in the world. It's driving me crazy not knowing.

EMILY (*Shaking her head sadly*): It really does. (*The three women move toward their escorts, each of whom nods knowingly.*)

HAROLDSON: Well, I don't want you to be frustrated, George.

DICKSON: I didn't think it was really that much of a mystery.

THOMPSON: I thought it was perfectly obvious.

DAISY, BLONDIE *and* MISS ERNEST (*Together*): I thought everyone knew that. . . . (*They pause and look at each each other.*)

DAISY: It was Tom!

MISS ERNEST: Dick!

BLONDIE: Harry!

DICKSON: What's going on here?

THOMPSON: Obviously, someone is playing a joke.

HAROLDSON: Some joke if you two have been telling people that you are me.

THOMPSON: I tell people I'm Harry Haroldson? I would never do such a thing. I'm no playboy.

HAROLDSON: And you are not the happiest man in the world either.

THOMPSON: I am, too.

DICKSON: You're not. I am.

HAROLDSON: Ha, that's a laugh, you old saver of worlds.

DICKSON: Don't shout at me, you playboy.

THOMPSON: Who are you calling a playboy? I happen to be a married man with sixteen children.

HAROLDSON: This is really making me very angry.

GEORGE (*Blowing his whistle*): Gentlemen. Gentlemen.

EMILY: Gentlemen. Gentlemen. George has something to say. (*They all stop and assume postures of complete calm.*)

GEORGE: Seemingly, there is some confusion. I was told that one of my friends had inherited the Happiest Hat, but I wasn't told which one. But don't any of you know?

THOMPSON: What do I have on my head? (*Points to his blue hat*)

HAROLDSON: A very funny hat. But if you will observe my hat—(*Points to his red hat*)

THOMPSON: That's a crazy hat.

DICKSON: Gentlemen, gentlemen, you have both been

cheated. If you look, you will see on my head, the original—the only—the one and only Happiest Hat.

HAROLDSON: That stupid hat.

DICKSON: I was given this stupid hat by Mr. Wandimiller himself.

THOMPSON (*Shaken for the first time; looking at* DICKSON): You were?

DICKSON (*Still with confidence*): I was.

HAROLDSON (*Removing his hat and looking at it*): I was given this crazy hat by Mr. Wandimiller, too.

DICKSON: But, there is only one Happiest Hat.

THOMPSON (*Removing his hat and looking at it sadly*): Mr. Wandimiller gave me my hat, too.

DICKSON (*Removing his hat*): Oh. Gentlemen, do you know what I think?

HAROLDSON: We've been swindled.

THOMPSON: Wandimiller is a crook.

GEORGE: But, gentlemen, one of you must have the Happiest Hat. Everyone knows that.

DICKSON: Of course.

THOMPSON: That's true.

HAROLDSON: But which one?

DICKSON: We'll go back to Mr. Wandimiller and demand that he tell us the truth.

HAROLDSON: We'll drag it out of him, if necessary.

THOMPSON: By reason, of course. I don't like force.

DICKSON: Gentlemen, are we agreed?

THOMPSON: We are.

HAROLDSON: We will go to Mr. Wandimiller and demand that he tell us which one has the Happiest Hat. (*They march off in step, swinging their arms in time. Blackout. Curtain*)

*   *   *   *   *

Scene 4

SETTING: *Mr. Wandimiller's office. The same as Scene 1.*
AT RISE: MAGGIE, *wearing a huge black armband and carrying a lily, is walking from up right to the desk.* THOMPSON, DICKSON, *and* HAROLDSON, *still in step, enter.*

THOMPSON: Where is Mr. Wandimiller?

DICKSON: We demand to see that crook.

HAROLDSON: We mean to have the truth if we have to drag it out of him by force.

MAGGIE: Mr. Wandimiller has gone. . . .

THOMPSON: Gone?

MAGGIE: To his reward.

DICKSON: You mean he's . . . ?

MAGGIE: I mean . . . he's in jail.

HAROLDSON: In jail?

MAGGIE: Very much in jail.

THOMPSON: Oh, this is terrible.

DICKSON: How long will he be gone?

MAGGIE: At least for life, maybe longer.

HAROLDSON: We'll just go to the jail. Prison bars can't keep me out.

MAGGIE: They weren't meant to. But they are keeping Mr. Wandimiller in.

THOMPSON: For life.

MAGGIE: For life.

HAROLDSON: Let's go to the jail then.

MAGGIE: It won't do you any good. He's in solitary confinement, and he can't have visitors.

DICKSON: Now we'll never know.

THOMPSON: This is annoying.

HAROLDSON: Frustrating.

DICKSON: Downright terrible.

MAGGIE: You mean about the Happiest Hat?

DICKSON: Do you know about the hat?

MAGGIE: Mr. Wandimiller told me just as they were dragging him off.

THOMPSON: Do you know which one is the *real* Happiest Hat?

MAGGIE: No, I don't know that.

HAROLDSON: I knew she wouldn't.

MAGGIE: But Mr. Wandimiller said you would know.

DICKSON: Mr. Wandimiller said *I* would know?

THOMPSON (*Pointing to* HAROLDSON): Mr. Wandimiller said *he* would know?

HAROLDSON (*Pointing to* DICKSON): Mr. Wandimiller said *you* would know?

ALL THREE (*Together*): Well, somebody tell us!

MAGGIE: I'll tell you what he said. First, all three of you put your hats on. (*They do.*) Now, he said, each of you look at the other two. Mr. Thompson, would you trade Daisy for the chance to save the world?

THOMPSON: I wouldn't have a world without Daisy.

MAGGIE: Mr. Haroldson, would you give up post office and Blondie for Daisy?

HAROLDSON: I . . . (*To* THOMPSON) I don't want to hurt your feelings, Tom.

MAGGIE: Mr. Dickson, would you give up saving the world for the privilege of burping the Thompson twins?

DICKSON (*Shuddering*): I wish you hadn't said that. I haven't had my dinner yet.

MAGGIE: Mr. Wandimiller said that if the real owner of the Happiest Hat would look at the others, he'd know who *really* has the Happiest Hat. (*All three stop and look at each other, shaking their heads, as they contemplate trading what they have with the others for what the others have.*)

THOMPSON (*Patting the other two on the shoulder comfortingly*): Well, I have to run. Daisy is waiting for me, the twins need burping, the triplets need their noses blown, the quadruplets need help with their lessons, and the quintuplets are going to let me sing with the band tonight. (*Starts off, stops and looks back, full of compassion*) Sorry, fellows, but we all can't be winners. (*Exits left*)

DICKSON (*Looking after him*): Poor old Thompson. Do you think he really believes he has the Happiest Hat? Poor old duffer. Well, I must be going, too. There's a country needs saving, and since Miss Ernest has bought a new dress, I should take her out to dinner. (*Starts off right*) I want to tell you, Harry, that I admire you. I think you're taking your loss like a real man. As Tom said, we all can't be winners. (*Exits right*)

HAROLDSON: For a smart man, Dick can jump to a wrong conclusion faster than anyone I ever saw.

MAGGIE: Do you have the Happiest Hat, Harry? (HAROLDSON *nods modestly.*) Really?

HAROLDSON: Well, let's put it this way, Maggie. Who's the only one left to play post office with you? (*Blackout. Fast curtain*)

THE END

Wishing Well Or Ill

Characters

CHARLIE, *the keeper of the Wishing Well*
BOGIE, *a happy retired man*
CAGNEY, *Bogie's friend*
MRS. BURGER ⎫
MRS. SANDS ⎬ *middle-aged widows*
AMY, *Mrs. Burger's daughter*
DAN, *Mrs. Sands' son*

TIME: *Evening.*

SETTING: *The patio of a small resort hotel. A wishing well, with sign reading* THE WISHING WELL, *is at center. Surrounding the patio is a low brick wall with four entrances. There are two matching benches, one against the right wall and the other against the left. A smaller bench is down center from well.*

AT RISE: CHARLIE *is pulling a cloth net from well and taking coins from it. He bites a coin, and mutters.* BOGIE, *dressed in imitation of Humphrey Bogart, and* CAGNEY, *dressed in imitation of James Cagney, are sitting on benches at right and left respectively.*

CHARLIE (*Looking at coin in disgust*): Counterfeit!
BOGIE: Everything is counterfeit, Charlie.

264

CHARLIE: You are, Bogie, that's for sure.

CAGNEY: The world is full of fakes. And that wishing well of yours, Charlie, is one of the worst.

CHARLIE: It's a good well. Everyday this wishing well proves that wishes do come true. But you have to be a real sport, not a piker, for it to work.

BOGIE: Sure, Charlie. (*Announces to the world in general*) People, throw your money away in Charlie's well. Thank you.

CAGNEY: Men find fortunes, young girls find husbands, just by throwing a coin in that well. That will be the day.

BOGIE: The only wish I've seen come true when anyone threw a coin in that well is yours, Charlie.

CAGNEY: You certainly hated it when silver dollars became scarce, didn't you, Charlie?

CHARLIE (*Grinning*): Silver dollars are luckier than pennies, that's the truth. How can you be a real sport with a penny?

BOGIE: Charlie, you ought to be ashamed of yourself taking advantage of people that way.

CHARLIE: I don't take advantage of anyone. (*Bites another coin*) People are always taking advantage of me. Another counterfeit coin. What's this world coming to when people try to buy their dreams with slugs?

CAGNEY: Maybe they want sluggish dreams.

BOGIE (*Good-naturedly*): One more bad pun like that, Jimmy, and I'll slug you.

CHARLIE: The wit here this morning is overpowering. That's the trouble with this town. We're so far behind the times that even our jokes come from the 1930's. (*Counting coins*) Two dollars and fourteen cents. For a whole week. Haven't wishers heard about the high cost of hoping? (*Fixes net in well*)

BOGIE: Two dollars and fourteen cents for a few minutes' work is not bad.

CAGNEY: I had an uncle who was paid a hundred dollars for two minutes work—and he didn't have to do anything but lie down.

CHARLIE: If you're waiting for me to ask what he did, Cagney, you'll wait a long time.

CAGNEY: He was shot out of a cannon. In a circus. It was a very big act.

CHARLIE: I didn't ask you.

BOGIE: That was a very big joke in 1928.

CHARLIE: Haven't you two loafers anything else to do but to sit around and annoy a working man?

CAGNEY: I don't know. Have we, Mr. Bogart?

BOGIE: I don't know, Mr. Cagney. What day is it?

CAGNEY: I don't know. Tuesday, maybe, or Wednesday.

BOGIE: On Tuesdays and Wednesdays, we have nothing else to do, Charlie. Now, if it were Thursday. . . .

CHARLIE: It is Thursday.

CAGNEY: On Thursdays, we have nothing else to do either.

CHARLIE: It would seem to me that active men would want to do something.

BOGIE: We're retired. That's something.

CAGNEY: That's right. For forty years all we did was work and get tired, and now we're *retired*. (*Stands up and stretches, takes a coin and throws it into well*) There you are, Charlie, go back to work.

BOGIE (*Standing, stretching, and throwing coin into well*): Yes, Charlie, make our wishes come true.

CHARLIE: If you weren't too lazy to make a wish, I might just do that.

CAGNEY: I wish. . . . (*Pauses*) There was something I was going to wish. Oh well, I'll think of it next week.

BOGIE (*Looking around restlessly*): I wish. . . . I wish

we'd have some excitement around here for a change.

CAGNEY: That's a good wish. I could stand some excitement for a change. And to think I was once "Public Enemy Number One." (*Pauses*) Want to go to the movies, Bogie?

BOGIE: We've seen the picture four times already, Jimmy.

CAGNEY: James Cagney as George M. Cohan is worth seeing a hundred times. I am a born Yankee Doodle Dandy. Come on.

BOGIE: I don't think so. Not again. No offense, Jimmy.

CAGNEY: Don't forget the second feature—with Humphrey Bogart.

BOGIE: Well, why not? (*Starts off, down left.* CAGNEY *joins him.*) See you around, Charlie.

CHARLIE: With my luck, I'll see you around.

CAGNEY: Don't take any wooden nickels, Charlie. They get waterlogged, you know. (*They exit, in imitation of* CAGNEY *and* BOGART, *laughing.*)

CHARLIE: Big joke. (*He bends over well and raises net. He does not see* MRS. BURGER *as she enters left. He takes coins from net, and yells.*) Wooden nickels! (MRS. BURGER *sits on left bench.* CHARLIE *hears bench move and turns, speaking before he sees her.*) Haven't you idiots anything better to do than pull dumb jokes?

MRS. BURGER (*Rising*): I beg your pardon. Were you addressing me?

CHARLIE (*Gulping*): I'm sorry. I thought you were someone else.

MRS. BURGER: I am not someone else. I am I, and no idiot.

CHARLIE: I can see that now.

MRS. BURGER: It's a little late for apologies.

CHARLIE: I wasn't apologizing. I was just explaining.

MRS. BURGER: It's a little late for explanations, too.

CHARLIE: That's the trouble with a retirement town like this. It's always too late for everything. Whole town's

just filled with people with nothing to do—too lazy even
to make decent wishes. (*Pauses*) I don't mean you,
madam.

MRS. BURGER: I should hope not. I have *never* been too
lazy to make a wish.

CHARLIE (*Sensing a customer*): This is a pretty good well
for wishing.

MRS. BURGER: That's not what the two old gentlemen I met
this morning told me.

CHARLIE: If those two answer to the names of Bogie and
Cagney, they are not gentlemen. And a lot they know.
You can't laugh at a wishing well and expect it to work.
You have to have faith.

MRS. BURGER: They say your well is nothing but a racket.

CHARLIE: Let me tell you about those characters. They
spent a whole lifetime working hard, and then suddenly
they decided that they weren't having much fun out of
life. So they quit work, which is fine; but they also quit
beings adults. And that's most annoying.

MRS. BURGER: I found them most charming.

CHARLIE: Oh, they're that all right. Charming nuts. That
Bogie. His real name is Albert. And that Cagney. His
name is Ralph. But they call themselves Bogie and Cagney now, because they've decided they are really Humphrey Bogart and James Cagney. Can you imagine that?

MRS. BURGER: I must admit that sounds odd. But I'm sure
they have their reasons.

CHARLIE (*Looking at her closely*): Don't I know you?

MRS. BURGER: How should I know that? (*Laughs*) But I
know you, Charlie. You haven't changed a bit in fifteen
years. I'm Mrs. Burger. My husband and I—he's dead
now. . . .

CHARLIE: The Burgers, of course. You had a little girl,
Amy, wasn't it?

MRS. BURGER: *Isn't* it? I still have a daughter and her name is still Amy. Of course, she is not a little girl any more.

CHARLIE: She's not *that* old.

MRS. BURGER: She's at that age when being old at all is *that* old.

CHARLIE (*Smiling*): That's a nice age, isn't it? (*Pauses*) I'm sorry to hear about Mr. Burger.

MRS. BURGER: It's been almost ten years. (*Looks about*) Nothing has changed much here. Except your two charming nuts. They're new, aren't they?

CHARLIE: They've been staying here—on and off—for the past five years.

MRS. BURGER: That's new, for me. Are they with their families?

CHARLIE: No families. Both widowers. No children either. They wouldn't be such happy clowns if they had families to worry them.

MRS. BURGER: That's true. He that has a child has given a hostage unto fortune. If they had a daughter like my Amy, they'd have worries. (*Quickly*) Not that Amy worries me. But I worry that people will take advantage of her—that friends will betray her.

CHARLIE: Ah, Mrs. Burger, people are all right. True, we don't have enough real sports and too many counterfeiters these days, but old friends are still old friends. Now, take your friend, Mrs. Sands. Now there's a. . . .

MRS. BURGER: Grace Sands! She's not my friend. I haven't seen her in fifteen years. I don't know why you say she's *my* friend. If I have one enemy in the world it's Grace Sands. My friend, indeed!

CHARLIE (*Taken aback*): But I thought you two were here. . . .

MRS. BURGER: When Grace Sands and I *used* to come here, I thought she was an entirely different person. Grace

Sands is a bull-headed, egotistical woman—just like her husband.

CHARLIE: Mr. Sands died. About ten years ago, I think.

MRS. BURGER: Oh. Well, I wouldn't have wished that, of course. But as for Grace Sands, naturally she had to be loyal to her husband, but she didn't have to be so bull-headed. Mr. Burger was right. Time has proved that. If Carl Sands had just listened to him, the business would have been much better off. Much better.

CHARLIE: I had forgotten. Your husbands were partners, weren't they?

MRS. BURGER: For nine years. Until Grace Sands betrayed me. She knew that Mr. Burger was right about what direction the company should take. But would she admit it? Not Grace Sands.

CHARLIE: I guess it doesn't make any difference now.

MRS. BURGER: I'm sure it doesn't make any difference to *you*. But it does to me. Oh, it isn't just the money. It isn't the fact that splitting the partnership set us back five years. It's just that . . . well, I thought Grace Sands was my friend, and she wouldn't say a word to Carl— not one word. He did well in his business, I suppose?

CHARLIE (*Trying to change the subject*): Well enough, I suppose. She still comes here for a vacation every year.

MRS. BURGER: I hope she doesn't come while I'm here. When I think how I trusted that woman—how I liked her. Do you know that we even hoped that our children would marry each other when they grew up?

CHARLIE: Dan and Amy?

MRS. BURGER: Yes, her Dan and my Amy. Why, I remember we were standing in this very spot. Grace Sands and I both threw coins into that well and wished that our children would marry. I don't think *she* ever cared. I sent her a telegram the night we left New York telling her we were going and that if she wanted to continue our friendship, I expected to hear from her. *She* never answered. I've never heard from her since. It wasn't easy for me to send that wire, her being in the wrong and all. Why, we were roommates in college together, and the way she dropped me, you'd have thought that our entire association was a fifteen-minute ride in the subway.

CHARLIE: Maybe she didn't get the wire.

MRS. BURGER: If I could send a wire, she could send a wire, too. I'd have answered her telegram if she had sent me one. Not Grace Sands.

CHARLIE: Don't think about it, Mrs. Burger, if it makes you unhappy. Make a wish in the well. Maybe it is a fraud; maybe it doesn't work every time; but it might make you feel good. Wish for happiness for Amy.

MRS. BURGER (*Taking coin from purse*): All right, I don't expect anything to happen, but I'll take a chance. (*Goes to well*) Do I just drop the coin into the well?

CHARLIE: Yes, in the middle.

MRS. BURGER (*Dropping coin and listening*): I didn't hear it hit.

CHARLIE: Well . . . er . . . it's a very deep well.

MRS. BURGER: That reaches all the way to the bottom of your pocket, I should imagine. But no matter. Now, I can make my wish, right?

CHARLIE: Right. Anything you want. Health for your mother. Beauty for your daughter. Fortune for your friend.

MRS. BURGER (*Grimly*): What about bad luck for an enemy?

CHARLIE: Now, Mrs. Burger, we were going to forget all about that.

MRS. BURGER: Maybe *you* are going to forget Grace Sands, but I'm not. I wish that she may know the sorrow she has brought me. I wish that someone she loves will refuse to answer a call from her as she refused to answer my telegram.

CHARLIE: Mrs. Burger, you're not the kind of woman to get pleasure from the unhappiness of others. Change your wish while you still have a chance.

MRS. BURGER: I will not. I've made my wish, and I'm going to keep it. Oh, I'm sorry I ever came back here. (*Pause*) But, since I am here, I'll take a walk about the town. Is dinner at seven? (*Starts off down right*)

CHARLIE: Yes, at seven. I wish that you would think about changing that wish, Mrs. Burger.

MRS. BURGER: I wish my own wishes with my money. (*Exits.* CHARLIE *draws up net, takes out coin, looks at it, then throws it into well.*)

CHARLIE: I wish that Mrs. Burger and Mrs. Sands would forget their quarrel and become friends. And I wish, that if they can't do that, at least that they don't find out they are both staying here. (*Starts to turn away*) And I wish this is the last time I'm so foolish as to throw my own money down this well. For real. (*Stands looking out thinking.* MRS. SANDS *comes in up right. She has a slight limp and carries a cane.*)

MRS. SANDS: Charlie, who was that lady I saw you talking to?

CHARLIE: Oh, hello, Mrs. Sands! I thought you were going up to the mountain lodge for a few days?

MRS. SANDS: I changed my mind. (*Sitting down on bench in front of well*) This is my favorite spot, here by your Wishing Well. (*Pauses*) This is really very lovely, Charlie. It always takes me back to the old days—when Carl was alive, and Dan was just a little boy.

CHARLIE: Is Dan joining you for this vacation?

MRS. SANDS: I don't know. I didn't decide to come until the last minute, and I sent him a wire, asking if he would

like to join me. He hasn't answered it yet. I suppose
young people get that way when they grow up.

CHARLIE: Oh, he's not neglecting you. He'll answer the
wire.

MRS. SAND: I hope so. Even if he can't join me, I hope
he answers. It's a lonely thing when someone you love
refuses to answer a call.

CHARLIE: Maybe he didn't get it.

MRS. SANDS: American Telephone and Telegraph is a most
reliable company. I have never failed to get my dividend.

CHARLIE: It could happen. (*Pauses*) Is Dan married yet?

MRS. SANDS: No, but I keep hoping . . . and wishing.
He has been rather secretive of late, and I think that's
a good sign.

CHARLIE: Secretive? That doesn't sound like Dan.

MRS. SANDS: No, it doesn't, does it? Ever since his father
died—and Dan was only a small boy then—he has always been anxious for me to meet his friends, especially
his girl friends.

CHARLIE: Maybe it's serious this time.

MRS. SANDS: I hope so. It's time Dan was getting married.
You didn't say who the lady was, Charlie. Is that your
secret?

CHARLIE: If I were Bogie or Cagney and you asked that
question, I'd say that was no lady, that was my wife.

MRS. SANDS (*Smiling*): They're still as charmingly foolish
as ever. And your mysterious lady?

CHARLIE: She's new. A guest at the inn. (*Pauses*) I don't
think I'd go out of my way to meet her, if I were you,
Mrs. Sands.

MRS. SANDS: Oh? She looks rather nice. She reminds me of
a friend I had once . . . (*Reflectively*) a very special
friend.

CHARLIE: I guess she's all right. But she certainly isn't

the kind of woman I think you'd want as a friend.

MRS. SANDS (*Rising*): You're probably right, Charlie. I don't think I want any special friends any more. I had a very good friend once, until I needed her. Then she simply disappeared without even telling me where she went.

CHARLIE: Disappeared?

MRS. SANDS: She moved without telling me, and that's the same thing. If she wanted to get away from me, I was not going to hunt her down. I know when I've been betrayed.

CHARLIE: Mrs. Sands, maybe there's something I'd better tell you. It's about that lady. . . . (BOGIE *and* CAGNEY *come in down left, singing "Sweet Betsy from Pike" in loud, cracked voices.* MRS. SANDS *turns, smiling and pleased.*)

BOGIE *and* CAGNEY:

O, do you remember Sweet Betsy from Pike,
Who crossed the wide prairie with her lover Ike,
With two yoke of cattle and one spotted hog,
A tall Shanghai rooster, and an old yeller dog.
(*They stop and with arms over each other's shoulders, sing refrain*) Singing too-ral-i oo-ral-i oo-ral-i ay.

MRS. SANDS (*Applauding*): Very good, gentlemen. Jeanette MacDonald and Nelson Eddy never sounded better.

BOGIE (*Bowing*): Thank you, gracious lady. I thought Cagney did very well in the Jeanette MacDonald part.

CHARLIE: Sounded more like two old coyotes baying at the moon.

CAGNEY: Let's throw Charlie down the well.

BOGIE: Down the well with Charlie. He hates music. (*They rush to* CHARLIE, *and with one on each side they try to lead him to well.* CHARLIE *stands firm, and they can't budge him.*)

CHARLIE (*With mild irritation*): Cut it out, you two idiots, before you strain a muscle or something.

CAGNEY: If I had a grapefruit, I'd push it in his face. That's what I did to Mae Murray and the audience just loved it.

BOGIE: Especially the grapefruit growers.

CHARLIE: Why don't you two stay in the movies where you belong?

CAGNEY: They've changed the bill. They've got one of those modern things. With that young fellow, Cary Grant.

CHARLIE: Then go play shuffleboard or something.

MRS. SANDS (*Laughing*): I think he's trying to get rid of you two.

CAGNEY: My dear Mrs. Sands, I haven't seen you in much too long, and I don't intend to be chased away from fair beauty by this old innkeeper.

MRS. SANDS (*Taking his arm*): You're just the charming man I've been waiting for, Jimmy. Come and take me for a walk.

CHARLIE: That's a good idea, Cagney. Why don't you and Mrs. Sands take a nice walk *down by the lake?*

MRS. SANDS: I think I'd rather walk through town.

CHARLIE: No, you'd like the lake better.

CAGNEY: My dear, shall we sail away into the sunset?

MRS. SANDS: You said that in *The Patent-Leather Kid,* right?

CAGNEY: Don't think I was in that movie, but I should have been. (MRS. SANDS *and* CAGNEY *exit left.* BOGIE *starts to follow, and* CHARLIE *stops him with his hand.*)

CHARLIE: I want to talk to you, Bogie.

BOGIE: You're not trying to drum up a little romance between Mrs. Sands and Jimmy, are you? I don't approve of match-making, Charlie.

CHARLIE: It's not match-making I'm trying to start. I'm just trying to stop a murder.

BOGIE: Now, that's more my speed. Murder. Why, when I played in *Key Largo*, I. . . .

CHARLIE: Not now, Bogie, I'm serious. I have a real problem. You met Mrs. Burger this afternoon, didn't you?

BOGIE: Yes, in the lobby. She said that she used to be a guest here every year.

CHARLIE: A long time ago, before you and Cagney started coming here for the season.

BOGIE: I'll bet she might remember Mrs. Sands.

CHARLIE: That's the problem. Mrs. Sands and Mrs. Burger were once the closest friends in the world.

BOGIE: They can have a nice reunion then. I remember in *Casablanca* I played Rick . . .

CHARLIE: Now they hate each other.

BOGIE: Hate? That's a pretty strong word.

CHARLIE: Maybe not hate, but something that will sound an awful lot like it. That's why I need your help. We have to keep the two of them from meeting.

BOGIE: That might be a pretty tall order.

CHARLIE: Not if you'll help. Mrs. Burger is going to leave here tomorrow, and if we can just keep them separated tonight, they'll never know. Cagney's walking Mrs. Sands on the beach now, and if you'll wait here and catch Mrs. Burger when she gets back. . . .

BOGIE: Do you want me to kidnap her?

CHARLIE: No, you idiot, take her to a show, or to dinner, or something. Mrs. Sands sleeps late in the morning, and. . . .

BOGIE: I know, "if we can just keep them separated tonight." You know, Charlie, this is more Cagney's style.

CHARLIE: Now, listen, Albert.

BOGIE: Albert! You're really serious, aren't you, Charlie?

CHARLIE: I'm really serious, Albert.

BOGIE: All right, Charlie, I'll guard the palace. (*Pretends he is on guard; marches in front of the well*) Charlie, how did you find out about all this? You're not the type women confide in.

CHARLIE: A lot you know. (*Pauses*) Besides when they talk about each other, they're not confiding. They're broadcasting. If they get together, both of them are going to say and do things that will make them very sorry later.

BOGIE: Don't worry, Charlie. Old Bogie will keep the world running smooth.

CHARLIE: Thank you. I'm going back to the inn. I'll give you all the details later, but in the meantime, if you need me. . . .

BOGIE: I'll call, Charlie. I'll call. Old Bogie's on guard. (*He marches up and down in front of the well.* CHARLIE *shakes his head and exits up right.* BOGIE *continues for a minute, then gets a catch in his back, looks about to be sure no one has seen this sign of age. Then limps to bench against left wall and sits. Stage lights dim from early evening to night with a single spot over well that leaves* BOGIE *almost invisible in the shadows. There is a short music bridge to indicate passage of time.* AMY *and* DAN *enter down left.* DAN *is carrying two suitcases, on one of which is a label,* JUST MARRIED.)

AMY: Do you want me to carry the suitcases again, Dan?

DAN: Again? You haven't carried them at all yet.

AMY: No, but you wanted me to. I could tell when you stumbled over that log and fell.

DAN: At that very moment, I knew our honeymoon was over, Amy.

AMY (*Laughing*): We made it. Here we are at the very well where our marriage was first planned. It's kind of romantic, isn't it, Dan?

DAN: Of course, it would have been more romantic if we

hadn't run out of gas two thousand miles down the road.

AMY: It wasn't even two miles.

DAN: If you had been carrying those suitcases, you wouldn't say that.

AMY: Make a wish, Dan. Throw a coin into the Wishing Well and make a wish.

DAN: It's a racket. Old Bogie and Cagney told me that Charlie has a bag rigged so that he can get all the coins that people throw into the well. Bogie even showed me the net the last time I was here with Mother.

AMY: I don't care. The well has magic. Your mother and my mother stood right here and wished that one day we would marry, and . . . well, here we are.

DAN: We certainly are. (*Puts down suitcases and takes coin from his pocket*) All right. Here goes. I wish that your mother and my mother knew about our wedding. (*Drops coin into well*)

AMY: And I wish that you're the one who tells them.

DAN: Me? That was my wish and my quarter. Anyhow, I thought you were going to tell them.

AMY: Me? I don't even know your mother. She's just some-body named Mrs. Sands who lives a thousand miles from here.

DAN: I wouldn't even know your mother if she came up and said, "I'm Mrs. Burger." I'd say, "Burger who?"

AMY: I'd say "Sand which?"

DAN: Now I know why my mother got angry at your mother.

AMY: My mother said everyone in your family was bull-headed.

DAN: Let me tell you something. I'm bull-headed about one thing.

AMY: You're bull-headed about lots of things.

DAN: No, I'm bull-headed about the fact that I love you, and our marriage is going to work.

AMY: As I've always said, being bull-headed is one of your more charming qualities. You're just the man to tell our mothers. *Bull-headed* is just another word for *brave*.

DAN: I stepped into that, didn't I?

AMY: I would do it, Dan, but . . . I don't think any young bride should start her married life with both her mother and her mother-in-law angry with her.

DAN: Do you think they are going to be angry?

AMY: I know *my* mother is going to be angry.

DAN: Maybe we could make it sound as if it were all their fault—they made the wish at this wishing well. Do you think it might work?

AMY: No. But since you're the one who has volunteered to do the telling, I think you should be allowed to make a mess of things in your own way.

DAN: Are you sorry you married me?

AMY: No. I may be after your mother and my mother get through with you, but right now, I think you're kind of cute.

DAN: Gee, thanks, Amy. Now I feel like a real tiger.

BOGIE: Growl.

AMY: What was that?

DAN: If it's a real tiger, I take back what I've said.

BOGIE (*Coming out of the shadows*): If I'm not a real tiger, may the *African Queen* sink with Katherine Hepburn aboard.

DAN: Bogie, what the devil are you doing here?

BOGIE: Eavesdropping. And you'd better be grateful.

AMY (*To Dan*): Is this the Bogie you told me about? (*Looks at him*) He's kind of cute, too, for an older man.

BOGIE (*In his best Bogart style*): You're real cute, too, baby.

AMY: Thank you, Mr. Bogart. If I weren't so startled, I'd squeal.

BOGIE: If you think you're startled now, wait until I tell you that your mothers are here. Both of them.

DAN: My mother is here?

AMY: My mother?

DAN: I don't believe it.

AMY: The place is still standing.

BOGIE: They haven't met yet. That's what I was here for, to make sure they didn't meet. But either I missed your mother, Amy, or I fell asleep.

DAN: My mother didn't say she would be here.

BOGIE: Your mother told Charlie she'd sent you a wire asking you to meet her here. And she's upset because you didn't answer it.

DAN: I never got it. But, of course, I haven't been back to my apartment in a week. We got married. We're on our honeymoon.

BOGIE: I'd never have guessed.

AMY: This is getting to be a fine mess. What do we do now?

BOGIE: If you're going to do the Antony and Cleopatra bit, why not jump off Lovers' Leap?

DAN: Gee, thanks, Bogie. You're going to be a great help.

AMY: I don't think you're so cute—even for an older man.

BOGIE: I do very well with the single crowd.

DAN: Our mothers here! This is a mess.

AMY (*Starting to pick up one of the suitcases*): Well, Dan, I'm sure you can handle it. I think I'll go back to the car and wait.

DAN: Now, wait a minute. Marriage is a fifty-fifty proposition.

BOGIE: Do you want my advice?

DAN *and* AMY: No.

BOGIE: Good. Now that I have your cooperation, here's what I would do. Send telegrams.

DAN: Telegrams?

AMY: My mother sent his mother a telegram and she didn't even bother to acknowledge it.

DAN: Now, let's not start that again.

BOGIE: Good, then it's settled. We'll send telegrams.

AMY: Couldn't we just go back to the car and drive away?

DAN: The car's broken. If *you* had carried the suitcases, you'd remember that.

AMY: All right, we'll send telegrams. But what do we say, Bogie?

BOGIE: I've been waiting for this chance for a long, long time. I really have this great idea, but this is the first chance I've had to work it out with real people. Of course, I see it best as a plot for Ingrid Bergman and me, but when life doesn't measure up to art, we just have to do the best we can. Now here's what we'll do. We send these telegrams. . . . (*Blackout. They exit. There is another short music bridge to indicate passage of time. When lights come up, it is early the next morning.* MRS. BURGER *comes in up left, followed by* CHARLIE. MRS. SANDS *comes in up right, followed by* CAGNEY. *Both women are waving telegrams and lamenting loudly. Both men are trying to console them. The women, followed by the men, come down around the well.*)

MRS. BURGER: My daughter. My little Amy. How could she do this to me?

CHARLIE: Now, now, Mrs. Burger.

MRS. SANDS: My son. My little Dan. How could he do this to me?

CAGNEY: Now, now, Mrs. Sands.

MRS. BURGER: How could she marry a man like that?

CHARLIE: Maybe he's not so bad.

MRS. SANDS: How could he marry a woman like that?

CAGNEY: Maybe she's not so bad. (*By this time, the two*

women have gone around the well and are almost face-to-face. In unison they turn back to the men following them.)

MRS. BURGER *and* MRS. SANDS: Not so bad! (*They have each caught sight of the other, just as they turned, and now they turn back and face each other.*) You!

CAGNEY: Now, now, ladies.

MRS. BURGER: Don't "*now, now*" me. This is the last straw. It was bad enough that shame should come to my daughter. But now my only enemy can laugh in my face. (*To* MRS. SANDS) Go on, laugh. Laugh at what my Amy has done.

MRS. SANDS: You know about what's happened to Dan, and you're just here to gloat. Go ahead, gloat. What did I ever to do to you that makes you happy now in my misery?

MRS. BURGER: Your misery? We're talking about *my* misery.

MRS. SANDS: You didn't even come to see me when I was in the hospital after the accident.

MRS. BURGER: What are you talking about?

MRS. SANDS: And it was all your fault, too. I was on my way to see you when I was hit by that car.

MRS. BURGER: How was I supposed to know you had an accident? I haven't seen you since we left New York.

MRS. SANDS: This was before you left—the summer of. . . .

MRS. BURGER: So that's why you didn't answer my telegram.

MRS. SANDS: What telegram?

MRS. BURGER: I sent you a telegram telling you that we were leaving New York and if you ever wanted to see me again. . . .

MRS. SANDS: I never got your telegram, but I heard you were leaving. I was on my way to . . . I was on my way to you when I had my accident.

MRS. BURGER: I didn't know. How can you ever forgive me? (*Sobs and throws her arms around* MRS. SANDS)

MRS. SANDS: I thought you knew and didn't care. If I had only gotten that telegram. I'm going to sell all my telegraph stock. Oh, Edna, I'm so sorry. I've missed you so.

MRS. BURGER: And I've missed you, Grace. (*They hug each other.*)

CAGNEY: And this is that terrible fight we've been trying to avoid? Gee, Charlie, I'm glad you weren't in my gang when I was running from the F.B.I.

CHARLIE: How did I know it was going to end this way? I'm a bachelor.

MRS. SANDS: And now Dan is married.

MRS. BURGER: So is my Amy.

MRS. SANDS: It's terrible. Listen. (*Reads telegram*) "Mom: Just married the most wonderful girl. Stop. You will meet her soon. Stop. Right now we have to flee country. Stop. She's wanted for bigamy in six states. Know you will understand. Love, Dan." Oh, what am I going to do?

MRS. BURGER: Listen to mine. (*Reads telegram*) "Mom: Just married the most wonderful man. Stop. You will meet him soon. Stop. Right now we have to flee country. Stop. He's wanted for bank robbery in four states. Stop. Know you will understand. Love, Amy." What am I going to do?

CAGNEY: The only parts of those telegrams that make sense are the stops. That's the worst dialogue I've ever heard. (*The women wail loudly, and* BOGIE *comes on down left.*)

BOGIE: What happened? Did the cat fall into the well?

MRS. BURGER: That well. It's a big fraud. Do you remember, Grace, we put our money into that well?

Mrs. Sands: And wished that our children would marry each other.

Mrs. Burger: And now my Amy has married a bank robber.

Mrs. Sands: And my Dan has married a bigamist.

Bogie: Mrs. Burger, would you be happier if Amy had married Dan?

Mrs. Burger: It was always my wish.

Mrs. Sands: And mine, too.

Bogie (*Taking coin and going to well*): Then, Well, we'll give you one more chance. (*Throws coin into well*) Straighten out this mess and have Dan and Amy married to each other. (*Takes whistle from pocket and blows it.*)

Mrs. Sands: This is no time for crazy jokes. (Dan *and* Amy *come on down left.* Bogie *whistles wedding march.*)

Mrs. Burger: Amy!

Mrs. Sands: Dan!

Bogie: Behold the blushing bride and bumbling groom— Mr. and Mrs. Dan Sands.

Mrs. Burger: You're married?

Mrs. Sands: To each other?

Dan *and* Amy (*Together*): We can explain, Mother.

Mrs. Sands: No, don't explain. I wouldn't understand. Just be happy. Everybody's happy now.

Charlie: For a day that started out rotten, this is turning out pretty well. So, you're married, Dan? And to your childhood sweetheart. Hi, Amy, you look . . . just as I thought you would look. I guess everybody's happy.

Mrs. Sands: I think I'm happy. I've always wanted Dan and Amy to marry. And here they are married. I must be happy.

Mrs. Burger: I'm not. I wanted to see my daughter married. I wanted to throw rice and cry a lot. Marriages are very happy occasions, and Amy's my only daughter.

AMY: Oh, Mama, we're married, and that's what is really important.

MRS. SANDS: You can just get married again. This morning. When kings and queens get married, I read about it in the paper. When my son marries, I want to see the ceremony.

MRS. BURGER: What a wonderful idea. They can be married—right here in the town where we wished this would all happen.

MRS. SANDS: You lead the way, Edna, and I'll follow.

DAN: But. . . .

MRS. SANDS: You have nothing to say about it, Dan. You're just the groom.

MRS. BURGER: Come, come. We have no time to waste. We have plans to make. Guests to invite. Dresses to order. (*To* MRS. SANDS) Let's not stand around. We've work to do. (*Starts off up right, followed by* MRS. SANDS) Grace, I'm going to depend on you to. . . .

MRS. SANDS: You can depend on me for *everything* this time. I'll never have another accident when you need me, Edna.

MRS. BURGER: I don't know how I ever got along without you. (*To* DAN *and* AMY) Come along, children, you'll have the rest of your lives to talk to each other. We have more important things to do now. The wedding. (DAN *and* AMY *start to speak, grin, and follow* MRS. BURGER *and* MRS. SANDS *off.*)

BOGIE: I don't know how I did it. But I was truly remarkable, wasn't I?

CAGNEY: Charming, Bogie, baby. Charming.

CHARLIE: You? You didn't do anything. It was my wishing well. Every wish that all of you made came true. Even yours—for a little excitement.

CAGNEY: He has a point, Bogie, baby.

BOGIE: No, wait a minute. I'm the hero.

CHARLIE: You are not. I am. Or at least the well is.

CAGNEY: Both of you shut up. I'm going to be the hero.

CHARLIE: You didn't do anything.

CAGNEY: No, but I'm going to. I'm going to blow up this well. We've had all the excitement we can stand around here for awhile. (CHARLIE *and* BOGIE *both start to answer, but merely shrug and* CAGNEY *gives an imitation of a James Cagney laugh as the curtain closes.*)

THE END

This Younger Generation

Characters

SARA, *16*
PETER, *17 her friend*
JOHN, *47, Peter's father*
PHYLLIS, *58, John's secretary*
ANDREW, *77, John's father*
DORIS, *76, John's mother*
JAMES, *107, Andrew's father*
ELIZABETH, *James' nurse*
TWO MEN
WOMAN

SETTING: *A park. Up center are three benches, one facing audience and the others flanking it, facing each other. A trash can is down left and a baby carriage is down right.*

AT RISE: 1ST MAN *is sleeping on the center bench, a newspaper covering his face.* 2ND MAN *enters up left, passes* 1ST MAN, *lifts one page of the newspaper from him, and walks off down right, reading it.* 1ST MAN *sits up, looks around suspiciously, lies down and goes back to sleep.* WOMAN *enters down right, passes the sleeping* MAN, *takes a single page from the newspaper, and walks off up left, reading it.* MAN *again sits up, looks around, and starts to return to sleep, when* SARA *and* PETER *enter. He watches them.* SARA *stops and looks in the baby carriage.*

SARA: Peter, look at the baby.

PETER: I don't want to.

SARA: Don't you like babies?

PETER: Oh, they're all right at that age, but the first thing you know they are my brother's age. I don't want to see it coming, that's all.

SARA: Oh. (*They walk toward benches.* 1ST MAN *looks at them, shakes his head, rises, and gathers his paper together, looking around for the missing pages. Then he shrugs and starts off down right. He peers into carriage, makes a face at the baby.*)

1ST MAN: This younger generation. Chee! (*Walks off right*)

SARA (*Sitting down*): Did you hear what he said?

PETER: Who?

SARA: That man. The one who just left.

PETER: I didn't hear him. I never listen to anyone over thirty, if I can help it.

SARA: You should have heard what he said.

PETER: Any time a man over thirty says anything to me it's always the same thing. Doesn't make any difference who the man is or what he's doing, it's always the same thing.

SARA: He said, "This younger generation. Chee!"

PETER: That's what I said. It's always the same thing. (*Sits*)

SARA: You're feeling pretty low, aren't you, Peter?

PETER: A little.

SARA: It sounds like a little more than a little. What is it? Your grades?

PETER: No, it's not my grades. I mean they're not all that hot, but they're good enough for me.

SARA: You don't have any money for my birthday present?

PETER: Your birthday's not for another six months.

SARA: You remembered! I was afraid you had forgotten.

PETER: It's my father.

SARA: What did you do?

PETER: I didn't do anything. I didn't do a thing. You don't have to do anything with my father. You just have to be something.

SARA: Oh?

PETER: I am "this younger generation," and no matter what anyone in this younger generation does, it's wrong. Our hair is too long; our trousers too short; we don't talk properly; we don't have any ambition; we don't have minds of our own; and everything we think is wrong. You know one thing, though?

SARA: What?

PETER: I'd rather belong to *this* generation than to *that* generation.

SARA: It's not as bad as that, now.

PETER: It's a lot worse. Maybe it's different for girls, but for boys! I belong to the "what-did-you-do-that-for" generation. No matter what happens—any place—I mean *any place!*—my father thinks I started it. College kids riot in Florida, and he tells *me* about it. Chinese kids march in China, and he looks at *me* as if I started it. I'll bet if some kid my age was elected President of the United States, he wouldn't tell me about that. That generation, chee!

SARA (*Laughing*): Oh, Peter, it's not that bad.

PETER: It's worse.

SARA: Why, just last week, you were telling me what a great guy your father is.

PETER: All right, maybe he is . . . with people of his own decrepit generation. He's mad at me now. For nothing.

Just because he doesn't know that times have changed.

SARA: You *did* do something!

PETER: I did not. I had an opinion. That's all. I had an opinion—an honest, logical, sensible opinion. Let me ask you something. What do you think of the Yankees?

SARA: You mean those people who live around Boston?

PETER: No, I mean the baseball Yankees.

SARA: I don't think anything about them.

PETER: That's what I told my father. I told him the Yankees are nothing, and he got mad. He told me I was a smart alecky kid.

SARA: Then you shouldn't have said it.

PETER: It's not the Yankees. He doesn't care anything about the Yankees. Two weeks ago he got angry at me because I said California had a larger population than New York.

SARA: I didn't think that was official yet.

PETER: Two weeks before that it all started because I told him that nobody read Sir Walter Scott except in school as freshmen.

SARA: Well, Peter, different people have. . . .

PETER: And a month ago, he was wild because I told him I had never heard of Greta Garbo. I mean he gets mad if I tell him this is the second half of the twentieth century. From now on, I'm not going to say anything to him except *forsooth, gadzooks,* and *sire.* (JOHN, PETER's *father, enters down left, looking back offstage.*)

SARA: You'd better start *gadzooking* right away, because here comes your father now.

PETER (*Rising*): Well, I'm in for it now.

JOHN (*Looking off downstage*): Hurry up, Phyllis! I'm hungry.

PHYLLIS (*Offstage*): Then you'd better come and help me. This stuff is heavy.

JOHN: Golly, I have to do everything. (*Goes back off left*)

SARA: Don't worry, Peter. Miss Hart is with him, and she's been sticking up for you for a thousand years.

PETER: I'm not a thousand years old.

SARA: But she is, Peter, and she has been standing up for the younger generation longer than you've been alive. (*Pauses*) Is she really a good secretary, Peter?

PETER: I guess so. My grandfather told me that Miss Hart taught *him* the business. (JOHN *enters carrying a paper, followed by* PHYLLIS *carrying a large lunch basket with both hands, and staggering under the load.*)

JOHN: You're right, Phyllis. This paper is heavy. (*Throws it in trash can*)

PETER: Hello, Dad. Hello, Miss Hart. (JOHN *and* PHYLLIS *turn and walk upstage toward* PETER *and* SARA.)

PHYLLIS: Hello, Peter. Hello, Sara. Soaking up the rural scene?

JOHN: Don't ask my son about the rural scene. That's too old-fashioned for him. My son doesn't like parks. Hello, Sara.

SARA: Hello, Mr. Melville. Have you come to the park to eat your lunch?

JOHN: Don't I always? But then I belong to a generation that likes parks . . . that likes a little fresh air and sunshine.

PETER: I like parks.

JOHN: It's too late to change your opinion now. Go on, be modern. See what it gets you. And don't expect me to share my lunch with you.

PETER: I've already eaten.

JOHN: Don't like lunch, either! All right, go ahead and sulk.

PETER: I'm not sulking.

JOHN: Call it what you want. (*Sits down*) Phyllis, what do we have for lunch today?

PHYLLIS (*Sitting down and looking in lunch basket*): Same

as always, Mr. Melville. Chicken salad sandwiches, boiled eggs, and milk.

JOHN: Oh, so now you're going to side with my son against me.

PHYLLIS: I didn't say anything.

JOHN: It's the way you said it. You don't like chicken salad sandwiches.

PHYLLIS: I love chicken salad sandwiches.

JOHN: You don't like boiled eggs.

PHYLLIS: I love boiled eggs.

JOHN: You don't like milk.

PHYLLIS: That's true. I don't. I brought a can of Metrecal.

JOHN: See, I knew you were going to side with my son.

PETER: I don't like Metrecal.

JOHN: Who asked you what you liked? Anyone who doesn't like the Dodgers is no one whose opinion means a thing to me.

PETER: It was the Yankees. I like the Dodgers.

JOHN: It's too late to change your mind now. (*Takes a bite of a sandwich*) Sara, are you sure you won't join us?

SARA: No, thank you, Mr. Melville. I have to go. I'm supposed to be at the library.

PETER: Me, too. (*Starts off*) Well, I'll see you, Dad. See you, Miss Hart.

PHYLLIS: See you, Peter. See you, Sara.

JOHN: And don't be late for supper.

PETER: I won't.

JOHN: Your mother told me to tell you not to be late to supper.

PETER: I'll be there early.

JOHN: Just be there on time.

PETER: I will. (SARA *and* PETER *start off right.* 1ST MAN *enters, almost bumps into them, and then goes upstage to* JOHN *and* PHYLLIS.)

1ST MAN: Do you have my paper?

JOHN: Sir?

1ST MAN: Do you have my paper? Don't you know what a paper is?

PETER (*Exiting with* SARA): That generation! Chee!

1ST MAN: Did you hear what that kid said?

JOHN: I never listen to that kid. He's my son.

1ST MAN: Well, maybe you should. Maybe he'd tell you it's against the law to take another man's paper.

JOHN: I didn't take your paper.

1ST MAN: It was the sports page, too. Now I'll never know how the Yankees came out.

JOHN: They lost. They always lose.

1ST MAN (*Turning away*): Boy, it's easy to see that you're hand-and-glove with this younger generation. (*Walks to trash can.* JOHN *and* PHYLLIS *watch him. He looks in trash can, takes out newspaper, turns around and stares at* JOHN *and* PHYLLIS.) What a crummy generation! (*Exits*)

JOHN: He thinks I took his paper.

PHYLLIS: Mr. Melville, do you want to tell me what to do about the Bennett contract now?

JOHN: I don't feel like working. This is very upsetting. That man thinks I took his paper.

PHYLLIS: We came to the park to work, Mr. Melville. We have to get that contract out this afternoon.

JOHN: Miss Hart, did I ever tell you that you remind me of my father?

PHYLLIS: Yes, Mr. Melville, you have told me. At least once a week for the past twenty years.

JOHN: I don't mean that as criticism. I appreciate your concern.

PHYLLIS: You have said that at least once a week for the past twenty years, too.

JOHN: I meant it, too. You are a superior secretary.

PHYLLIS: Good, then shall we get on with the Bennett contract?

JOHN: You are very much like my father.

PHYLLIS: Last year, we did the work for fourteen cents a unit. But wages have gone up since then.

JOHN: My father always pushed me. Even when I was a child.

PHYLLIS: And materials have gone up, too.

JOHN: He said it was for my own good.

PHYLLIS: Taxes are up, too.

JOHN: And I suppose he meant it. Or at least, he thought he meant it.

PHYLLIS: The price should be fifteen cents a unit.

JOHN: What really bothered my father was that we are not of the same generation. I remember once he was angry because I wanted to wear long pants to high school. He thought I should wear knickers.

PHYLLIS: Of course, we could make it fifteen and an eighth. That has a psychological advantage. The one-eighth gives the impression that we arrived at the figure precisely.

JOHN: Everyone else in high school was wearing long pants. But he thought I should wear knickers.

PHYLLIS: And then, too, that extra one-eighth of a cent would give us a little safeguard.

JOHN: When I was in grade school, he made me wear Buster Brown collars.

PHYLLIS: Transportation costs are bound to go up.

JOHN: The kids all called me a sissy. I wonder if kids still call other kids sissies.

PHYLLIS: We could, of course, offer a straight 15-cent price if they would order in ten-thousand-unit lots. It would be cheaper to ship by carloads.

JOHN: And he thought my hair was too short. It's healthier and cleaner to have short hair. He said I looked like an Indian on a raiding party.

PHYLLIS: Wooton and Lynch will charge at least fifteen and a sixth, I'm sure of that. (ANDREW *and* DORIS *enter down right. They are looking off down right and do not see* JOHN *and* PHYLLIS. ANDREW *waves his cane at someone off right.*)

ANDREW: Nice to see you, Charlie.

DORIS: That wasn't Charlie.

ANDREW: It wasn't? It certainly looked like Charlie.

DORIS: It did not. Charlie has red hair.

ANDREW: Charlie Jones has red hair? Since when?

DORIS: I thought you were talking about Charlie Smith. I don't know any Charlie Jones.

ANDREW: Well, it's Charlie Somebody. I can tell by the way he wears his glasses. (*Waves off right*) Wait, Charlie, wait a minute. (*Exits right*)

DORIS (*Following* ANDREW *off*): Andrew! Andrew, don't make a fool of yourself. (*Exits right*)

JOHN: My parents! Did you see them, Phyllis? That was Mom and Dad. Let's get out of here.

PHYLLIS: Why should we get out of here?

JOHN: Because I don't want Dad telling me I've been doing something wrong.

PHYLLIS: What *have* you been doing wrong?

JOHN: Nothing. Not a thing. But that doesn't make any difference to my father. I was born in the wrong generation, and that's enough for him. (*They start upstage.*)

PHYLLIS (*Following* JOHN): We're never going to get that Bennett contract finished.

JOHN: Hurry up. He'll see us.

PHYLLIS: I'm hurrying, but the Bennett contract. . . .

JOHN: Oh, that! I mailed it this morning—fifteen cents a

unit, and they pay transportation. (*They exit.* DORIS *and* ANDREW *enter, looking upstage cautiously.*)

ANDREW: Are they gone, Doris?

DORIS: They're gone, Andrew. But I've never seen a father and son like you and John, always playing games of hide-and-seek.

ANDREW: It's no game, Doris. That boy can't face me.

DORIS: You pick on John too much.

ANDREW: He wasn't wearing his knickers. Did you notice that?

DORIS: Nobody wears knickers anymore.

ANDREW: Didn't have a Buster Brown collar on either.

DORIS: Nobody wears Buster Brown collars anymore.

ANDREW: Hair looked awful short, too.

DORIS: He's getting bald, Andrew.

ANDREW: That's his trouble. I told him that no good would come of cutting his hair down to the roots like an Indian on a raiding party.

DORIS: You're getting bald, too, Andrew.

ANDREW: You're getting to be a nosy old woman, Doris.

DORIS: You talk fresh to me, Andrew Melville, and I'll give you nothing but chicken salad sandwiches for a week.

ANDREW: Oh, now, Dorrie.

DORIS: Don't Dorrie me. And boiled eggs, too.

ANDREW: You're just trying to make me sick. (*Walks upstage and sits on bench*)

DORIS (*Yelling after him*): And milk. (2ND MAN *crosses stage with paper from down right. He gives* ANDREW *a sheet of the paper.*)

2ND MAN: Here, young fellow, find yourself a job.

ANDREW: I don't want a job. I'm retired.

2ND MAN: Chee! This younger generation. (*He exits up left.*)

DORIS (*Coming up to* ANDREW): What did that young fellow want?

ANDREW: He wanted to know where he could buy a pair of knickers.

DORIS: Knickers?

ANDREW: Yes, and a Buster Brown collar.

DORIS (*Sitting down*): This younger generation! I don't know what will come of it.

ANDREW: I'm worried about John, Dorrie.

DORIS: John's all right. He's a good boy.

ANDREW: He has a lot of wild ideas.

DORIS: Well, he's young yet.

ANDREW: He ought to be growing up. Facing responsibility. When I was his age, I walked six miles to school everyday.

DORIS: John's forty-seven years old now, Andrew.

ANDREW: Makes no difference. Lots of kids younger than that walked six miles to school when I was a boy.

DORIS: I don't think our Johnny is very strong.

ANDREW: That's what comes from cutting his hair so short. Saps the strength. Always has. Always will. Look at what happened to Hercules when his hair was cut!

DORIS: That wasn't Hercules. That was Samson.

ANDREW: That's the trouble with young people today. They're always changing things. (WOMAN *enters, takes paper from* ANDREW *and gives him another sheet.*)

WOMAN: Here, I'll trade you.

ANDREW: I don't want to trade. I like the paper I have.

WOMAN: That's the trouble with this younger generation. Everyone is selfish. Take both. (*Throws paper down on bench and exits up right*)

DORIS: Who was that girl, Andrew?

ANDREW: I never saw her before in my life.

DORIS: She was awfully friendly for a stranger. Giving you

presents and all. In my generation, girls didn't behave like that with strange men.

ANDREW: I'm not a strange man. I'm your husband.

DORIS: I didn't say you weren't.

ANDREW: It's a terrible thing when a man's wife of fifty years doesn't even know him anymore. Stranger, indeed!

DORIS: You're just trying to change the subject. (1ST MAN *enters.*)

1ST MAN (*Pointing to* ANDREW): Ah-ha!

DORIS: Is that Charlie Jones?

ANDREW: I don't know any Charlie Jones.

DORIS: Then how do you know that's not Charlie Jones?

ANDREW: I think it's Charlie Smith.

DORIS: It can't be. You don't know any Charlie Smith. You said you didn't.

ANDREW: I don't know this man either, so he must be Charlie Smith. (*To* 1ST MAN, *who has come up to them*) Hey, there, Charlie Smith.

1ST MAN: Sir, you have me at a disadvantage.

ANDREW: What happened to your red hair?

1ST MAN: My hair is black.

ANDREW: And you've taken on weight. You certainly have changed, Charlie Smith.

1ST MAN: Sir, my name is not Charlie Smith.

ANDREW: Boy, you really have changed. What's your name now, Charlie?

1ST MAN: Sir, I don't wish to bandy words with you. I want my paper. I intend to have my paper. If you don't give me my paper this instant, I shall call a policeman and have you carted off to juvenile court. There's been entirely too much of this sort of crime among this younger generation.

DORIS: He's seventy-seven years old, Charlie Smith, a lot older than you.

1ST MAN: I tell you my name is not Charlie Smith, and

hasn't anyone ever told you, young lady, that you are not supposed to speak to adults until you are spoken to?

DORIS: That's old-fashioned.

1ST MAN: Good manners are never old-fashioned.

DORIS: Hah! That went out with high button shoes.

1ST MAN: Button your lip, little girl. And you, sir, are you going to give me my papers, or do I call a policeman?

ANDREW: Take your old papers. I don't want them anyway.

1ST MAN: Why did you say that?

ANDREW: I just did that's all.

1ST MAN: Do you think that was a smart thing to say? Do you think being fresh with adults makes you grown up?

ANDREW: Oh, peanut brittle.

1ST MAN: The trouble with your generation, sir, is they rush from knickers to long trousers before they're dry behind the ears. Good day. (*Takes papers and marches off up right*)

ANDREW: I don't like that man, Dorrie.

DORIS: He's a bully, I can tell you that.

ANDREW: He talks just like Father. He's always picking on me.

DORIS: You never saw him before.

ANDREW: I didn't say I did.

DORIS: Then, how could he be always picking on you?

ANDREW: I mean Father. Father's always picking on me.

DORIS: Your father doesn't always pick on you.

ANDREW: He does, too. He does, too.

DORIS: He does not.

ANDREW: He didn't want me to marry you. He said you were fat.

DORIS: Your father is a mean man.

ANDREW: He said you'd try to boss me after we were married.

DORIS: Hah! That's because he bosses you all the time.

ANDREW: You're right, Dorrie. Father picks on me.

DORIS: Did he really say I was fat?

ANDREW: I don't want to discuss it. I just wanted you to agree that Father picks on me.

DORIS: He didn't really say I was fat, did he?

ANDREW: He said something like that. (JAMES, *pushed in wheelchair by* ELIZABETH, *enters down left.*) There's Father now. He's come to pick on me. Quick, Dorrie, let's hide. (ANDREW *and* DORIS *get on their hands and knees and hide behind benches. During the following scene, their "stage whispers" are almost shouted, and they make a farcical business of hiding every time* JAMES *or* ELIZABETH *looks in their direction.*)

JAMES (*Yelling, pointing at baby carriage*): Who's the old goat in that wheelchair?

ELIZABETH: That's not a wheelchair, Mr. James.

JAMES: It is too. I can see it with my own pretty blue eyes.

ELIZABETH: It's a baby carriage, Mr. James.

JAMES: A what?

ELIZABETH: A baby carriage. A wheelchair for babies.

JAMES: Tell that baby to get his wheelchair out of my way. That's the trouble with this younger generation. No consideration for anyone.

ELIZABETH: I'll move the carriage.

JAMES: Why should you move the carriage? Let the baby move it. You're not his nurse. (ELIZABETH *goes to carriage, moves it a little and peers in it, making cooing sounds.*)

ELIZABETH (*Whispering to* JAMES): It's not a he, Mr. James. It's a she.

JAMES: Oh! (*To carriage*) I'm sorry about that, little lady. (ANDREW *and* DORIS *have moved upstage behind the bench, half-hiding and looking on.*)

ANDREW: There he is—making a fool of himself over that young baby. Just because it's a lady.

DORIS: Now, if he's going to complain about anyone being fat, he should look at that baby.

ANDREW: Look at him. Making faces and trying to be sweet.

DORIS: That baby's really fat.

ANDREW: Let's get out of here before he sees us.

DORIS: That baby's fatter than I ever was.

ANDREW: Let's go. I don't want to see him now. He'll pick on me. (*Starts off up right.*)

DORIS (*Following*): If I was as fat as that baby, then he'd have something to talk about. (*Follows* ANDREW *off.* ELIZABETH *continues to push* JAMES *upstage center.*)

JAMES: Andrew thinks I didn't see him.

ELIZABETH: You shouldn't pick on that boy, Mr. James.

JAMES: I don't pick on him. It's that Dorrie. She tells him I pick on him. (*Pauses*) She's a skinny little thing, isn't she?

ELIZABETH: She's pretty, and she's made Andrew a good wife.

JAMES: She's too skinny. But that's all the rage with this younger generation. I'll tell you something, though. She wouldn't be much good in an Indian fight. Good wind would blow her away.

ELIZABETH: Doris has been a good daughter-in-law to you, Mr. James, and you should be ashamed.

JAMES: And she wears paint on her face. Like an Indian. What kind of a woman wears paint on her face? (*Sadly*) They don't have the kind of women I knew when I was a boy. And they don't have the same kind of men either. (1ST MAN *enters.*)

1ST MAN: Excuse me, sir. Don't I know you?

JAMES: I never saw you before in my life.

1ST MAN: Come, come, sir. I just talked to you a few minutes ago. You were sitting here reading *my* paper.

JAMES: Oh, no sir, that was not I.

1st Man: It looked very much like you. Or to put it another way, it looked the way you must have looked forty years ago. Confess, sir, it was you, and you have aged forty years during the past few minutes.

James: I tell you it wasn't I. A man doesn't age forty years in a few minutes. Have sense, man.

1st Man: Sir, I saw a lady go into a beauty shop and an hour later she was forty years younger.

James: I don't go to beauty shops.

1st Man: That, sir, is why you look forty years older. Come now, confess.

James: Sit down and I'll tell you something.

1st Man (*Sitting*): Speak away, sir. I love to hear confessions.

James: The man you spoke to earlier was not I. . . .

1st Man (*Starting to rise*): Sir, you are trying to make a fool of me.

James: Sit down! He was my son.

1st Man: Of course, how stupid of me. He looked very much like you, and he told me that he had a father who looked very much like him. So . . . he is telling the truth, he has a father who looks like him, which means that his father has a son who looks like him, which means the father looks like the son just as much as the son looks like the father.

James: I don't look like Andrew.

1st Man: He said you were nothing alike.

James: Sir, I do have a confession.

1st Man: I knew it.

James: I failed with my son.

1st Man: It is a common complaint.

James: He is not the man I was.

1st Man: One seldom is.

James: He does not have my courage.

1ST MAN: One never does.

JAMES: He does not have my charm.

1ST MAN: What son does?

JAMES: He doesn't have my family background.

1ST MAN: Indeed he did tell me that his father was an extraordinary man.

JAMES: He wasn't as good as my father. Not by a long shot. This younger generation doesn't have the kind of parents we used to have. It's sad. Elizabeth, take me home.

ELIZABETH (*Pushing him off*): Now, now, Mr. James!

JAMES: This younger generation! It just can't do anything right! (JAMES *and* ELIZABETH *exit.* 1ST MAN *lies down on bench, spreads newspaper over his face, as if dozing.* 2ND MAN *enters, passes* 1ST MAN, *lifts one page of newspaper from him, and walks off down right, reading it. After he has disappeared,* 1ST MAN *sits up, looks around suspiciously, lies down, and returns to sleep.* SARA, PETER, JOHN *and* PHYLLIS, ANDREW *and* DORIS, JAMES *and* ELIZABETH *enter from right and left and converge on the sleeping* MAN.)

PETER: Wake up. Wake up.

JOHN: You have been having a nightmare.

ANDREW: About us.

JAMES: And we don't like it.

PETER: Wake up. Hurry or there'll be another generation on its way.

JOHN: He won't wake up.

SARA: Not until you all go away.

PHYLLIS: He can't see you. You're just parts of his nightmare.

DORIS: And as long as you're around, he has to keep nightmaring.

ANDREW: Nightmaring? What kind of a word is that?

Doris: It's good enough for this dream. (*They all turn and exit.* 1st Man *sits up, looks about, rises, and goes down right. He peers into carriage.*)

1st Man: Another generation! Welcome to the world, kid. (*The curtain falls and the loud wail of a baby's crying can be heard.*)

THE END

Production Notes

A VIEW OF THE SEA
Characters: 4 male; 5 female.
Playing Time: 35 minutes.
Costumes: Modern, everyday dress. Officer Smathers wears uniform; Cap wears old sweater and sailor's cap.
Properties: Broom, book.
Setting: The stage is empty except for a doorstep, at center, and a trash can, labeled THE KELSONS, which stands up left. Trash can contains book, telescope, bag of apples, croquet mallet, and ball of cotton. Exits are at right and left.
Lighting: Lights dim at end of play, as indicated in text.

GOING STEADY
Characters: 4 male; 4 female.
Playing Time: 25 minutes.
Costumes: Modern, everyday dress. During Sharon's dream, Woody wears a knight's helmet. Mr. Jackman wears a pith helmet, and Mr. Flyboy holds a space helmet. Dean Broth wears academic robes. Pritchard Merton is dressed flashily, with a sport coat, white scarf, beret, and dark glasses.
Properties: Bunch of artificial roses.
Setting: The Jennings living room. There is a sofa at center; a wall mirror, lamps, chairs and tables complete the furnishings.

Lighting: Stage lights dim and go out at opening and close of Sharon's dream, as indicated.

THE IN-GROUP
Characters: 12 actors. Cast may be all-male, all-female, or mixed.
Playing Time: 30 minutes.
Costumes: One, Two, and Three wear white; Four, Five, and Six, blue; Seven, Eight, and Nine, white and black; Ten, Eleven, and Twelve, green.
Properties: Books, handkerchiefs.
Setting: An elevated platform with three kitchen stools is up center. In front of the platform are several mats and pillows. Five chairs are down left, and slightly downstage from them is an easel with a painting on it. Down right are five chairs and a typing table with typewriter and paper on it.
Lighting: A bright spot shines on platform so that it is the center of attention, but the other areas can still be clearly seen.

WHAT'S ZYMURGY WITH YOU?
Characters: 4 male; 4 female.
Playing Time: 30 minutes.
Costumes: Timothy, Hiram, and Iris wear appropriate "hippy" outfits. Timothy's "hippy" garments should be limited to those he can remove easily (coat, hat,

beads, etc.). Jack wears a sweat-suit. Others wear modern, every-day dress.
Properties: Basketball, pile of books.
Setting: A park in the small town of Centerville. A bench is down center, and a path runs across the stage in front of it. Trees, bushes, fountains, other benches, etc., complete the setting. Exits are down right and left and up center.
Lighting: No special effects.

THE MOON'S UP THERE
Characters: 6 male; 4 female.
Playing Time: 30 minutes.
Costumes: Modern dress. Kimball and Dietlin wear army uniforms. Actress and her Agent wear flashy clothes. Mrs. Hefley and Mrs. Patton wear working clothes.
Properties: Rifles for Kimball and Dietlin, suitcase for Actress, camera for Agent.
Setting: The area in front of a rocket site. A low fence, about three feet high, runs for about six feet across the stage, down center. About five feet upstage from the fence are two benches. A large yellow paper moon hangs on back wall.
Lighting: No special effects.

HAPPY ENDING
Characters: 7 male; 4 female. (Balliol and Belcher are female roles; Helen is a male role.)
Playing Time: 30 minutes.
Costumes: Faust, Lucifer, and devils wear traditional costumes. Lucifer has a long, full cape. Shakespeare is dressed in Elizabethan costume, and has a short pointed beard. Others may wear appropriate historical costume, exaggerated for comic effect, or they may wear modern-comic dress.

Properties: Pitchforks, baby carriage, hot dogs, picnic basket, sunglasses, cameras.
Setting: Faust's laboratory. Up center is an elevated platform, on which is a high-back chair. Down right is a laboratory table, with odd-shaped bottles and machines. A stool is up center from table. Down left is a small platform. Exits are up center, down left, and down right.
Lighting: At beginning of play, stage is dimly lit, with red lighting suggesting the Inferno. Lights gradually come up during play, then return to original lighting for curtain.

TRASH AND TREASURE
Characters: 6 male; 4 female.
Playing Time: 35 minutes.
Costumes: Modern, everyday dress.
Properties: Checker board and checkers, scarves, dresses, hats, box of wooden blocks, bag of tin cans, two wastebaskets with newspapers, two earrings, large brown envelope containing manuscript.
Setting: The basement of an apartment house, the room in which the trash cans are kept. A small table with two chairs is down right. Up center is a large trash can, in front of which is a bench. Six or seven medium-sized trash cans are placed in various positions so they form an irregular border around stage. Exits are right and left, and at back.
Lighting: No special effects.

THE WHOLE CITY'S DOWN BELOW
Characters: 5 male; 5 female.
Playing Time: 30 minutes.
Costumes: Modern, everyday dress for Mr. and Mrs. Bons, Emily and Joe. Others wear appropriate

historical costumes. Romeo and Cyrano wear swords.

Properties: Chessmen and chessboard, blanket, two swords.

Setting: The living room of the Bons' apartment, as seen through an apartment window that overlooks the city below. Mr. Bons' wheelchair is down center. In front of it is a small table with chessmen and chessboard on it. At right is a sofa, and down left is an armchair. Exits are at right and left and at back.

Lighting: Only the area at center is lighted. The rest of the stage at back and at sides is in shadow. The curtains may be drawn so that only the down center area can be seen directly.

Sound: Soft, somber background music may be used to bridge episodes, as indicated in text.

A YOUNG MAN
OF CONSIDERABLE VALUE

Characters: 6 male; 4 female.

Playing Time: 40 minutes.

Costumes: Modern, everyday dress.

Properties: Account book, coins, pile of books, pen and ink stand.

Setting: Mr. Jones' treasury room. A huge gold-colored sack covered with dollar signs is up center, and arranged about the stage are smaller sacks, as well as treasure chests, huge precious stones, etc. A table and a chair are down center. Three small sacks are lined up on one side of table to serve as chairs. Two money trees with stage money for leaves stand right and left of table. Exits are down right and left and up center.

Lighting: No special effects.

TAKE IT FROM THE BEGINNING

Characters: 5 male; 4 female.

Playing Time: 35 minutes.

Costumes: Modern, everyday dress.

Properties: Scripts, papers.

Setting: A theater stage during tryouts. Flats are leaning against walls, and furniture is piled in various corners. A stool is down center, and to the left of it are a small table and chair.

Lighting: At beginning, stage is in semi-darkness, except for spot on couple at center. Later overhead lights come on, then go out as spot is again used for actors.

HI DOWN THERE

Characters: 4 male; 4 female.

Playing Time: 35 minutes.

Costumes: Modern, everyday dress.

Properties: Newspaper, banner, knitting, suitcase, book.

Setting: A vacant lot between two high buildings. Tall stepladders, about six feet high, are at right and left. A smaller ladder, about four feet high, is in the middle. A trash can is down left, and three soap boxes, painted with alternating blue and white stripes, are down right. Exits are down right and left and up center.

Lighting: A spotlight may shine on each ladder.

TREE TO THE SKY

Characters: 4 male; 4 female.

Playing Time: 35 minutes.

Costumes: Everyday, modern dress. Mrs. Meriwether carries a handbag containing deed. Peter has coins and box containing a button in his pocket. Mrs. Mauer has a quarter in her pocket, and diamond ring, which she places on the mound of earth when setting up fence. Moore may wear artist's smock; Wagner, a business suit, and Judge, a black robe, if desired.

Properties: Canvas chair, bag containing small shovel, watering can and fence, box containing button, coins, deed, chair and beach umbrella, gaily-painted cardboard house, picket fence, camp chair, easel, frame, palette, gaily-painted hamburger stand and stool, diamond.

Setting: A bare stage, with a little mound of earth at center. There are exits right and left.

Lighting: If desired, bright, stark lighting, gradually softening as indicated, may be used.

Sound: Offstage music, bird song, waves, breeze, as indicated in text.

AN ANTON CHEKHOV
SORT OF EVENING
Characters: 4 male; 3 female.
Playing Time: 35 minutes.
Costumes: Ordinary, everyday dress for Blairs, Harold, and Mrs. Wingfield. Duke and Lennie are dressed in the style of gangster movies of the 1930's.
Properties: Two guns and a rifle; books, note pad, pencils.
Setting: The family room of the Blair home. A desk with telephone, piles of books, and papers is down right. Easy chairs, tables, lamps, etc., complete the setting. A book with a blue cover is on one of the tables. An exit up left leads to front door, and another down right leads to the outside. Exit to kitchen is down left.
Lighting: All lights but one are turned off, and come on again, as indicated in text.
Sound: Gunshots, telephone, doorbell, offstage horn and door slamming, as indicated in text.

THE HAPPIEST HAT
Characters: 5 male; 5 female.
Playing Time: 35 minutes.
Costumes: Modern, everyday dress. Maggie wears a black armband in last scene.
Properties: Dictation pad, pencil, newspapers, papers and maps, tennis racket, party invitations, iron, whistle, party hat, lily, three hat boxes, painted red, white, and blue, each containing a hat. The three hats (red for Haroldson, white for Dickson, and blue for Thompson) suggest the kind of happiness each character represents—marital bliss, public service, and personal pleasures.
Setting: The four scenes are all rearrangements of one basic set. Scene 1 is Mr. Wandimiller's office. Up center are a desk and chair. Down right of them are six kitchen chairs in a row, painted alternately red, white, and blue. Down left from desk are six orange crates, painted alternately red, white, and blue. The chairs and crates serve as arrows in Scene 1 leading the action to the upstage center area. Scene 2 shows the three homes of Thompson, Dickson, and Haroldson. The division between Thompson's and Dickson's homes is made by a blue and white streamer, running from the top of the upstage wall, right corner, down to the floor, right center, by the footlights; the division between Dickson's and Haroldson's homes is made by a red and white streamer that runs from the left corner of the upstage wall down to the floor by the footlights, left center. These two streamers divide the downstage area into three separate acting

areas. In Area 1, the Thompson area, a blue chair and blue orange crate are moved to downstage right position to serve as a chair and footstool, and the desk is a little upstage from them. In Area 2, the Dickson area, two white crates and one blue are placed together for a worktable in the center of the area, back of which is a blue chair, and downstage left and right of it are two white chairs. In Area 3, the Haroldson area, the two red chairs are placed side-by-side, with two red crates set on their sides to suggest a couch and coffee table. Scene 3 uses the whole stage for a party scene. The streamers are draped across the upstage wall. The desk at center is covered with a white tablecloth, and a punch bowl is placed on top of it. The six chairs and crates are arranged in three conversational groups, with the crates serving as end tables. Scene 4 returns the stage to exactly the same arrangement as Scene 1. These changes in scenes should take about one minute each, and the theatrical surprise should come from the different arrangements of the simple stage props.

Lighting: Transitions between scenes may be made with a blackout and fast curtain. If varied lighting effects are available, each scene should be lit differently.

Sound: If music is available, the scene changes should be covered by a music bridge—mood music played by a single instrument.

WISHING WELL OR ILL
Characters: 4 male; 3 female.
Playing Time: 40 minutes.

Costumes: Modern, everyday dress, with Bogie and Cagney dressed as much like Humphrey Bogart and James Cagney as possible.

Properties: Coins, cane, suitcases with "Just Married" sign, whistle, telegrams.

Setting: The patio of a small resort hotel. A wishing well, with sign reading, THE WISHING WELL, is at center. Surrounding patio is a low brick wall, with entrances up and down right and left. There is a bench against the right wall, and a matching bench against left wall. A smaller bench is down center from well.

Lighting: Following first scene, lights are dimmed for the night scene, and come up again for morning in last scene.

Sound: Music bridges may be used to indicate passage of time between scenes.

THIS YOUNGER GENERATION
Characters: 6 male; 5 female.
Playing Time: 30 minutes.

Costumes: Modern, everyday dress. There should be considerable exaggeration in costume and make-up, however—almost bordering on circus-clown appearance, especially for the older generation.

Properties: Newspapers, lunch basket containing sandwiches, etc., wheelchair.

Setting: A park. Three benches are up center, one facing the audience and the other two flanking it, facing each other. Down left is a trash can and down right, a baby carriage. Exits are up and down right and left.

Lighting: No special effects.

Sound: Baby's cry, as indicated in text.